ADVANCED
COMPLEX CALCULUS

HARPER'S MATHEMATICS SERIES

Charles A. Hutchinson, Editor

ADVANCED
COMPLEX
CALCULUS

by

KENNETH S. MILLER, Ph.D.

Professor of Mathematics,
New York University

HARPER & BROTHERS, PUBLISHERS

New York

ADVANCED COMPLEX CALCULUS

Library of Congress catalog card number: 59–12675

CONTENTS

Contents

PREFACE

This is a text for a first course in complex variable theory designed to follow a course in real variables such as may be found in *Advanced Real Calculus*.* It is designed for upper class mathematics majors and beginning graduate students. Notes on which this book is based have also been successfully used for graduate engineering students. The level of rigor is on a par with that found in *ARC*, that is, an exact ϵ, δ-treatment. Keeping in mind the class of readers to whom the book is addressed, we have made the exposition detailed and uniform throughout the whole text. The only important theorem that we do not prove is the Jordan separation theorem, which, however, is extensively discussed. It is the opinion of the author that a logically satisfying proof of this theorem would take us too far afield. The interested reader can quickly see that for our practical purposes it is not necessary.

The organization of the book is patterned after that of *ARC*. The first chapter treats complex numbers and convergence of complex sequences. The analogy to real numbers and real sequences is emphasized. Many proofs are reduced to an application of real variable theory. Chapter 2 is devoted to topological preliminaries and includes a discussion of continuous curves and functions of bounded variation. In Chapter 3 we start function theory proper with a definition of function, continuity, and differentiability as applied to complex functions. The elementary functions are introduced by their (real) series expansions and then extended to the complex domain. Thus we have a repertoire of concrete functions for later applications. Careful attention is paid to multi-valued functions, including a discussion of "Riemann axes" (the analog of Riemann surfaces for real functions), which helps to clarify the use and significance of multi-valued complex functions. Analytic functions and the Cauchy-Riemann equations are introduced; the distinction between analyticity and differentiability is clearly discussed. The chapter concludes with a brief interpretation of analytic functions as mappings. Chapter 4 is

---

* K. S. Miller, *Advanced Real Calculus*, Harper & Brothers, 1957. Throughout this book we shall use the abbreviation *ARC* for *Advanced Real Calculus*.

vii

a detailed study of the integral. Starting with complex-valued functions of a real variable, the development parallels the real case. The great divergence from this parallel development lies in the Cauchy integral theorem and the Cauchy integral formula. In Chapter 5 we return to sequences and series of complex numbers and functions, including the usual theorems which are the analogs for real sequences and series. Special attention is focused on sequences of analytic functions. Thus the first five chapters are in one to one correspondence with the first five chapters of *ARC* and introduce the reader to the basic fundamentals concerning functions of a complex variable. Care is exercised in pointing out the "natural" extensions from the real to the complex so that complex variable theory appears as a logical continuation rather than as a bizarre offshoot of real variable theory. Correspondingly the important properties of analytic functions that have no real counterpart are carefully delineated.

In the remaining four chapters we depart from the parallel development of real variable theory. Chapter 6 is a rather detailed discussion of the calculus of residues with special emphasis on integration around branch points. For example, the loop and double loop integrals which reappear in Chapter 9 are discussed. Chapter 7 is a "catch-all" chapter of important theorems such as Rouché's theorem, Liouville's theorem, and the maximum modulus theorem; even so, the chapter exhibits a reasonable cohesiveness. While most of the results could have been presented at earlier points in the book, it seemed best to collect them all in one place rather than interrupt the main thread of development in each previous chapter. Chapter 8 is a brief but mathematically exact introduction to conformal mapping and includes a discussion of the elliptic integral. In Chapter 9 we indulge ourselves with a discussion of the method of Laplace integrals. This is an interesting application of complex variable theory to differential equations. Furthermore, it can be given without going into a detailed study of existence, uniqueness, properties of solutions, and singular points of linear differential equations. Of course, the subject matter of linear differential equations in the complex domain is in itself material for a complete textbook.

It is a pleasure to acknowledge the help of my former students Mr. L. E. Blumenson of New York University and Mr. H. R. Gluck of Princeton University, who read the entire manuscript and offered many valuable suggestions for the improvement of the text. I am also indebted to my father, Mr. W. A. Miller, for the preparation of the many excellent diagrams.

K. S. M.

June, 1959

ADVANCED
COMPLEX CALCULUS

CHAPTER I

Numbers and Convergence

1.1 Introduction

The reader will recall that the study of functions of real variables was prefaced by a study of real numbers, limits, and certain topological considerations. Thus it was not possible to plunge immediately into a rigorous treatment of the theory of differentiation without first having an appreciation of the meaning of "number." It will therefore come as no surprise that if we are to study the theory of functions of a *complex* variable we had best begin with a preliminary examination of *complex* numbers, limits of sequences of complex numbers, and certain topological questions.

Fortunately, our treatment will be briefer than that necessary for real variables. The reason for this is that we have already laid a broad foundation in our study of real variables. (Essentially what we do is to reduce the complex case to the real case and apply the great wealth of material developed in advanced calculus.) For example, the reader has an intuitive notion of a complex number, $a + ib$ where $i = \sqrt{-1}$ and a and b are real. We shall show that to study the convergence of a sequence of *complex* numbers such as $\{a_n + ib_n\}$ we need only study the convergence of the two *real* sequences $\{a_n\}$ and $\{b_n\}$. Thus, for example, a Cauchy convergence theorem for sequences of complex numbers can be given short shrift, compared to the long and delicate arguments needed for the real case.*

We do not wish to mislead the reader. While the technique of considering a complex number as two real numbers enables us to prove many theorems, this method of approach should not be carried to extremes. The essential beauty and utility of the theory of analytic

---

* See K. S. Miller, *Advanced Real Calculus*, Harper & Brothers, 1957, p. 10. Throughout this book we shall use the abbreviation *A RC* for *Advanced Real Calculus*.

functions rests on the treatment of the complex variable as an *entity* and not as a pair of real variables.

1.2 Complex Numbers

We recall the definition of a real number. By a *complex number* we shall mean an *ordered pair of real numbers* (a,b). Thus in the symbol (a,b) the quantities a and b are real numbers. By an *ordered* pair we mean that (a,b) and (b,a) are distinct unless $a = b$. Two complex numbers (a,b) and (c,d) are equal if and only if $a = c$ and $b = d$.

The *sum* of two complex numbers is defined by the equation

$$(a,b) + (c,d) = (a + c, b + d) \tag{1.1}$$

and the *product* by the equation

$$(a,b) \cdot (c,d) = (ac - bd, ad + bc). \tag{1.2}$$

Clearly if (a,b) and (c,d) are ordered pairs of real numbers, so are the right-hand sides of Equations 1.1 and 1.2.

Assuming the associativity and commutativity of addition and multiplication of real numbers, as we did in *ARC*, we can easily show that complex numbers also enjoy the same properties, viz.:

$$(a,b) + [(c,d) + (e,f)] = [(a,b) + (c,d)] + (e,f) \quad \text{(Assoc. of add.)} \tag{1.3}$$

$$(a,b) + (c,d) = (c,d) + (a,b) \quad \text{(Comm. of add.)} \tag{1.4}$$

$$(a,b) \cdot [(c,d) \cdot (e,f)] = [(a,b) \cdot (c,d)] \cdot (e,f) \quad \text{(Assoc. of mult.)} \tag{1.5}$$

$$(a,b) \cdot (c,d) = (c,d) \cdot (a,b) \quad \text{(Comm. of mult.)} \tag{1.6}$$

One can also show that multiplication is distributive with respect to addition, namely:

$$(a,b) \cdot [(c,d) + (e,f)] = (a,b) \cdot (c,d) + (a,b) \cdot (e,f). \tag{1.7}$$

The proofs of Equations 1.3—1.7 are elementary exercises in high school algebra and will be left to the reader.

The *zero complex number* is $(0,0)$. From Equations 1.1 and 1.4 it is evident that

$$(a,b) + (0,0) = (0,0) + (a,b) = (a,b).$$

The *negative* of a complex number (a,b) is $(-a,-b)$ since

$$(a,b) + (-a,-b) = (0,0).$$

It is customary to write $(-a,-b)$ as $-(a,b)$. Clearly the negative is unique.

Given any complex numbers (a,b) and (c,d) with $(c,d) \neq (0,0)$ we can always find a complex number (u,v) such that

$$(a,b) = (c,d) \cdot (u,v). \tag{1.8}$$

In other words, division by any complex number (except zero) is always possible.   For if

$$u = \frac{ac + bd}{c^2 + d^2}, \qquad v = \frac{bc - ad}{c^2 + d^2},$$

then Equation 1.8 is satisfied.   The reader may convince himself that (u,v) is unique.

In brief, we have shown that the complex numbers form a *field*.*

1.3 The Imaginary Unit

From the relations of the previous section we see that

$$(a,0) + (b,0) = (a + b,0)$$
$$(a,0) \cdot (b,0) = (ab,0)$$
$$\frac{(a,0)}{(b,0)} = \left(\frac{a}{b},0\right), \qquad b \neq 0.$$

Thus we may identify the complex number $(a,0)$ with the real number a since it obeys all the arithmetic laws.   (Precisely speaking, we say that the subfield $(a,0)$ of all complex numbers is *isomorphic* to the real numbers.)†

Now any complex number (a,b) may be written in the form

$$(a,b) = (a,0) \cdot (1,0) + (b,0) \cdot (0,1)$$
$$= a + b(0,1).$$

For convenience and custom we shall use the symbol i for the complex number $(0,1)$.   Thus

$$(a,b) = a + bi.$$

From Equation 1.2 we see that

$$(0,1) \cdot (0,1) = (-1,0),$$

so that $i^2 = -1$.   Thus we sometimes write $i = \sqrt{-1}$.   This is just another symbol for the complex number $(0,1)$.   Of course, the reader has already observed that our abstract formulation of complex numbers was motivated by a formal manipulation of the symbol $a + b\sqrt{-1}$

---

* See K. S. Miller, *Elements of Modern Abstract Algebra*, Harper & Brothers, 1958, p. 57 and chap. 3, for a detailed discussion of abstract fields.
    † See Miller, *op. cit.*, pp. 22, 60.

where a and b are real numbers. We sometimes call complex numbers of the form $(0,b)$ *imaginary* or *purely imaginary* numbers.

While real numbers may be arranged geometrically on a straight line according to magnitude with some arbitrary point taken as the origin, we need a plane in order to represent a complex number. This is customarily done by labeling the axis of abscissas the real axis (Re) and the axis of ordinates the imaginary axis (Im). Thus the complex number $a + ib$ is represented on the cartesian plane as the point with coordinates (a,b). We call such a plane the *complex plane*.

For completeness, we now mention a few terms with which the reader probably is already familiar. The *conjugate* of a complex number

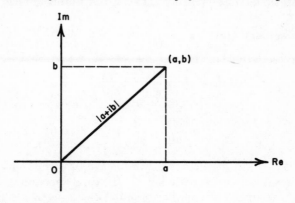

Figure 1.1

$a + ib$ is defined as $a - ib$. We shall indicate conjugates by a bar. Thus

$$\overline{a + ib} = a - ib.$$

The *modulus* of a complex number $a + ib$ is written $|a + ib|$ and is defined as

$$|a + ib| = +\sqrt{a^2 + b^2}.$$

Clearly $|a + ib|$ is always nonnegative. We see that "modulus" is the natural extension of the notion of "absolute value" of a real number. For if $b = 0$, the above equation becomes

$$|a| = +\sqrt{a^2},$$

which is the definition of the absolute value of a real number, namely, $|a| = a$ if $a \geq 0$ and $|a| = -a$ if $a < 0$. Geometrically, the modulus is the distance from the origin to the point (a,b) in the complex plane (see Fig. 1.1).

I.4 Properties of Complex Numbers

We now shall discontinue our abstract notation (a,b) of a complex number (which was necessary to formulate clearly our system of complex numbers) and hereafter use the notation $a + ib$. Of course, it frequently will be convenient to use a single symbol such as α to denote a complex number, for example, $\alpha = a + ib$.

For *real* numbers we recall the relations $|ab| = |a||b|$ and $|a + b| \leq |a| + |b|$. Let us show that these relations are still true if a and b are complex numbers and $|\cdots|$ is interpreted as "modulus."

Theorem I. If α and β are any complex numbers, then

$$|\alpha\beta| = |\alpha| \cdot |\beta|.$$

Proof: Let $\alpha = a + ib$, $\beta = c + id$. Then

$$|\alpha\beta| = |(a + ib)(c + id)| = |(ac - bd) + i(bc + ad)|$$
$$= \sqrt{(ac - bd)^2 + (bc + ad)^2}$$

by definition of modulus. But

$$(ac - bd)^2 + (bc + ad)^2 = a^2c^2 + b^2d^2 + b^2c^2 + a^2d^2$$
$$= c^2(a^2 + b^2) + d^2(a^2 + b^2)$$
$$= (c^2 + d^2)(a^2 + b^2)$$

and

$$|\alpha\beta| = +\sqrt{a^2 + b^2}\sqrt{c^2 + d^2} = |\alpha| \cdot |\beta|.$$

Immediate corollaries are $|\alpha|^2 = |\alpha^2| = \alpha\bar{\alpha}$ and $|\bar{\alpha}| = |\alpha|$.

As was remarked in the introduction, we can prove theorems involving complex numbers by reducing them to theorems about real numbers. We used this device in Theorem 1 and shall use it also to prove Theorem 2 known as the *triangle inequality*.

Theorem 2. If α and β are complex numbers, then

$$|\alpha + \beta| \leq |\alpha| + |\beta|. \tag{1.9}$$

Proof: First we note that

$$(|\alpha| + |\beta|)^2 = |\alpha|^2 + |\beta|^2 + 2|\alpha| \cdot |\beta|.$$

As before, let $\alpha = a + ib$, $\beta = c + id$. Then

$$|\alpha| \cdot |\beta| = \sqrt{(a^2 + b^2)(c^2 + d^2)} = \sqrt{(ac + bd)^2 + (ad - bc)^2}$$
$$\geq \sqrt{(ac + bd)^2} = |ac + bd|.$$

But

$$|\alpha + \beta|^2 = (a + c)^2 + (b + d)^2 = (a^2 + b^2) + (c^2 + d^2) + 2(ac + bd)$$
$$= |\alpha|^2 + |\beta|^2 + 2(ac + bd).$$

Thus

$$(|\alpha| + |\beta|)^2 - |\alpha + \beta|^2 \geq 2|ac + bd| - 2(ac + bd) \geq 0$$

or

$$(|\alpha| + |\beta|)^2 \geq |\alpha + \beta|^2,$$

from which our theorem follows.

Corollary. $|\alpha - \beta| \geq ||\alpha| - |\beta||$.

Proof: Write $\alpha = \beta + (\alpha - \beta)$. Then from Theorem 2

$$|\alpha| \leq |\beta| + |\alpha - \beta|$$

or

$$|\alpha - \beta| \geq |\alpha| - |\beta|.$$

Interchanging the roles of α and β yields the corollary.

Other trivial consequences are $|a + ib| \geq |a|$, $|a + ib| \geq |b|$.

1.5 Sequences of Complex Numbers

Suppose that we are given a rule which associates with every positive integer n a complex number α_n. Then we call

$$\alpha_1, \alpha_2, \cdots, \alpha_n, \cdots \tag{1.10}$$

—or more compactly $\{\alpha_n\}$—a *sequence* of complex numbers. We shall say that the sequence *converges* to the limit α if: Given any $\epsilon > 0$ there exists an N such that for all $n > N$

$$|\alpha_n - \alpha| < \epsilon. \tag{1.11}$$

This is, of course, the same as the definition of convergence of sequences of real numbers. We shall use the notation

$$\lim_{n \to \infty} \alpha_n = \alpha$$

or

$$\{\alpha_n\} \to \alpha$$

as well as Equation 1.11 to imply that the sequence $\{\alpha_n\}$ converges to α.

If a sequence has a limit, this limit is *unique*. Suppose $\{\alpha_n\}$ converged to α and β with $\alpha \neq \beta$. Then given $\epsilon = \frac{1}{2}|\alpha - \beta| > 0$, choose an N so large that

$$|\alpha_n - \alpha| < \frac{\epsilon}{2} \qquad \text{and} \qquad |\alpha_n - \beta| < \frac{\epsilon}{2}$$

for all $n > N$. This is possible since by hypothesis $\{\alpha_n\}$ converges to both α and β. Then by the triangle inequality

$$2\epsilon = |\alpha - \beta| = |\alpha - \alpha_n + \alpha_n - \beta| \leqq |\alpha - \alpha_n| + |\alpha_n - \beta|$$

$$< \frac{\epsilon}{2} + \frac{\epsilon}{2} = \epsilon,$$

which is absurd.

The fundamental theorem on the convergence of sequences of complex numbers which relates them to the convergence of real sequences follows.

Theorem 3. Let $\{\alpha_n\}$ be a sequence of complex numbers where $\alpha_n = a_n + ib_n$. Then a necessary and sufficient condition that $\{\alpha_n\}$ converge to $\alpha = a + ib$ is that $\{a_n\}$ converge to a and $\{b_n\}$ converge to b.

Proof: Necessity. Let $\epsilon > 0$ be assigned. Then there exists an N such that

$$|\alpha_n - \alpha| < \epsilon \qquad (1.12)$$

for all $n > N$. But Equation 1.12 is equivalent to

$$|(a_n + ib_n) - (a + ib)| = |(a_n - a) + i(b_n - b)| < \epsilon$$

for all $n > N$. Since

$$\epsilon > |(a_n - a) + i(b_n - b)| \geqq |a_n - a|$$

and

$$\epsilon > |(a_n - a) + i(b_n - b)| \geqq |b_n - b|$$

for all $n > N$, we conclude that $\{a_n\} \to a$ and $\{b_n\} \to b$.

Sufficiency: Let $\epsilon > 0$ be assigned. Choose an N so large that

$$|a - a_n| < \frac{\epsilon}{2} \qquad \text{and} \qquad |b - b_n| < \frac{\epsilon}{2}$$

for all $n > N$. Then for $n > N$,

$$|\alpha_n - \alpha| = |(a_n + ib_n) - (a + ib)| = |(a_n - a) + i(b_n - b)|$$

$$\leqq |a - a_n| + |b - b_n| < \frac{\epsilon}{2} + \frac{\epsilon}{2} = \epsilon.$$

A fundamental theorem in the theory of real sequences was the *Cauchy convergence theorem*. We state and prove it for complex sequences in Theorem 4.

Theorem 4. Let $\{\alpha_n\}$ be a sequence of complex numbers. A necessary and sufficient condition that the sequence converge is: Given an $\epsilon > 0$ there exists an N such that for all $n > N$ and all positive integers p,

$$|\alpha_n - \alpha_{n+p}| < \epsilon.$$

Proof: Necessity. Suppose $\{\alpha_n\}$ converges to α. Choose an N so large that

$$|\alpha_n - \alpha| < \frac{\epsilon}{2}$$

for all $n > N$. Now if p is a positive integer, $n + p > N$ and hence

$$|\alpha_{n+p} - \alpha| < \frac{\epsilon}{2}.$$

But by the triangle inequality,

$$|\alpha_n - \alpha_{n+p}| = |\alpha_n - \alpha + \alpha - \alpha_{n+p}| \leqq |\alpha_n - \alpha| + |\alpha - \alpha_{n+p}|$$
$$< \frac{\epsilon}{2} + \frac{\epsilon}{2} = \epsilon.$$

Sufficiency: Let $\epsilon > 0$ be assigned. Suppose there exists an N such that

$$|\alpha_n - \alpha_{n+p}| < \epsilon$$

for all $n > N$ and all $p > 0$. Let $\alpha_n = a_n + ib_n$. Then the above inequality implies

$$|(a_n + ib_n) - (a_{n+p} + ib_{n+p})| = |(a_n - a_{n+p}) + i(b_n - b_{n+p})| < \epsilon,$$

which in turn implies

$$|a_n - a_{n+p}| < \epsilon \qquad \text{and} \qquad |b_n - b_{n+p}| < \epsilon.$$

But by the Cauchy convergence theorem for real sequences, $|a_n - a_{n+p}| < \epsilon$ for all $n > N$ and $p > 0$ implies $\{a_n\}$ converges, say to a. Similarly $\{b_n\}$ converges, say to b. By Theorem 3 this implies $\{\alpha_n\}$ converges to $a + ib$.

A sequence $\{\alpha_n\}$ of complex numbers is said to be *bounded* if there exists a real number M, independent of n, such that

$$|\alpha_n| \leqq M$$

for all n, $n = 1, 2, 3, \cdots$. A bounded sequence need not converge. For example, $\{(-1)^n\}$ is a bounded sequence which does not converge. However, the converse of this proposition *is* true.

Theorem 5. Let $\{\alpha_n\}$ be a convergent sequence of complex numbers. Then $\{\alpha_n\}$ is bounded.

Proof: Let $\{\alpha_n\}$ converge to α. Then for any n,

$$|\alpha_n| = |(\alpha_n - \alpha) + \alpha| \leq |\alpha_n - \alpha| + |\alpha|.$$

If we let $\epsilon = 1$, then there exists an N such that

$$|\alpha_n - \alpha| < 1$$

for all $n > N$. Thus

$$|\alpha_n| < 1 + |\alpha|$$

for all $n > N$. Choose

$$M = \max (|\alpha_1|, |\alpha_2|, \cdots, |\alpha_N|, 1 + |\alpha|).$$

Then

$$M \geq |\alpha_n|$$

for *all* n.

The next three theorems on the sum, product, and quotient of sequences of complex numbers are identical with Theorems 4, 5, and 6 of Chapter 1 of *ARC* for real sequences. We include their proofs here for completeness. As the reader goes through these proofs he should convince himself that every step is justified in terms of the rules laid down for the manipulation of complex numbers. He should be especially careful to interpret $|\cdots|$ as "modulus" rather than "absolute value."

Theorem 6. Let $\{\alpha_n\}$ and $\{\beta_n\}$ be two convergent sequences of complex numbers with limits α and β respectively. Then the sequence $\{\alpha_n + \beta_n\}$ converges and its limit is $\alpha + \beta$.

Proof: Let $\epsilon > 0$ be assigned. Choose an N such that

$$|\alpha_n - \alpha| < \frac{\epsilon}{2} \quad \text{and} \quad |\beta_n - \beta| < \frac{\epsilon}{2}$$

for all $n > N$. Then by the triangle inequality

$$|(\alpha_n + \beta_n) - (\alpha + \beta)| = |(\alpha_n - \alpha) + (\beta_n - \beta)|$$

$$\leq |\alpha_n - \alpha| + |\beta_n - \beta| < \frac{\epsilon}{2} + \frac{\epsilon}{2} = \epsilon.$$

Theorem 7. Let $\{\alpha_n\} \to \alpha$ and $\{\beta_n\} \to \beta$. Then the sequence $\{\alpha_n\beta_n\}$ converges to $\alpha\beta$.

Proof: Let $\epsilon > 0$ be assigned. By Theorem 5 there exists an A such that $A > |\alpha_n|$ for all n. Let $K = \max(|\beta|, A)$. Now choose an N so large that

$$|\alpha_n - \alpha| < \frac{\epsilon}{2K} \quad \text{and} \quad |\beta_n - \beta| < \frac{\epsilon}{2K}$$

for all $n > N$. Then by the triangle inequality,

$$|\alpha_n \beta_n - \alpha\beta| = |\alpha_n \beta_n - \alpha_n \beta + \alpha_n \beta - \alpha\beta| = |\alpha_n(\beta_n - \beta) + \beta(\alpha_n - \alpha)|$$

$$\leq |\alpha_n|\,|\beta_n - \beta| + |\beta|\,|\alpha_n - \alpha| < K\frac{\epsilon}{2K} + K\frac{\epsilon}{2K} = \epsilon$$

for all $n > N$.

Theorem 8. Let $\{\alpha_n\}$ converge to $\alpha \neq 0$. Then the sequence $\{1/\alpha_n\}$ converges to $1/\alpha$.

Proof: Note that if some α_k is zero, $1/\alpha_k$ is not defined. Thus the sequence $\{1/\alpha_n\}$ is not well defined. (However, we know that when investigating the convergence or divergence of a sequence we can neglect any finite number of terms without affecting the convergence or divergence.) Thus we shall first show the existence of an N such that $\alpha_n \neq 0$ for $n > N$. Then if we consider the sequence

$$\alpha_{N+1}, \alpha_{N+2}, \cdots,$$

it will also have the limit α, *and* the sequence

$$\frac{1}{\alpha_{N+1}}, \frac{1}{\alpha_{N+2}}, \cdots$$

also will be well defined. We proceed with this portion of the proof.

Since $\alpha \neq 0$ and $\{\alpha_n\}$ converges to α, we may choose an N so large that

$$|\alpha_n - \alpha| < \frac{|\alpha|}{2}$$

for all $n > N$. Now from the corollary to Theorem 2,

$$|\alpha_n| \geq |\alpha| - |\alpha - \alpha_n| > \frac{|\alpha|}{2} > 0.$$

Thus $\alpha_n \neq 0$ for $n > N$, and the sequence of reciprocals $\{1/\alpha_n\}$ is well defined for $n > N$.

Now

$$\left|\frac{1}{\alpha_n} - \frac{1}{\alpha}\right| = \frac{|\alpha - \alpha_n|}{|\alpha_n| \cdot |\alpha|}.$$

Thus if an $\epsilon > 0$ is assigned, we can choose a $P > N$ such that

$$|\alpha_n - \alpha| < \frac{|\alpha|^2\epsilon}{2}$$

for all $n > P$. Then for $n > P$,

$$\left|\frac{1}{\alpha_n} - \frac{1}{\alpha}\right| < \frac{\dfrac{|\alpha|^2\epsilon}{2}}{\dfrac{|\alpha|}{2}|\alpha|} = \epsilon.$$

EXERCISES

1.1. If α and β are complex numbers, prove that

$$\overline{\alpha + \beta} = \bar{\alpha} + \bar{\beta}$$

and

$$\overline{\alpha\beta} = \bar{\alpha}\bar{\beta}.$$

1.2. Let z be a complex number. By Re $[z]$ we mean the real part of z and by Im $[z]$ we mean the imaginary part of z. Thus if $z = x + iy$, Re $[z] = x$ and Im $[z] = y$. Prove that if α and β are any complex numbers then

$$\text{Re}\,[\alpha + \beta] = \text{Re}\,[\alpha] + \text{Re}\,[\beta]$$
$$\text{Im}\,[\alpha + \beta] = \text{Im}\,[\alpha] + \text{Im}\,[\beta]$$

and

$$\text{Re}\,[\alpha\beta] = \text{Re}\,[\alpha]\,\text{Re}\,[\beta] - \text{Im}\,[\alpha]\,\text{Im}\,[\beta]$$
$$\text{Im}\,[\alpha\beta] = \text{Re}\,[\alpha]\,\text{Im}\,[\beta] + \text{Im}\,[\alpha]\,\text{Re}\,[\beta].$$

1.3. If α is a complex number, prove that

$$|\alpha| \geq |\text{Re}\,[\alpha]|, \qquad |\alpha| \geq |\text{Im}\,[\alpha]|$$

and

$$|\alpha| \leq |\text{Re}\,[\alpha]| + |\text{Im}\,[\alpha]|.$$

1.4. If α and β are complex numbers with $\beta \neq \alpha \neq 0$, prove the identity

$$\frac{1}{\alpha - \beta} = \frac{1}{\alpha} + \frac{\beta}{\alpha^2} + \frac{\beta^2}{\alpha^3} + \cdots + \frac{\beta^n}{\alpha^{n+1}} + \frac{\beta^{n+1}}{\alpha^{n+1}(\alpha - \beta)}.$$

1.5. If α_i and β_i are complex numbers, prove that

$$\left|\sum_{i=1}^{n} \alpha_i\beta_i\right|^2 \leq \sum_{i=1}^{n} |\alpha_i|^2 \sum_{i=1}^{n} |\beta_i|^2.$$

(This is the *Cauchy-Schwarz* inequality.)

1.6. If α_i and β_i are complex numbers, prove that

$$\left[\sum_{i=1}^{n} |\alpha_i + \beta_i|^2\right]^{1/2} \leq \left[\sum_{i=1}^{n} |\alpha_i|^2\right]^{1/2} + \left[\sum_{i=1}^{n} |\beta_i|^2\right]^{1/2}.$$

(This is the *triangle* or *Minkowski* inequality.)

1.7. If α is a complex number with the property that $|\alpha| < \epsilon$ for all $\epsilon > 0$, prove that $\alpha = 0$.

1.8. If the sequence of complex numbers $\{\alpha_n\}$ converges to α, prove that $\{|\alpha_n|\}$ converges to $|\alpha|$.

1.9. Let $\{\alpha_n\}$ be a sequence of positive real numbers. Let $\{\beta_n\}$ be a sequence of complex numbers with the property that $|\beta_n| \leq \alpha_n$. If $\{\alpha_n\}$ converges to zero, prove that the sequence $\{\beta_n\}$ converges.

1.10. If the sequence $\{\alpha_n\}$ converges to α, prove that the sequence $\{\beta_n\}$, where

$$\beta_n = \frac{1}{n}\sum_{k=1}^{n} \alpha_k,$$

also converges to α.

1.11. Let $\{\alpha_n\} \to \alpha$ and $\{\beta_n\} \to \beta$. If

$$\gamma_{n+1} = \frac{\alpha_1\beta_n + \alpha_2\beta_{n-1} + \cdots + \alpha_n\beta_1}{n}, \qquad n = 1, 2, \cdots,$$

prove that the sequence $\{\gamma_{n+1}\}$ converges to $\alpha\beta$.

CHAPTER 2

Topological Preliminaries

2.1 Introduction

In this chapter we shall consider some elementary properties of point sets in the plane. Of course, we considered some of these properties when we studied functions of two real variables (cf. Chapter 6 of *ARC*). The results obtained there will be quickly summarized in Section 2.2. The wording will reflect the complex plane approach. For example, the cumbersome statement

$$\sqrt{(x - x_0)^2 + (y - y_0)^2} < \epsilon \qquad (2.1)$$

needed to describe a spherical neighborhood about the point (x_0,y_0) in the xy-plane in real variable theory may be replaced by the succinct statement

$$|z - z_0| < \epsilon \qquad (2.2)$$

in the complex plane. Thus this last inequality represents all points interior to a circle of radius ϵ with center at z_0. If we identify z with $x + iy$ and $z_0 = x_0 + iy_0$, Equations 2.1 and 2.2 become identical.

It is possible to discuss many properties of functions of two real variables without probing too deeply into the structure of the domain of definition. For example, in Chapter 6 of *ARC* we frequently considered a function $f(x,y)$ defined and continuous on an open region $\mathfrak{A}$ of the xy-plane. Then around any point (x_0,y_0) in $\mathfrak{A}$ we could draw a closed rectangular neighborhood $\mathfrak{R}$ of (x_0,y_0) such that $f(x,y)$ was defined and continuous on $\mathfrak{R}$. We then proceeded to prove various properties about f in $\mathfrak{R}$. Thus we avoided any discussion of the boundary of $\mathfrak{A}$. However, we cannot side-step this issue indefinitely. At some stage we must explicitly define what we mean by a curve or boundary in the plane. For example, if we pushed our study of real variables to Peano-Jordan content or the study of line integrals we

13

would be squarely faced with this issue.   Because the character of complex variables is essentially two-dimensional, we must come to grips with some phases of the problem even in the most elementary portions of the theory.

2.2 Point Sets

We mention again that we shall use the words *point* and *complex number* interchangeably.   Geometric language is convenient, but all our proofs will be arithmetic.

Let z_0 be any point in the complex plane.   The set of points z satisfying the inequality

$$|z - z_0| < \epsilon \tag{2.3}$$

for any $\epsilon > 0$ will be called a *neighborhood* of z_0, or more explicitly, an *ϵ-neighborhood* of z_0.   Clearly any point has an infinity of neighborhoods, one for every $\epsilon > 0$.   The neighborhood we have specified is a *spherical neighborhood*, that is, it consists of all points interior to a circle of radius ϵ with center at z_0.   Most proofs in complex variable theory use spherical neighborhoods, although it is, of course, possible to use rectangular neighborhoods as we sometimes did in the theory of functions of two real variables (see Chapter 6 of *ARC*).

We recall a few definitions.   Let E be a point set.   We say z_0 is a *limit point* of E if every neighborhood of z_0 contains points of E distinct from z_0.   A point set F is said to be *closed* if it contains all its limit points or else has none.   A point set G is said to be *open* if every point of G has a neighborhood entirely contained in G.   We introduce the term *perfect* to describe a closed set F such that every point of F is a limit point of F.   This rules out certain degenerate closed sets.   For example, if $\{\alpha_n\}$ is a sequence of complex numbers converging to α, then the point set consisting of the numbers $\alpha, \alpha_1, \alpha_2, \cdots$ is closed but not perfect.

The *complement* of a set E is defined as all points *not* in E.   An intimate relation between closed and open sets is expressed in the following theorem.

Theorem 1.   The complement of a closed set is open and the complement of an open set is closed.

Proof: Let F be a closed set and G its complement.   Suppose G is not open.   Then there exists a point z_0 in G such that every neighborhood of z_0 contains points of F.   By definition, z_0 is a limit point of F.   But F, being closed, contains all its limit points.   Thus z_0 is in F—a contradiction.

Let G be an open set and F its complement. Suppose F is not closed. Then there must exist a limit point z_0 of F which is not in F. Thus z_0 must be in G. But G is open. Therefore there exists a neighborhood of z_0 entirely contained in G. If this is so, z_0 cannot be a limit point of F, since every neighborhood of a limit point contains points of F distinct from the limit point—a contradiction.

One of the basic theorems of point set topology in real variables was the Heine-Borel covering theorem. We state it below for convenient reference, the proof being identical with that given in Chapter 6 of *ARC*. (We recall that a point set E is said to be *bounded* if there exists a rectangle R of finite dimensions such that every point of E is interior to R.)

Theorem 2: (*Heine-Borel*). Let E be a closed bounded point set. Let $\{C_i\}$ be a finite or infinite collection of circles such that every point of E is interior to at least one C_i. Then there exists a finite subset of the $\{C_i\}$ such that every point of E is interior to at least one member of this finite subset.

2.3 Continuous Curves

Section 2.2 covered essentially all the topological notions that were absolutely necessary to the study of the elementary theory of real variables, for example, as given in *ARC*. As we have noted in the introduction, a more penetrating analysis would have been necessary if certain aspects of real variable theory were to have been more deeply probed. In the present section we shall consider such topics as *continuous curves* and *rectifiability*.

Let

$$x = \phi(t), \qquad y = \psi(t)$$

be two real-valued continuous functions of the real variable t defined on the t-interval $[\alpha,\beta]$. We shall call such a pair of functions a *continuous curve, C*. The totality of points $z = x + iy$ obtained by allowing t to range over the closed interval $[\alpha,\beta]$ will be called the *points of the curve*. If no two distinct values of t yield the same point on the curve, we shall call the curve a *simple curve*. Thus a simple curve is a continuous curve with the property that

$$\phi(t_2) = \phi(t_1) \qquad \text{and} \qquad \psi(t_2) = \psi(t_1)$$

cannot be simultaneously true for $t_1 \neq t_2$. If $\phi(\alpha) + i\psi(\alpha) = \phi(\beta) + i\psi(\beta)$, we shall call the continuous curve C a *closed curve*. A closed curve will be called a *simple closed curve* if the only values of t which yield the same point on the curve are $t = \alpha$ and $t = \beta$. We see that the definition of simple curve rules out curves which have multiple points, such as, for example, the lemniscate or four-leaved rose.

One would imagine at first that "continuous curve" would be coextensive with our intuitive notion of "smooth curve." Such is not the case. Peano showed that there are continuous curves that pass through every point of a square!* Thus we see once more that geometric ideas must be replaced by precise arithmetical definitions if we are to build a logical theory.

In Chapter 4 of *ARC* when we introduced the Riemann integral of a function $f(x)$, the interval over which $f(x)$ was defined was *finite*; that is, its length was a finite number. We shortly shall consider curvilinear or contour integrals, that is, integrals of functions defined along continuous curves. It will turn out, as seems intuitively reasonable, that we shall have to require that our curve have finite length. Thus we now shall consider the problem of giving a precise meaning to the term *length* of a continuous curve.

Let $z_1 = x_1 + iy_1$ and $z_2 = x_2 + iy_2$ be two points in the complex plane. Then by the *line segment* joining z_1 and z_2 we mean the set of points

$$z = [x_1 + t(x_2 - x_1)] + i[y_1 + t(y_2 - y_1)], \qquad 0 \leqq t \leqq 1.$$

Thus a line segment can be described by a continuous curve. By the *length* of the segment $[z_1, z_2]$ we shall mean $|z_1 - z_2|$. A finite number of segments $[z_1, z_1'], [z_2, z_2'], \cdots, [z_n, z_n']$ is called a *polygon*, G, if $z_i' = z_{i+1}$, $i = 1, 2, \cdots, n - 1$. If G has no multiple points, we call it a *simple polygon*. If $z_1 = z_n'$ we call G a *closed polygon*, and if G is closed with no multiple points, we say G is a *simple closed polygon*. These definitions parallel those of continuous curve, simple curve, closed curve, and simple closed curve given earlier in this section. However, the *length* of a polygon is well defined; namely, it is the sum of the lengths of the segments comprising the polygon.

Now let

$$C: \begin{cases} x = \phi(t) \\ y = \psi(t) \end{cases} \qquad \alpha \leqq t \leqq \beta$$

be a continuous curve. Let π be a partition of $[\alpha, \beta]$,

$$\alpha = t_0 < t_1 < \cdots < t_n = \beta$$

* See, for example, P. Dienes, *The Taylor Series*, Oxford, Clarendon Press, 1931, p. 175.

and let $z_j = \phi(t_j) + i\psi(t_j)$, $j = 0, 1, \cdots, n$. The line segments $[z_0, z_1]$, $[z_1, z_2], \cdots, [z_{n-1}, z_n]$ form a polygon G, which we shall call a polygon *inscribed* in C. Let $\lambda(G)$ denote the length of the polygon. If l.u.b. $\lambda(G)$ exists where the l.u.b. is extended over all partitions of $[\alpha, \beta]$, then we say C is *rectifiable* and call L,

$$L = \text{l.u.b. } \lambda(G),$$

the *length* of C.

We shall now show that as the norm* Δ of the partition approaches zero, the lengths of the inscribed polygons approach the length of the curve.

Theorem 3. Let C be a rectifiable curve,

$$C: \begin{cases} x = \phi(t) \\ y = \psi(t) \end{cases} \quad \alpha \leq t \leq \beta.$$

Let π be a partition of $[\alpha, \beta]$ and Δ its norm. Then

$$L = \lim_{\Delta \to 0} \lambda(G_\pi),$$

where L is the length of C and $\lambda(G_\pi)$ is the length of the polygon G_π inscribed in C corresponding to the partition π.

Proof: Let $\epsilon > 0$ be assigned. Since $L = \text{l.u.b. } \lambda(G)$, there exists a partition π of $[\alpha, \beta]$ of norm δ such that

$$L - \lambda(G_\pi) < \frac{\epsilon}{2}.$$

Let n be the number of subdivisions in π. Now $\phi(t)$ and $\psi(t)$ are continuous and hence uniformly continuous on $[\alpha, \beta]$. Thus we may choose a $\delta' > 0$ so small that

$$\sqrt{[\phi(t) - \phi(u)]^2 + [\psi(t) - \psi(u)]^2} < \frac{\epsilon}{4n}$$

whenever $|t - u| < \delta'$.

Let π' be any partition of norm less than or equal to δ', and let ρ be a refinement of π and π' consisting of the points of subdivision belonging to both π and π'. Then, of course, $\lambda(G_\rho) \geq \lambda(G_{\pi'})$, $\lambda(G_\rho) \geq \lambda(G_\pi)$. If $\lambda(G_\rho) > \lambda(G_{\pi'})$, it will be because certain points of π lie between two consecutive points of π'. The excess of $\lambda(G_\rho)$ over

---

* By the *norm* of the partition we mean the maximum of the positive numbers $t_i - t_{i-1}$. See p. 48 of *ARC*.

$\lambda(G_{\pi'})$ corresponding to such points will be less than $n(2\epsilon/4n) = \epsilon/2$. Thus

$$\lambda(G_{\rho}) - \lambda(G_{\pi'}) < \frac{\epsilon}{2}$$

Since $\lambda(G_{\rho}) \geq \lambda(G_{\pi})$, we also have

$$\lambda(G_{\pi}) - \lambda(G_{\pi'}) < \frac{\epsilon}{2}.$$

But

$$L - \lambda(G_{\pi}) < \frac{\epsilon}{2}$$

by construction. These last two inequalities imply

$$L - \lambda(G_{\pi'}) < \epsilon.$$

We shall call a simple rectifiable curve a *Jordan arc* and a simple rectifiable closed curve a *Jordan curve*.

In the elementary calculus it was shown that the length of a curve could be expressed as

$$\int_{\alpha}^{\beta} \sqrt{[\phi'(t)]^2 + [\psi'(t)]^2} \, dt.$$

We give a precise statement and proof of this formula.

Theorem 4. Let C be a rectifiable curve,

$$C : \begin{cases} x = \phi(t) \\ y = \psi(t) \end{cases} \quad \alpha \leq t \leq \beta,$$

and let $\phi(t)$ and $\psi(t)$ have continuous first derivatives on $[\alpha,\beta]$. Then the length L of C is given by

$$L = \int_{\alpha}^{\beta} \sqrt{[\phi'(t)]^2 + [\psi'(t)]^2} \, dt.$$

Proof: Since $\phi'(t)$ and $\psi'(t)$ are continuous by hypothesis, the sum of their squares is also continuous on $[\alpha,\beta]$. We leave it to the reader to show that the square root is continuous. Thus the above integral is well defined. Let π be a partition of $[\alpha,\beta]$. Then the length of the inscribed polygon G_{π} corresponding to π is given by

$$\lambda(G_{\pi}) = \sum_{i=1}^{n} \sqrt{(x_i - x_{i-1})^2 + (y_i - y_{i-1})^2},$$

where, of course, $x_i = \phi(t_i)$ and $y_i = \psi(t_i)$, $i = 1, 2, \cdots, n$. By the Law of the Mean, there exist points ξ_i and η_i, $t_{i-1} < \xi_i < t_i$, $t_{i-1} < \eta_i < t_i$ such that

$$\phi(t_i) - \phi(t_{i-1}) = \phi'(\xi_i)(t_i - t_{i-1})$$

and

$$\psi(t_i) - \psi(t_{i-1}) = \psi'(\eta_i)(t_i - t_{i-1}).$$

Hence

$$\lambda(G_\pi) = \sum_{i=1}^{n} \sqrt{[\phi'(\xi_i)]^2 + [\psi'(\eta_i)]^2}\,(t_i - t_{i-1}).$$

The reader may easily verify that the function $f(u,v) = \sqrt{[\phi'(u)]^2 + [\psi'(v)]^2}$ is jointly continuous in the square $\alpha \leq u, v \leq \beta$. Now let $\epsilon > 0$ be assigned. Choose a $\delta > 0$ so small that

$$|f(u,v) - f(u',v')| < \frac{\epsilon}{2(\beta - \alpha)}$$

whenever $|u - u'| < \delta$ and $|v - v'| < \delta$, and also so small that

$$\left| \int_\alpha^\beta \sqrt{[\phi'(t)]^2 + [\psi'(t)]^2}\,dt - \sum_{i=1}^{n} \sqrt{[\phi'(t_i')]^2 + [\psi'(t_i')]^2}\,(t_i - t_{i-1}) \right| < \frac{\epsilon}{2}$$

$$(2.4)$$

whenever $t_i - t_{i-1} < \delta$ and t_i' is any point in $[t_{i-1}, t_i]$. Let π have norm less than or equal to δ. Then, since

$$|\xi_i - t_i'| < \delta \qquad \text{and} \qquad |\eta_i - t_i'| < \delta,$$

we have

$$\left| \lambda(G_\pi) - \sum_{i=1}^{n} f(t_i', t_i')(t_i - t_{i-1}) \right| < \frac{\epsilon}{2}. \qquad (2.5)$$

Equations 2.4 and 2.5 imply

$$\left| \lambda(G_\pi) - \int_\alpha^\beta \sqrt{[\phi'(t)]^2 + [\psi'(t)]^2}\,dt \right| < \epsilon.$$

Theorem 3 completes the proof.

2.4 Functions of Bounded Variation

Since curves may be described by pairs of real functions of a real variable, we need only consider real variable theory in order to analyze them. A convenient criterion is to require that the functions be of *bounded variation*. This in itself is a useful way to classify real functions. We shall define the term *bounded variation* and deduce some theorems based on this definition. Other properties of functions of bounded variation will be found in the exercises at the end of this chapter.

Let $f(x)$ be a function of the real variable x defined on $[a,b]$.   Let π,

$$a = x_0 < x_1 < \cdots < x_n = b,$$

be a partition of $[a,b]$ and consider the sum

$$S_\pi = \sum_{k=1}^{n} |f(x_k) - f(x_{k-1})|.$$

If the totality of sums $\{S_\pi\}$ for all partitions of $[a,b]$ forms a bounded set, then we shall say $f(x)$ is of *bounded variation* on $[a,b]$.   We call

$$V(f) = \text{l.u.b.} \, S_\pi$$

the *variation* of $f(x)$ on $[a,b]$.

A function of bounded variation is of necessity bounded; however, a function of bounded variation need not be continuous.   This does not imply that every continuous function is of bounded variation, as we can show by the following example.

Let $f(x)$ be defined on the closed interval $[0,1]$ as

$$f(x) = x \sin \frac{1}{x}, \qquad x \neq 0$$

$$f(x) = 0, \qquad\quad x = 0.$$

It is easy to see that $f(x)$ is continuous on $[0,1]$.   Using the elementary properties of the trigonometric functions (see Section 3.4), we shall show that $f(x)$ is not of bounded variation on $[0,1]$.

Let

$$S_p = \sum_{k=1}^{p} |f(x_k) - f(x_{k-1})|,$$

where

$$0 = x_0 < x_1 < \cdots < x_p = 1.$$

We shall show that for any preassigned positive number M there exists an integer p and a partition of $[0,1]$ such that $S_p > M$.   This will then imply that $f(x)$ is not of bounded variation on $[0,1]$.

For any positive integer $n > 2$ choose the partition

$$x_0 = 0$$

$$x_k = \frac{1}{\dfrac{\pi}{2} + (n - k - 1)\pi}, \qquad k = 1, 2, \cdots, n - 1$$

$$x_n = 1.$$

Then

$$S_n = \sum_{k=1}^{n} |f(x_k) - f(x_{k-1})| = \frac{1}{\frac{\pi}{2} + (n-2)\pi}$$

$$+ \sum_{k=2}^{n-1} \left| \frac{1}{\frac{\pi}{2} + (n-k-1)\pi} + \frac{1}{\frac{\pi}{2} + (n-k)\pi} \right| + \left| \sin 1 - \frac{2}{\pi} \right|$$

$$> \sum_{k=2}^{n-1} \left| \frac{1}{(n-k)\pi} + \frac{1}{(n-k+1)\pi} \right| > 2 \sum_{k=2}^{n-1} \frac{1}{(n-k+1)\pi}$$

$$= \frac{2}{\pi} \sum_{\beta=2}^{n-1} \frac{1}{\beta}.$$

Now let N be an integer which exceeds $4M$ and let $p = 2^N + 1$. Then if S_p is the sum corresponding to the partition of the above form for $n = p$,

$$S_p > \frac{2}{\pi} \sum_{\beta=2}^{2^N} \frac{1}{\beta} > \frac{2}{\pi} \left(\frac{N}{2} \right) = \frac{N}{\pi} > \frac{4M}{\pi} > M.$$

However, while not every continuous function is of bounded variation, we can show that if it has a bounded derivative it *is* of bounded variation.

Theorem 5. Let $f(x)$ be differentiable on $[a,b]$ and let $|f'(x)| \leq M$ for all x in $[a,b]$. Then $f(x)$ is of bounded variation on $[a,b]$.

Proof: Let π be any partition of $[a,b]$ and let

$$S = \sum_{k=1}^{n} |f(x_k) - f(x_{k-1})|.$$

By the Law of the Mean there exist points ξ_k such that

$$f(x_k) - f(x_{k-1}) = f'(\xi_k)(x_k - x_{k-1}), \qquad x_{k-1} < \xi_k < x_k.$$

Then

$$|f(x_k) - f(x_{k-1})| = |f'(\xi_k)| \cdot |x_k - x_{k-1}| \leq M(x_k - x_{k-1})$$

and

$$S \leq M(b - a)$$

for any partition of $[a,b]$. Thus $f(x)$ is of bounded variation on $[a,b]$.

Corollary. If $f'(x)$ is continuous on $[a,b]$, then $f(x)$ is of bounded variation on $[a,b]$.

Proof: If $f'(x)$ is continuous on $[a,b]$, it is bounded on $[a,b]$ and hence Theorem 5 applies.

Note that it was necessary to include the boundedness of $f'(x)$ in the statement of Theorem 5. That is, the mere existence of $f'(x)$ on $[a,b]$ does not imply its boundedness, as can be seen by the following example.

Let $f(x)$ be defined on $[0,1]$ as

$$f(x) = x^2 \sin \frac{1}{x^2}, \qquad x \neq 0$$

$$f(x) = 0, \qquad\qquad x = 0.$$

Clearly $f(x)$ is continuous on $[0,1]$. If $x \neq 0$,

$$f'(x) = 2x \sin \frac{1}{x^2} - \frac{2}{x} \cos \frac{1}{x^2},$$

and if $x = 0$,

$$f'(0) = \lim_{\substack{h \to 0 \\ h > 0}} \frac{f(h) - f(0)}{h} = \lim_{\substack{h \to 0 \\ h > 0}} h \sin \frac{1}{h^2} = 0.$$

Thus $f'(x)$ exists for all x on $[0,1]$. However, $f'(x)$ is not bounded. For suppose that there existed an M such that $M \geqq |f'(x)|$ for all x in $[0,1]$. Let N be an odd integer greater than M. Then

$$f'\left(\frac{1}{N\sqrt{\pi}}\right) = -2N\sqrt{\pi} \cos N^2\pi = -2N\sqrt{\pi}(-1)^{N^2} = 2N\sqrt{\pi} > M,$$

which is a contradiction. (This function is not of bounded variation.)

We do not wish to mislead the reader with the above counterexample. Theorem 5 expresses a *sufficient* condition on $f(x)$ that it be of bounded variation; for, as we have noted, a function may be of bounded variation without even being continuous, let alone differentiable. Thus while differentiability in itself is neither necessary nor sufficient to insure bounded variation, the existence of a *bounded* derivative *is* sufficient.

The key result of this section is the following theorem.

Theorem 6.   Let C,

$$C: \begin{cases} x = \phi(t) \\ y = \psi(t) \end{cases} \qquad \alpha \leqq t \leqq \beta,$$

be a continuous curve.   A necessary and sufficient condition that C be rectifiable is that $\phi(t)$ and $\psi(t)$ be of bounded variation on $[\alpha,\beta]$.

Proof: Necessity. Let C be rectifiable of length L. Let π be any partition of $[\alpha,\beta]$. Then from

$$(x_i - x_{i-1})^2 + (y_i - y_{i-1})^2 \geq (x_i - x_{i-1})^2$$

follows

$$L \geq \sum_{i=1}^{n} [(x_i - x_{i-1})^2 + (y_i - y_{i-1})^2]^{1/2} \geq \sum_{i=1}^{n} |\phi(t_i) - \phi(t_{i-1})|.$$

Thus $\phi(t)$ is of bounded variation with variation $V(\phi) \leq L$. Similarly $V(\psi) \leq L$.

Sufficiency: Let $\phi(t)$ and $\psi(t)$ be of bounded variation on $[\alpha,\beta]$ with variations $V(\phi)$ and $V(\psi)$ respectively. Then from the inequality

$$[(x_i - x_{i-1})^2 + (y_i - y_{i-1})^2]^{1/2} \leq |x_i - x_{i-1}| + |y_i - y_{i-1}|$$

follows

$$\sum_{i=1}^{n} [(x_i - x_{i-1})^2 + (y_i - y_{i-1})^2]^{1/2} \leq \sum_{i=1}^{n} |x_i - x_{i-1}| + \sum_{i=1}^{n} |y_i - y_{i-1}|$$

$$\leq V(\phi) + V(\psi)$$

and C is rectifiable of length $L \leq V(\phi) + V(\psi)$.

2.5 Jordan's Theorem

Let C be the unit circle $|z| = 1$ in the complex plane. Then it seems self-evident that the circle divides the plane into two regions—the interior of the circle and the exterior of the circle, which have the circumference of C as their common boundary. Interior points are values of z satisfying the relation $|z| < 1$; exterior points are those values of z satisfying the inequality $|z| > 1$; and the boundary points of C are the set of points $|z| = 1$. However, after learning about such a pathological curve as the Peano curve we would hesitate to surmise without a formal proof that every Jordan curve Γ has this property of dividing the plane into two distinct regions with Γ as a common boundary. Fortunately such a formal proof can be given. However, before giving a precise statement of the "separation theorem" we would like to recall a few more definitions of point set topology and introduce some new ones.

A point α belonging to a set E is called an *interior* point if α has a neighborhood entirely contained in E. Thus if E is an open set, every point of E is an interior point. Conversely, a point γ not belonging to E is called an *exterior* point if γ has a neighborhood containing no points of E. If β is a point in the plane with the property that every neighborhood of β contains both points *in* E and points *not* in E, then we say β is a *boundary* point of E. For example, if E is the set of points satisfying the inequality $|z| < 1$, then the interior points, exterior points, and boundary points are exactly those described in the first paragraph of this section. An immediate consequence of these definitions is the following theorem.

Theorem 7. Let E be a point set. The set B of all boundary points of E forms a closed set.

Proof: If B has no limit points, the theorem is trivial. Suppose, then, that it has limit points. Let α be any such limit point. Then every neighborhood $\mathfrak{N}_\alpha$ of α contains points of B. Let β be a point of B in $\mathfrak{N}_\alpha$. Then there exists a neighborhood $\mathfrak{N}_\beta$ of β entirely contained in $\mathfrak{N}_\alpha$. Since $\mathfrak{N}_\beta$ contains points in E and not in E, $\mathfrak{N}_\alpha$ also has this property. Hence α is a boundary point of B. Thus B is closed.

Note that the *boundary* as defined above need not coincide with our intuitive notion of boundary. For example, if E is the whole plane, every point is an interior point. There are no exterior points or boundary points. If E consists of all complex numbers $a + ib$ where a is rational and b irrational, then every point of E is a boundary point. In fact, every point of the plane is a boundary point. If E is the real axis, then every point not on the real axis is an exterior point and every point on the real axis is a boundary point.

Two points α and β in an open set G are said to be *connected* if there is a continuous curve lying entirely in G which connects α to β. Equivalently, we can say α and β are connected if there exists a finite sequence of overlapping circles, entirely contained in G, with the property that α is in the first circle and β is in the last. The proof of the equivalence is as follows: (i) Let C be the continuous curve. Around every point of C draw a circle entirely contained in E. This is possible since G is open. Now apply the Heine-Borel theorem to obtain a finite sequence. (A continuous curve is a closed bounded set.) (ii) Conversely, if we have a finite sequence of overlapping circles, we can draw a polygon entirely contained in these circles which connects α to β. Such a polygonal path is a continuous curve. If every pair of points in an open set G is connected we say G is *connected*.

The Jordan separation theorem may now be stated.

Theorem 8: (*Jordan's Theorem*). A simple closed curve C divides the plane into two connected open sets having C for their common boundary. One of these connected open sets is bounded, the other unbounded. Any continuous curve which connects a point of the unbounded region to a point of the bounded region contains at least one point of C.

A complete proof of this theorem may be found in such books as those of Newman or Dienes.* However, the proof is very involved and would take us too far afield since many topological preliminaries are needed. We therefore shall content ourselves with the statement of the theorem. In all practical situations it is obvious that the theorem is satisfied since in most *applications* the most complicated type of region considered is a circle or trivial variation thereof.

Finally, we would like to introduce some additional terminology and discuss some consequences of the Jordan curve theorem. It is customary to call the *unbounded* connected open set the *exterior* of C and the *bounded* connected open set the *interior* of C. This is in harmony with our geometric intuition. If every simple closed curve which lies in an open set G has the property that its interior also lies in G, then we call G *simply connected*. For example, if G is the set of points z defined by the inequalities $1 < |z| < 2$, then G is connected but not simply connected. The interior of a Jordan curve is simply connected.

Let C,

$$C: \begin{cases} x = \phi(t) \\ y = \psi(t) \end{cases} \quad \alpha \leq t \leq \beta,$$

be a continuous curve. Suppose that C',

$$C': \begin{cases} x = f(\tau) \\ y = g(\tau) \end{cases} \quad a \leq \tau \leq b,$$

is also a continuous curve which bears the following relation to C: There exists a monotonically increasing function $\tau = \tau(t)$ continuous on $[\alpha,\beta]$ such that

$$\begin{aligned} f(\tau(t)) &= \phi(t) \\ g(\tau(t)) &= \psi(t) \end{aligned} \quad \alpha \leq t \leq \beta \tag{2.6}$$

and

$$\tau(\alpha) = a, \qquad \tau(\beta) = b. \tag{2.7}$$

Then we say C and C' are *equivalent*. Clearly they have the same points.

If $\tau = \tau(t)$ is a monotonically decreasing function, continuous on $[\alpha,\beta]$ with the property that Equations 2.6 are verified, but that

$$\tau(\beta) = a, \qquad \tau(\alpha) = b$$

---

* M. H. A. Newman, *Elements of the Topology of Plane Sets of Points*, Cambridge University Press, pp. 115 ff.; Dienes, *op. cit.*, pp. 177 ff.

replaces Equations 2.7, then we say C and C' are *inversely equivalent*. Again they have the same points.

Consider now a circle C of radius R with center at $x_0 + iy_0$,

$$C: \begin{cases} x = x_0 + R\cos t \\ y = y_0 + R\sin t \end{cases} \quad 0 \leqq t \leqq 2\pi, \tag{2.8}$$

(See Section 3.4 for a definition of the trigonometric functions.) Then we shall call C a *positively sensed circle*. By this we mean that as t increases from 0 to 2π, the corresponding points $z = x + iy$ on C move in a *counterclockwise* direction around the circle. If C' is a circle inversely equivalent to C, then we shall call C' a *negatively sensed circle*. While the idea of "clockwise" and "counterclockwise" as applied to circles is clear, this concept is not necessarily so obvious when applied to general simple closed curves. Nevertheless, by using Theorem 8 it is not too difficult to give precise meanings to the terms positively and negatively sensed even in these cases. In all applications there will be no ambiguity.

EXERCISES

2.1. Let $\{G_\alpha\}$ be a collection of sets. Let G be the set with the property that z is a point in G if and only if z is in some G_α. Then we call G the *union* of the sets G_α. Show that the union of any collection of open sets is again open. Show that the union of any collection of closed sets is not necessarily closed.

2.2. Let E be a point set. A point α is called a *point of closure* of E if every neighborhood of α contains points of E. If $\bar{E}$ is the set of all points of closure of E, prove that $\bar{E}$ is a closed set.

2.3. A point set E is said to be *compact* if every infinite set of points in E has at least one limit point in E. Prove that a necessary and sufficient condition that E be compact is that it be closed and bounded.

2.4. The set of all limit points of E is called the *derived set* E' of E. Prove that $\bar{E} = E + E'$. That is, show that every point in the closure of E is either in E or E' and that every point in E or in the derived set is in $\bar{E}$.

2.5. If $f(x)$ is monotonic on $[a,b]$, show that it is of bounded variation on $[a,b]$.

2.6. If $f(x)$ is of bounded variation on $[a,c]$ and on $[c,b]$, prove that $f(x)$ is of bounded variation on $[a,b]$. Conversely, if $f(x)$ is of bounded variation on $[a,b]$ and c is an interior point of the interval, prove that

$$V_{ab} = V_{ac} + V_{cb},$$

where V_{ab}, V_{ac}, V_{cb} represent the variation of $f(x)$ on the intervals $[a,b]$, $[a,c]$, and $[c,b]$ respectively.

2.7. If $f(x)$ and $g(x)$ are of bounded variation on $[a,b]$, prove that $f(x) + g(x)$, $f(x)g(x)$, and $1/f(x)$ (provided $|f(x)|$ is bounded away from zero) are of bounded variation on $[a,b]$.

2.8. If $f(x)$ is of bounded variation on $[a,b]$, show that there exist two positive monotonically increasing functions $g(x)$ and $h(x)$ such that

$$f(x) = g(x) - h(x).$$

2.9. Prove that a function of bounded variation is Riemann integrable.

2.10. Let $\mathfrak{A}$ be a connected open set. Prove that every pair of points in $\mathfrak{A}$ can be joined by a rectifiable curve lying entirely in $\mathfrak{A}$.

2.11. Let E be the set of all complex numbers $a + ib$ where a and b are both rational. Prove that the complement of E is connected. Furthermore, show that any two points in the complement of E can be joined by a polygon of not more than three sides.

2.12. Show that if two simple curves have the same points they are either equivalent or inversely equivalent.

CHAPTER 3

Functions of a Complex Variable

3.1 Introduction

In this chapter we shall discuss certain elementary properties of functions of a complex variable. By a *complex variable* we mean a number of the form $z = x + iy$ where x and y are real independent variables. Limits, continuity, uniform continuity, and boundedness of functions will be defined and various theorems proved. They will be analogous to the corresponding definitions and theorems for the real case. The *elementary functions* such as the trigonometric and exponential functions will be defined and their extension to the complex domain will be examined. These functions together with the rational functions will give us a repertoire of functions that will be useful in later applications. We shall then be able to discuss such functions as the logarithm of a complex variable and the (complex) power of a complex variable. After a brief discussion of multi-valued real functions we shall present an interesting discussion of multi-valued complex functions by the use of *Riemann surfaces*. We shall then be in a position to give precise and crisp proofs of theorems on differentiability and analyticity. The concept of analyticity is perhaps the most important single idea in the elementary theory of functions of a complex variable. Among other things, we shall derive the Cauchy-Riemann equations. The material presented in this chapter will lay a solid foundation for the detailed and, we believe, fascinating theory of integration that will be unfolded in Chapters 4 and 6.

3.2 Functions

Let $\mathfrak{C}$ be any set of points z in the complex plane. Suppose that a rule has been given that associates with every point z in $\mathfrak{C}$ at least one point w. We indicate this by writing

$$w = f(z)$$

and calling f a *function* of the complex variable z. The *domain* of f is $\mathfrak{C}$ and the *range* of f is the set of values assumed by w. For example, if $\mathfrak{C}$ is the unit circle $|z| \leq 1$, and $w = f(z) = 3z^2 + 1 + i$, then the range $\mathfrak{B}$ of f is the set of points $|w - (1 + i)| \leq 3$. That is, $\mathfrak{B}$ is a circle of radius 3 with center at $1 + i$ (see Fig. 3.1). We sometimes say f is a *mapping* of the region $\mathfrak{C}$ onto the region $\mathfrak{B}$.

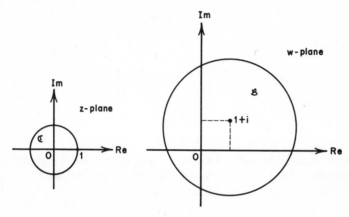

Figure 3.1

Suppose then that $f(z)$ is defined and single-valued on some open set $\mathfrak{A}$. Let z_0 be a point in $\mathfrak{A}$. If there exists a complex number A such that for every $\epsilon > 0$ there exists a $\delta > 0$ such that

$$|f(z) - A| < \epsilon \tag{3.1}$$

whenever

$$0 < |z - z_0| < \delta, \tag{3.2}$$

then we say $f(z)$ *has A for a limit as z approaches z_0*. We sometimes write

$$\lim_{z \to z_0} f(z) = A \tag{3.3}$$

to indicate this fact. That is, Equation 3.3 is nothing more than a shorthand notation for the precise definition of limit embodied in Equations 3.1 and 3.2.

Note that our complex limit is essentially that of functions of *two* real variables, since Equation 3.2 may be written

$$0 < |(x + iy) - (x_0 + iy_0)| = \sqrt{(x - x_0)^2 + (y - y_0)^2} < \delta.$$

Thus we actually have two degrees of freedom, and the statement "z approaches z_0" implies the *joint* approach of x and y to x_0 and y_0 respectively.

For example, the function

$$f(z) = \frac{z^2}{|z|^2}, \qquad z \neq 0$$

does *not* have a limit as z approaches zero.   For if we let $x = \text{Re}\,[z] = 0$, then

$$f(z) = \frac{(iy)^2}{|y|^2} = -1,$$

and if we let $y = \text{Im}\,[z] = 0$,

$$f(z) = \frac{x^2}{|x|^2} = +1.$$

Thus

$$\lim_{z \to 0} f(z)$$

does not exist.

The fundamental theorems on limits are given in Theorem 1 below. Their proofs will be omitted since they are identical with the corresponding proofs in the real case.

Theorem I.   Let $f(z)$ and $g(z)$ be defined and single-valued on some open region $\mathfrak{A}$ of the complex plane.   Let $f(z)$ and $g(z)$ have α and β respectively as limits as z approaches z_0 (some point in $\mathfrak{A}$).   Then

(i) $\lim\limits_{z \to z_0} [f(z) + g(z)] = \alpha + \beta$

(ii) $\lim\limits_{z \to z_0} f(z)g(z) = \alpha\beta$

(iii) $\lim\limits_{z \to z_0} \dfrac{1}{f(z)} = \dfrac{1}{\alpha},$ provided $\alpha \neq 0$.

3.3 Continuity

Let $w = f(z)$ be defined and single-valued on an open region $\mathfrak{A}$ of the complex plane.   Let z_0 be a point in $\mathfrak{A}$.   Clearly $f(z_0)$ is defined.   If for every $\epsilon > 0$, there exists a $\delta > 0$ such that

$$|f(z) - f(z_0)| < \epsilon$$

whenever $|z - z_0| < \delta$, then we say $f(z)$ is *continuous* at z_0.   Again we emphasize that continuity of a function of a *single* complex variable is essentially the same as the *joint* continuity of functions of *two* real variables.

For example, $f(z) = z^2$, where z is defined in the unit circle

$\mathfrak{C}:\{|z| < 1\}$, is continuous at every point of $\mathfrak{C}$.   For let z_0 be any point in $\mathfrak{C}$.   Then

$$|z^2 - z_0^2| = |(z - z_0)(z + z_0)| \leq (|z| + |z_0|)|z - z_0| < 2|z - z_0|.$$

Thus if $\epsilon > 0$ is assigned, choose $\delta = \frac{1}{2}\epsilon$.   The function $f(z) = |z|$ is also continuous for any z since

$$||z| - |z_0|| \leq |z - z_0|$$

by the corollary to Theorem 2 of Chapter 1, and we need only let $\delta = \epsilon$.

The sums, products, and quotients of continuous functions are also continuous; and the function of a function rule holds.   We formally state these results.

Theorem 2.   Let $f(z)$ and $g(z)$ be defined and single-valued in an open region $\mathfrak{A}$ and be continuous at some point z_0 in $\mathfrak{A}$.   Then $f(z) \pm g(z)$, $f(z)g(z)$, and $1/f(z)$ (provided $f(z_0) \neq 0$) are continuous at $z = z_0$.   If $h(\zeta)$ is defined in a neighborhood of $\zeta_0 = f(z_0)$ and continuous at $\zeta = f(z_0)$, then $h(f(z))$ is continuous at $z = z_0$.

The proof of this theorem parallels the corresponding proofs for real variables and will be omitted here.   (See also Theorem 1 of this chapter.)

If $f(z)$ is defined and single-valued on an open set $\mathfrak{A}$ and continuous at every point of $\mathfrak{A}$, then we shall say that $f(z)$ is *continuous on* $\mathfrak{A}$.   It is sometimes necessary, or at least convenient, to define continuity on a closed set.   Suppose then that $f(z)$ is defined on a set E.   Let z_0 be a point of E.   We have seen that continuity at z_0 is meaningful only if z_0 is a limit point.   (Note that every point of an open set $\mathfrak{A}$ is a limit point of $\mathfrak{A}$).   Now it may be that even though z_0 is a limit point of E belonging to E, it may fail to have a neighborhood entirely contained in E.   (For example, z_0 may be a boundary point of E.)   We therefore adopt the following convention: If for any $\epsilon > 0$ there exists a $\delta > 0$ such that

$$|f(z) - f(z_0)| < \epsilon$$

for all z *in* E with the property that $|z - z_0| < \delta$, then we say $f(z)$ is continuous at z_0.   (This definition parallels the definition of continuity for real variables at the end points of a closed interval.)   Thus we can extend the definition given in the first sentence of this paragraph to any set $\mathfrak{B}$ such that every point of $\mathfrak{B}$ is a limit point—for example, to perfect sets.

For real variables we showed that a function continuous on a closed interval was uniformly continuous.   We can prove a similar theorem for complex functions. Of course, we must replace the "closed interval" by some appropriate two-dimensional closed set. For example, a closed rectangle or, more generally, a bounded perfect set will suffice.

Our definition of uniform continuity is the expected one. Let $f(z)$ be defined and single-valued on a set $\mathfrak{B}$ such that every point of $\mathfrak{B}$ is a limit point, and let $f(z)$ be continuous at every point of $\mathfrak{B}$. If, given an $\epsilon > 0$, there exists a $\delta > 0$ such that

$$|f(z_1) - f(z_2)| < \epsilon$$

whenever $|z_1 - z_2| < \delta$, then we shall say $f(z)$ is *uniformly continuous* on $\mathfrak{B}$. Of course the important point to note is that δ is independent of the points z_1, z_2.

Theorem 3. Let $f(z)$ be continuous on a bounded perfect set E. Then $f(z)$ is uniformly continuous on E.

Proof: Let $\epsilon > 0$ be assigned. Then for every point z' in E there exists a $\delta > 0$, $\delta \equiv \delta(z')$ such that

$$|f(z) - f(z')| < \frac{\epsilon}{2}$$

whenever $|z - z'| < \delta(z')$. Now consider a circle of radius $\frac{1}{2}\delta(z')$ with center at z', for all z' in E. We have therefore covered every point of E by a spherical neighborhood of positive radius. By the Heine-Borel theorem (Theorem 2 of Chapter 2) there exists a finite subset of the $\delta(z')$, say $\delta_1, \delta_2, \cdots, \delta_N$, such that every point of E is interior to at least one of these δ_k-neighborhoods. Let

$$\delta = \frac{1}{2} \min [\delta_1, \delta_2, \cdots, \delta_N].$$

We assert that this is the uniform δ for the given ϵ. That is, we shall show that

$$|f(\zeta) - f(\eta)| < \epsilon$$

for any two points ζ, η in E such that $|\zeta - \eta| < \delta$.

Let ζ be any point in E. By the above construction there exists a δ_k such that ζ is interior to the neighborhood which has $\frac{1}{2}\delta_k$ as its radius. Let z_k' be the center of this circle. Then

$$|\zeta - z_k'| < \frac{1}{2}\delta_k < \delta_k. \qquad (3.4)$$

Now if η is any point such that

$$|\eta - \zeta| < \delta \leqq \frac{1}{2} \delta_k,$$

then

$$|\eta - z_k'| = |(\eta - \zeta) + (\zeta - z_k')| \leqq |\eta - \zeta| + |\zeta - z_k'|$$
$$< \frac{1}{2} \delta_k + \frac{1}{2} \delta_k = \delta_k. \qquad (3.5)$$

From Equation 3.4

$$|f(\zeta) - f(z_k')| < \frac{\epsilon}{2}$$

and from Equation 3.5

$$|f(\eta) - f(z_k')| < \frac{\epsilon}{2}.$$

These last two inequalities imply

$$|f(\eta) - f(\zeta)| < \epsilon$$

whenever $|\zeta - \eta| < \delta$.

There are other properties of continuous functions that we could mention. For example, a function $f(z)$ defined and single-valued on a region $\mathfrak{B}$ is said to be *bounded* if there exists a real number M such that

$$|f(z)| \leqq M$$

for all z in $\mathfrak{B}$. We can thus prove the following theorem.

Theorem 4. Let $f(z)$ be continuous on a bounded perfect set E. Then $f(z)$ is bounded on E.

Proof: Suppose $f(z)$ is not bounded. Then there exists a point z_1 in E such that

$$|f(z_1)| > 0.$$

Also there exists a point z_2 in E such that

$$|f(z_2)| > |f(z_1)| + 1.$$

For if this were not the case, we could use $|f(z_1)| + 1$ as our bound. Similarly, we construct an infinite sequence of distinct points, z_1, $z_2, \cdots$, in E with the property that

$$|f(z_{k+1})| > |f(z_k)| + 1, \qquad k = 1,2,\cdots.$$

By the Bolzano-Weierstrass theorem,* the set of points $\{\mathrm{Re}\,[z_n]\}$ has a limit point, say x_0. Let $\{x_{n_k}\}$, $k = 1, 2, \cdots$, where $x_{n_k} = \mathrm{Re}\,[z_{n_k}]$,

* See *ARC*, p. 21.

be a sequence of x's converging to x_0. Then $\{y_{n_k}\}$, $k = 1, 2, \cdots$, where $y_{n_k} = \text{Im}\,[z_{n_k}]$ is a bounded sequence. Again by the Bolzano-Weierstrass theorem the sequence $\{\text{Im}\,[z_{n_k}]\}$ has a limit point, say y_0. Let

$$\{y_{n_{k_\alpha}}\}, \qquad \alpha = 1, 2, \cdots$$

be a subsequence of $\{y_{n_k}\}$ which converges to y_0. Then the sequence $\{\zeta_\alpha\}$, where

$$\zeta_\alpha = x_{n_{k_\alpha}} + iy_{n_{k_\alpha}}$$

converges to $x_0 + iy_0$. Since E is closed, $z_0 = x_0 + iy_0$ is in E.

Now $f(z)$ is continuous at z_0 by hypothesis. Let $\epsilon = \frac14$. Then there exists a $\delta > 0$ such that

$$|f(z_0) - f(z)| < \frac{1}{4}$$

whenever $|z_0 - z| < \delta$. Since z_0 is a limit point, there exists an infinite number of the ζ_α points such that $|z_0 - \zeta_\alpha| < \delta$. Let ζ_p and ζ_q be any two such distinct points. Then

$$|f(\zeta_p) - f(z_0)| < \frac{1}{4}, \qquad |f(\zeta_q) - f(z_0)| < \frac{1}{4}.$$

But

$$\begin{aligned}
1 \leq |p - q| &< \big||f(\zeta_p)| - |f(\zeta_q)|\big| \leq |f(\zeta_p) - f(\zeta_q)| \\
&= |f(\zeta_p) - f(z_0) + f(z_0) - f(\zeta_q)| \\
&\leq |f(\zeta_p) - f(z_0)| + |f(z_0) - f(\zeta_q)| < \frac{1}{4} + \frac{1}{4} = \frac{1}{2},
\end{aligned}$$

which is absurd.

3.4 The Elementary Functions

A *polynomial* is a function of z of the form

$$f(z) = a_0 z^n + a_1 z^{n-1} + \cdots + a_n,$$

where n is a nonnegative integer and the a_i are complex constants. If $a_0 \neq 0$, we say $f(z)$ is a *polynomial of degree n*. Thus a non-zero constant is a polynomial of degree zero. We do not assign a degree to the polynomial which is identically zero.* From Theorem 2 we see that $f(z)$ is continuous. A *rational function* of z is the ratio of two polynomials. For example,

$$g(z) = \frac{a_0 z^n + a_1 z^{n-1} + \cdots + a_n}{b_0 z^m + b_1 z^{m-1} + \cdots + b_m},$$

* Some authors say such a polynomial has degree "minus infinity."

where not all the b_k are zero, is a rational function; and $g(z)$ is continuous for all z which do not make the denominator vanish.

The reader is also familiar with other elementary functions, for example, the trigonometric functions, the exponential, and the logarithm for *real* argument. We wish to extend their definitions to the complex plane. However, let us first give a precise meaning to sin x, cos x, e^x, and log x when x is *real*. One way of doing this is to consider the following infinite series:

$$E(x) = \sum_{n=0}^{\infty} \frac{x^n}{n!} \tag{3.6}$$

$$S(x) = \sum_{n=1}^{\infty} (-1)^{n-1} \frac{x^{2n-1}}{(2n-1)!} \tag{3.7}$$

$$C(x) = \sum_{n=0}^{\infty} (-1)^n \frac{x^{2n}}{(2n)!}. \tag{3.8}$$

It is easily seen that they all converge for all values of x. Thus they represent power series which converge uniformly and absolutely in every finite closed interval, which can be integrated and differentiated any number of times, and the resulting series will still be a uniformly and absolutely convergent power series in any interval.

We shall sketch a line of argument to show that the functions defined by Equations 3.6, 3.7, and 3.8 are actually the familiar e^x, sin x, and cos x functions, respectively. One easily verifies that

$$E(0) = 1, \qquad S(0) = 0, \qquad C(0) = 1$$

$$E'(x) = E(x), \qquad S'(x) = C(x), \qquad C'(x) = -S(x)$$

and that $S(x)$ is an odd function while $C(x)$ is an even function. Since all series converge absolutely we may multiply the series together, rearrange terms, and still have a convergent series. Doing this, we can establish the formulas

$$S(x + y) = S(x)C(y) + C(x)S(y) \tag{3.9}$$

$$C(x + y) = C(x)C(y) - S(x)S(y) \tag{3.10}$$

and letting $x = -y$ in Equation 3.10, we have the corollary

$$S^2(x) + C^2(x) = 1. \tag{3.11}$$

From this last identity we infer

$$|S(x)| \leqq 1, \qquad |C(x)| \leqq 1. \tag{3.12}$$

Similar to Equations 3.9 and 3.10 we can establish the *addition formula*

$$E(x + y) = E(x)E(y)$$

for $E(x)$. We then define e^x as $E(x)$.

Since $C(0) = 1$ and by a direct calculation $C(2) < 0$, there must be a point in the closed interval $[0,2]$ at which $C(x)$ vanishes. Let $x = p$ be the smallest value (if there is more than one) for which $C(x)$ vanishes. From Equation 3.11 we see that $S(p) = \pm 1$. We assert that $S(p) = +1$. For, by the Law of the Mean,

$$S(p) - S(0) = C(\xi)(p - 0),$$

where $0 < \xi < p$. Since $C(\xi) > 0$ and $S(0) = 0$,

$$S(p) = C(\xi)p > 0$$

and hence $S(p) = +1$. From Equations 3.9 and 3.10 it is easy to see that $S(x)$ and $C(x)$ are periodic of period $4p$. For

$$S(x + p) = S(x)C(p) + S(p)C(x) = C(x)$$

$$C(x + p) = C(x)C(p) - S(x)S(p) = -S(x)$$

and

$$S(x + 2p) = S(x + p)C(p) + C(x + p)S(p) = C(x + p) = -S(x)$$

$$C(x + 2p) = C(x + p)C(p) - S(x + p)S(p) = -S(x + p) = -C(x),$$

while finally

$$S(x + 4p) = S(x + 2p)C(2p) + C(x + 2p)S(2p)$$

$$= [-S(x)][-S(p)] + [-C(x)][-S(0)] = S(x)$$

$$C(x + 4p) = C(x + 2p)C(2p) - S(x + 2p)S(2p) = C(x).$$

It is easy to see that

$$\Gamma(t) = C(t) + iS(t), \qquad 0 \le t \le 4p$$

is a simple closed curve. By Theorem 4 of Chapter 2, its length is

$$L = \int_0^{4p} \sqrt{[C'(t)]^2 + [S'(t)]^2}\, dt = \int_0^{4p} \sqrt{S^2(t) + C^2(t)}\, dt$$

$$= \int_0^{4p} dt = 4p.$$

But Equation 3.11 implies Γ is a unit circle. Thus $4p = 2\pi$ and

$p = \pi/2$. If we consider the triangle of Fig. 3.2, it is easily seen that our analytical definition of the trigonometric functions given by Equations 3.7 and 3.8 coincides with our geometric definition.

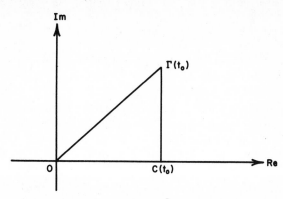

Figure 3.2

3.5 Extension to the Complex Plane

If $\alpha = a + ib$ is any nonzero complex number, then we may write

$$\alpha = |\alpha|\left(\frac{a}{|\alpha|} + i\,\frac{b}{|\alpha|}\right).$$

Since $a/|\alpha|$ and $b/|\alpha|$ are real numbers both less than one in absolute value and

$$\left(\frac{a}{|\alpha|}\right)^2 + \left(\frac{b}{|\alpha|}\right)^2 = 1,$$

it is possible to find a real θ such that

$$\frac{a}{|\alpha|} = \cos\theta, \qquad \frac{b}{|\alpha|} = \sin\theta.$$

Then we may write

$$\alpha = |\alpha|(\cos\theta + i\sin\theta), \qquad 0 \leq \theta < 2\pi.$$

Of course, this is nothing more than the *polar form* of a complex number. The number θ is called the *argument* of α,

$$\theta = \arg\alpha$$

and, of course, $|\alpha|$ is the modulus of α.

Another elementary result is de Moivre's theorem, which states that if

$$\alpha = r(\cos \theta + i \sin \theta), \qquad r = |\alpha|, \qquad \theta = \arg \alpha$$

$$\beta = s(\cos \phi + i \sin \phi), \qquad s = |\beta|, \qquad \phi = \arg \beta$$

are any two complex numbers, then

$$\alpha\beta = rs[\cos (\theta + \phi) + i \sin (\theta + \phi)].$$

We shall not bore the reader with a proof.

However, the results of the previous paragraphs enable us to define the trigonometric functions and the exponential function for *complex* argument. Thus if y is real, we *define* e^{iy} as

$$e^{iy} = \cos y + i \sin y. \tag{3.13}$$

By de Moivre's theorem we can prove the addition formula

$$e^{iy}e^{i\eta} = e^{i(y+\eta)}.$$

For if e^{iy} is written as in Equation 3.13 and

$$e^{i\eta} = \cos \eta + i \sin \eta,$$

then

$$e^{iy}e^{i\eta} = (\cos y + i \sin y)(\cos \eta + i \sin \eta) = \cos (y + \eta) + i \sin (y + \eta)$$
$$= e^{i(y+\eta)}.$$

If $z = x + iy$ is a complex number, we *define* e^z as

$$e^z = e^x e^{iy} = e^x(\cos y + i \sin y).$$

Thus

$$|e^z| = e^x \qquad \text{and} \qquad \arg e^z = y + 2n\pi,$$

where n is an integer. It is easy to see that $e^{z_1}e^{z_2} = e^{z_1+z_2}$ for any two complex numbers z_1 and z_2.

From Equation 3.13 we are invited to define $\sin z$ and $\cos z$ for complex z as

$$\sin z = \frac{e^{iz} - e^{-iz}}{2i}$$

$$\cos z = \frac{e^{iz} + e^{-iz}}{2}.$$

If, in particular, z is purely imaginary, say $z = iy$,

$$\sin iy = \frac{e^{-y} - e^{y}}{2i} = i \sinh y$$

and

$$\cos iy = \frac{e^{-y} + e^y}{2} = \cosh y,$$

which is the customary definition of the hyperbolic functions. In particular,

$$e^y = \cosh y + \sinh y.$$

We also define $(e^z)^\zeta$ as $e^{z\zeta}$. Thus, for example,

$$(e^{iy})^i = e^{-y} = \cosh y - \sinh y.$$

From the definition of e^{iy} (Equation 3.13) we see that

$$e^{i(y+2n\pi)} = \cos (y + 2n\pi) + i \sin (y + 2n\pi)$$
$$= \cos y + i \sin y = e^{iy}$$

where n is any integer, positive, negative, or zero. Thus e^{iy} is a periodic function in iy of complex period $2\pi i$. Of course, so is e^z.

Since $y = e^x$ (x real) is a strictly monotonically increasing positive valued function, its inverse is well defined. We write this as

$$x = \log y, \qquad y > 0.$$

Now if z is a complex number unequal to zero, we define $\log z$ as a number w which has the property that $e^w = z$, and write

$$w = \log z.$$

But $z = |z|e^{i(\theta+2n\pi)}$ where $\theta = \arg z$ and n is an integer, positive, negative, or zero. Thus,

$$w = \log |z| + i(\theta + 2n\pi)$$

and $\log z$ is a multi-valued function.* We customarily define the *principal value* of $\log z$ as $\log |z| + i\Theta$ where $-\pi < \Theta \leq \pi$ and $\log |z|$ is real. Sometimes we use $\mathrm{Log}\, z$ to emphasize this principal value. Thus

$$\log z = \mathrm{Log}\, z + 2n\pi i$$

and

$$\mathrm{Log}\, z = \log |z| + i \Theta, \qquad -\pi < \Theta \leq \pi, \qquad \log |z| \text{ real.}$$

---

* If x is real and positive, then according to our formula its logarithm is

$$\log x + 2n\pi i, \qquad n = 0, \pm 1, \pm 2 \cdots \tag{†}$$

Thus considered in the complex domain, the logarithm of a real positive number is a multi-valued complex function. We adopt the convention that the logarithm of a real positive number is always to be taken as a real number. Then in (†) we always let $n = 0$. A similar remark applies to the general case. Thus $\log |z|$ where z is any complex number unequal to zero is always assumed to be real. In this case we sometimes call $\log |z|$ the *arithmetical logarithm* of $|z|$.

The logarithm enables us to give a definition of z^α ($z \neq 0$) where α is an arbitrary complex number.   Namely, we define it as

$$z^\alpha = e^{\alpha \log z} = e^{\alpha[\log |z| + i(\theta + 2n\pi)]}.$$

$$= e^{\alpha(\text{Log } z)} e^{\alpha 2n\pi i}.$$

When α is not an integer, z^α is multi-valued.   For example if $\alpha = \tfrac{1}{2}$,

$$z^\alpha = \pm e^{\alpha(\text{Log } z)}$$

since $e^{\frac{1}{2}(2n\pi i)} = e^{n\pi i} = (-1)^n$.   If $\alpha = i$, $z^i = e^{i \text{ Log } z} e^{-2n\pi}$, and the real multiplicative factor $e^{-2n\pi}$ may be made arbitrarily large by choosing n large and negative.

3.6 Multi-valued Real Functions

Let us consider for a moment real multi-valued functions of the real variable x.   Typical examples are $y = \sqrt{x}$ and $y = \arcsin x$. Since we are concerned only with real values, we must insist that $x \geqq 0$ for $y = \sqrt{x}$ and that $-1 \leqq x \leqq 1$ for $y = \arcsin x$.

We recall that one of the ground rules of real analysis is inevitably to assume that all functions are *single*-valued.   Thus in any analysis involving $\sqrt{x}$ we stated beforehand whether we would be considering $+\sqrt{x}$ or $-\sqrt{x}$.   Rarely did we consider the multi-valued function $\sqrt{x}$ where either the plus or the minus sign could be taken.   For convenience of terminology let us call $+\sqrt{x}$ and $-\sqrt{x}$ the *branches* of the function $\sqrt{x}$.   Thus $\sqrt{x}$ has two branches while arcsin x has an infinite number of branches.   This definition will be in harmony with the terminology to be introduced later in connection with complex functions.

In real variable theory it is not too difficult to sidestep the use of multi-valued functions (for example, by considering $+\sqrt{x}$ in the case $y = \sqrt{x}$ or by considering the principal value Arcsin x in the case $y = \arcsin x$).   However, the same situation does not prevail in the complex case.   There is an essential characteristic of multi-valued functions in the complex domain which cannot and should not be ignored.   In fact, many beautiful theories, for example, the theory of linear differential equations in the complex domain, depend precisely on these multi-valued properties.

It is the purpose of this section to explain a point of view which enables us to consider multi-valued functions as single-valued ones. We shall first describe the technique for the real variable case.   While it is perhaps pedantic to do so, since multi-valuedness may be analyzed by other, simpler methods, it nevertheless illuminates the procedures which may be applied in the complex case where such a treatment is mandatory.

We shall examine first the function $y = \sqrt{x}$. Suppose we are given a positive value of x, say x_1. Then we must decide whether to define y_1 as $+\sqrt{x_1}$ or $-\sqrt{x_1}$. Let us agree to define it as $+\sqrt{x_1}$, as illustrated in Fig. 3.3. Choose another positive value of x, say x_2. Again we must

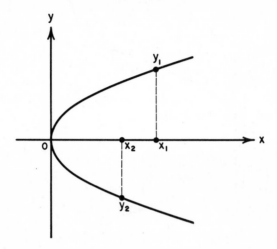

Figure 3.3

define y_2 as either $+\sqrt{x_2}$ or $-\sqrt{x_2}$. Let us define it as $-\sqrt{x_2}$. Now here is an embarrassing situation. If x_1 is close to x_2, then y_1 will not be close to y_2 (unless we are at the origin). Thus, among other things y is not continuous. But while our choice of $-\sqrt{x_2}$ for y_2 is admissible, it violates our intuition. Certainly, if we define y_1 as $+\sqrt{x_1}$ and x_2 is close to x_1, it seems plausible that we should define y_2 as $+\sqrt{x_2}$.

Let us see if we can place the above preliminary discussion on a more precise footing. To do this, let us imagine that the xy-plane is cut along the x-axis from 0 to ∞. Let us label the upper half of the cut x^* and the lower half x^{**}. This is illustrated in Fig. 3.4. Actually x^* and x^{**} coincide as do the three points labeled 0. For purposes of visualization and illustration we draw them as distinct. We shall call each of the lines x^* and x^{**} a *ray*. If x is a value on the x^*-ray, let us define y as $+\sqrt{x}$, and if x is a number on the x^{**}-ray, let us define y as $-\sqrt{x}$, as suggested by Fig. 3.4. Furthermore, let us adopt the convention that we cannot cross over the cut. Since the only place where x^* and x^{**} coincide is at the origin, the only way we can get from the x^*-ray to the x^{**}-ray is to pass through zero. We shall call the combination of x^* and x^{**} the *Riemann axis* associated with $\sqrt{x}$. We see then that if $x_0 \neq 0$ is a numerical value of x on the x^*-axis it is not "near" x_0 when considered on the x^{**}-axis. That is, points which are physically close or identical are not necessarily close or identical when considered on the Riemann axis. If we are given a value of x

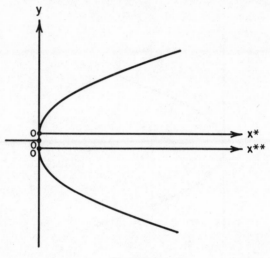

Figure 3.4

on the Riemann axis, there is a unique value of y associated with it. Thus the function $\sqrt{x}$ is single-valued and continuous on the Riemann axis. Also we note that the branches $+\sqrt{x}$ and $-\sqrt{x}$ are single-valued (and continuous) on the rays x^* and x^{**} respectively.

A more convenient way to represent the Riemann axis of $\sqrt{x}$ is shown in Fig. 3.5. Of course, x^* and x^{**} coincide and the three

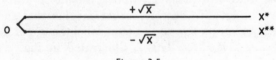

Figure 3.5

heavily indicated points all coincide with the origin. Again we emphasize that the rays x^* and x^{**} are connected only at the origin. Thus the Riemann axis is connected; but it is not possible to transfer from x^* to x^{**} without first going through the origin. Similarly, the Riemann axis of arcsin x is illustrated in Fig. 3.6. In this case we have an infinite number of rays labeled $x^{(\pm n)}$, $n = 0, 1, 2, \cdots$, with $x^{(0)}$

corresponding to the principal value Arcsin x of arcsin x. Of course, all these rays coincide with the x-axis. The numbers in parentheses indicate the values of arcsin x at these points. Thus we see that arcsin x is single-valued (and continuous) on its Riemann axis.

Figure 3.6

The above analyses indicate that, in general, if we are given a multi-valued function of a real variable, we can reduce it to a *single*-valued function on its Riemann axis. Thus all branches of the function are represented, and each branch is single-valued on its ray. The construction of Riemann axes is not the easiest task. In fact, in many cases it is extremely difficult. For example, let

$$x = y^4 - 2y^2 + 1$$

define y as a function of x. The Riemann axis for y is sketched in Fig. 3.7. Here we have four rays, and even in this relatively trivial

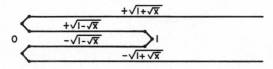

Figure 3.7

example it takes a little time to ascertain the appropriate values on the rays and the correct connections of the various branches.

As an application of this little theory, the reader could develop a theory of integration of multi-valued functions with segments of Riemann axes playing the role of the intervals of the classical theory. For example, in the terminology introduced above,

$$\int_{1^{**}}^{1^{*}} \sqrt{x}\, dx = \int_{1}^{0} (-\sqrt{x})\, dx + \int_{0}^{1} (+\sqrt{x})\, dx = 2 \int_{0}^{1} \sqrt{x}\, dx = \frac{4}{3}.$$

3.7 Riemann Surfaces

The discussion in the previous section leads us to consider the analogous construction for multi-valued functions of a complex variable. Let us examine $f(z) = \sqrt{z} = z^{1/2}$ where z is complex. We saw in Section 3.5 that there were two complex numbers whose square was z. If we write

$$z = |z|e^{i\theta}$$

then these numbers are

$$w_1 = \sqrt{|z|}e^{i\theta/2} \quad \text{and} \quad w_2 = \sqrt{|z|}e^{i(\theta+2\pi)/2} = -w_1.$$

As before, we shall call w_1 and w_2 the *branches* of $f(z)$. Suppose that at some point on the complex plane, say, for convenience, a point on the positive real axis, we define $f(z) = +\sqrt{z} \equiv +\sqrt{x}$ (see Fig. 3.8).

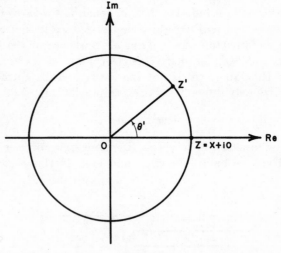

Figure 3.8

Now consider a circle of radius $|z| = x$ with center at the origin. If z' is any point on the circumference we can define $\sqrt{z'}$ as $\sqrt{|z|}e^{i\theta'/2} = \sqrt{x}\,e^{i\theta'/2}$ where $\theta' = \arg z'$, or we may define it as $\sqrt{|z|}e^{i(\theta'+2\pi)/2} = -\sqrt{x}\,e^{i\theta'/2}$. Our analysis of the previous section suggests $\sqrt{x}\,e^{i\theta'/2}$. Now as we continue around the circle, maintaining this definition of $\sqrt{z}$ at every point, the argument θ' increases from 0 to 2π. When we arrive back at our initial point, $\sqrt{z} = +\sqrt{x}\,e^{i(2\pi)/2} = -\sqrt{x}$ and the function does *not* return to its initial value.

To overcome this difficulty let us consider the following construction. Imagine that we have two identical planes, one on top of the other.

Slit both planes along the positive real axis, and connect the upper
edge of the top plane to the lower edge of the bottom plane and the
lower edge of the top plane to the upper edge of the bottom plane.
We have attempted to draw a three-dimensional sketch of this construction in Fig. 3.9.   The planes are to be thought of as coincident just

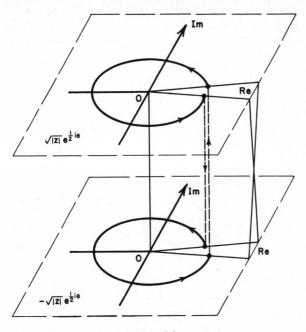

Figure 3.9

like the rays of a Riemann axis.   We draw them displaced for purposes
of visualization.

   The two-sheeted surface of Fig. 3.9 is called the *Riemann surface**
of the function $\sqrt{z}$.   We have labeled the upper plane by $\sqrt{|z|}\,e^{i\theta/2}$,
$0 \leq \theta < 2\pi$, and the lower plane by $\sqrt{|z|}\,e^{i(\theta+2\pi)/2} = -\sqrt{|z|}\,e^{i\theta/2}$.
Thus on its Riemann surface, $\sqrt{z}$ is *single-valued*.   Note that the two
sheets of the Riemann surface are connected, and if we make *two*
complete circulations around the origin we arrive back at the *same
point on the Riemann surface*.   *One* circulation yields the same point in
the *complex plane*, but *not* the same point on the Riemann surface.
The point $z = 0$, where the two branches coalesce, is called a *branch
point* of $\sqrt{z}$.

   * For a more detailed discussion of Riemann surfaces see P. Dienes, *The Taylor Series*,
Oxford, Clarendon Press, 1931, pp. 123–135.

The angle of the branch cut is immaterial.   We have slit the plane along the real axis, but any line, for example, a line making an angle of $125°$ with the positive direction of the real axis would also be satisfactory.   In fact, any simple continuous curve which starts at the origin and recedes indefinitely would be admissible.

The function $\sqrt[n]{z}$ where n is a positive integer has an n-sheeted Riemann surface.   The function $\log z$ has a Riemann surface with an infinite number of sheets.   However, if we keep circulating about zero

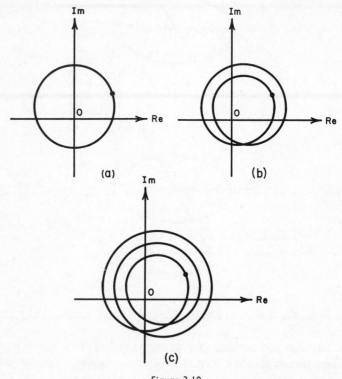

Figure 3.10

in a positive sense, the argument of $\log z$ will advance 2π every circulation.   Thus while we arrive at the *same* point on the plane after every complete circulation, we arrive at *different* points on the Riemann surface.   The only way we can arrive at the same point on the Riemann surface is to make an equal number of complete circulations in the negative sense.   In the case of $\sqrt[n]{z}$, n complete circulations bring us back to the same point on its Riemann surface.

This semi-intuitive mental picture of a Riemann surface which we have deduced above will be very helpful in our future work. It will clearly indicate the distinction between multi-valued and single-valued functions. That is, single-valued functions have a Riemann surface consisting of only one sheet, for example, functions such as z^2, $1/z$. In these cases the complex plane itself *is* the Riemann surface. A function such as $z^{1/3}$ has a three-sheeted Riemann surface, while the functions z^{1+i}, arccos z have infinite-sheeted Riemann surfaces.

We also wish to emphasize again the distinction between curves closed on the Riemann surface and closed in the plane. In the case of $\sqrt{z}$, a circle about the origin is closed in the plane but not on the Riemann surface of $\sqrt{z}$ (see Fig. 3.10a). Two complete circulations

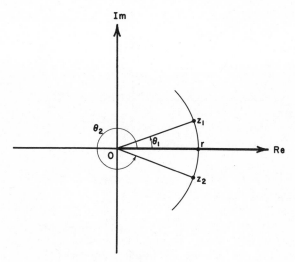

Figure 3.11

(see Fig. 3.10b) represent a curve not only closed in the plane but closed on the Riemann surface of $\sqrt{z}$. The curve of Fig. 3.10b considered as drawn on the Riemann surface of $\sqrt[3]{z}$ is *not* closed. However, the loop of Fig. 3.10c *is* closed in the plane and on the Riemann surface of $\sqrt[3]{z}$ (but not on the Riemann surface of $\sqrt{z}$).

One final comment. If we consider again the function $f(z) = \sqrt{z}$ and slit the complex plane along the positive direction of the real axis, then $f(z)$, or more precisely a branch of $\sqrt{z}$, is single-valued on this *slit plane*. Of course, we must specify which branch. For example, let

$$\sqrt{z} = \sqrt{|z|}e^{i\theta/2}, \qquad 0 \leqq \theta < 2\pi.$$

Then the values of $\sqrt{z}$ are uniquely specified on the slit plane. However, the function is not continuous on the positive real axis (see Fig. 3.11) since

$$\lim_{\theta_1 \to 0} \sqrt{z_1} = \sqrt{r} \lim_{\theta_1 \to 0} e^{i\theta_1/2} = \sqrt{r}$$

while

$$\lim_{\theta_2 \to 2\pi} \sqrt{z_2} = \sqrt{r} \lim_{\theta_2 \to 2\pi} e^{i\theta_2/2} = -\sqrt{r}.$$

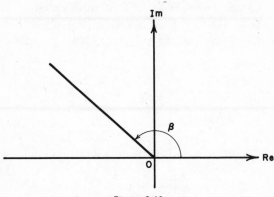

Figure 3.12

If we had slit the plane along, say, the ray $\theta = \beta$ (see Fig. 3.12), then we could have defined a branch of $\sqrt{z}$ as

$$\sqrt{z} = \sqrt{|z|} e^{i\theta/2}, \qquad \beta \leq \theta < \beta + 2\pi$$

and the function $f(z)$ would be single-valued on this slit plane and discontinuous on the cut $\theta = \beta$.

3.8 Differentiability

Let

$$w = f(z)$$

be defined and single-valued on an open region $\mathfrak{A}$ of the complex plane. Let z_0 be a point in $\mathfrak{A}$, and consider the difference quotient

$$\frac{f(z_0 + h) - f(z_0)}{h}, \tag{3.14}$$

where $h \neq 0$ is a complex number. At present, the only other restriction we place on h is that it be so small that the totality of points z satisfying the inequality $|z_0 - z| \leq |h|$ remain in $\mathfrak{A}$. If there exists a complex number A such that: given any $\epsilon > 0$ there exists a $\delta > 0$ such that

$$\left| \frac{f(z_0 + h) - f(z_0)}{h} - A \right| < \epsilon \qquad (3.15)$$

whenever $0 < |h| < \delta$, then we say $f(z)$ has a *derivative* at $z = z_0$ or is *differentiable* at z_0, and call A its derivative. We shall use any of the usual notations for A, namely,

$$A = f'(z_0) = \frac{d}{dz} f(z) \bigg|_{z=z_0} = \frac{d}{dz} f(z_0) = w'(z_0) = \left(\frac{dw}{dz} \right)_{z=z_0}.$$

We also write Equation 3.15 in the perhaps more familiar form

$$\lim_{\substack{h \to 0 \\ h \neq 0}} \frac{f(z_0 + h) - f(z_0)}{h} = f'(z_0). \qquad (3.16)$$

Sometimes we use Δz in place of h for a more colorful notation.

If $f(z)$ is defined and single-valued on an open region $\mathfrak{A}$ and has a derivative at every point of $\mathfrak{A}$, then we shall say $f(z)$ is *differentiable on* $\mathfrak{A}$. This is *not* the same thing as saying that $f(z)$ is differentiable at every point of $\mathfrak{A}$. For in this latter case different neighborhoods could be taken for different points. As an illustration, consider the function $f(z) = z^{3/2}$ in the unit circle $\mathfrak{C} : \{|z| < 1\}$. Let $f(z) = |z|^{3/2} e^{3i\theta/2}$ with $0 \leq \theta < 2\pi$ in a neighborhood of $z = 0$. Then at $z = 0$, $f'(z) = 0$. If $z = z_0 \neq 0$ is any other point in $\mathfrak{C}$, then we can find an open neighborhood $\mathfrak{A}_0$ of z_0 excluding $z = 0$ and define a (single-valued) branch of $f(z)$ in $\mathfrak{A}_0$. Thus $f(z)$ has a derivative at $z = z_0$. However, $f(z)$ is not differentiable on $\mathfrak{C}$, since if $f(z)$ is defined as $|z|^{3/2} e^{3i\theta/2}$, $0 \leq \theta < 2\pi$ in $\mathfrak{C}$, then the derivative will not exist for z real and positive. Similarly the statement "$\cdots f(z)$ is defined and single-valued on an open set $\mathfrak{A}$ and continuous at every point of $\mathfrak{A} \cdots$" (see p. 31) is not coextensive with saying "$f(z)$ is continuous at every point of $\mathfrak{A}$."

It means much more for a function of a complex variable to have a derivative than for a function of a real variable. This is due to the inherent two-dimensional character of a complex variable. We have already pointed out this phenomenon in connection with our discussion of limits. Thus if $h = h_1 + ih_2$, the statement "$h \to 0$" is equivalent to the *joint* approach to zero of h_1 and h_2. Also, because of this, most of the functions that one would write down are *not* differentiable, While a complex constant α and the functions z, z^2, e^z *are* differentiable such simple functions as $\bar{z}$ and $|z|$ are *not* differentiable. The proof of the differentiability of α, z, z^2 is trivial and will be left as an exercise for the reader.   The proof of the differentiability of e^z and $\sin z$ will be deferred until after the proofs of Theorems 7 and 8 of this chapter.

Let us show that $\bar{z}$ is *not* differentiable.   We must thus investigate the ratio

$$\frac{\overline{(z + h)} - \bar{z}}{h} = \frac{\bar{h}}{h}$$

as h approaches zero.   If we write $h = h_1 + ih_2$ and let $h_1 = 0$, then $\bar{h}/h = -1$, and if $h_2 = 0$, $\bar{h}/h = +1$.   Thus

$$\lim_{\substack{h \to 0 \\ h \neq 0}} \frac{\bar{h}}{h}$$

does not exist.   Similarly, we shall show that $|z|$ is not differentiable. Suppose $z \neq 0$.   Then we must consider the limit of

$$R = \frac{|z + h| - |z|}{h} \tag{3.17}$$

as h approaches zero.   If we multiply numerator and denominator by $|z + h| + |z|$, the above expression becomes

$$R = \frac{2xh_1 + 2yh_2 + h_1^2 + h_2^2}{h[|z + h| + |z|]}$$

and in this form it is easy to see that

$$\lim_{\substack{h \to 0 \\ h_1 = 0}} \frac{|z + h| - |z|}{h} = -i\frac{y}{\sqrt{x^2 + y^2}},$$

while

$$\lim_{\substack{h \to 0 \\ h_2 = 0}} \frac{|z + h| - |z|}{h} = \frac{x}{\sqrt{x^2 + y^2}}.$$

If $z = 0$, then

$$R = \frac{\sqrt{h_1^2 + h_2^2}}{h_1 + ih_2}$$

and

$$\lim_{\substack{h \to 0 \\ h_1 = 0 \\ h_2 > 0}} R = -i, \qquad \lim_{\substack{h \to 0 \\ h_2 = 0 \\ h_1 > 0}} R = +1.$$

Since Equation 3.16 implies that the limit must be the same no matter how h approaches zero, the conjugate of z and the modulus of z are not differentiable.

The elementary properties of the derivative that hold for real variables are also true in the complex case.   We state them in Theorem 5.

Theorem 5. Let $f(z)$ and $g(z)$ be defined and single-valued in some open region $\mathfrak{A}$ of the complex plane. Let $f(z)$ and $g(z)$ be differentiable at some point z_0 in $\mathfrak{A}$. Then at $z = z_0$ the functions $f(z) + g(z)$, $f(z)g(z)$, $\dfrac{1}{f(z)}$ (provided $f(z_0) \neq 0$) are differentiable and:

(i) $\dfrac{d}{dz}[f(z_0) + g(z_0)] = \dfrac{d}{dz}f(z_0) + \dfrac{d}{dz}g(z_0)$

(ii) $\dfrac{d}{dz}[f(z_0)g(z_0)] = f(z_0)\dfrac{d}{dz}g(z_0) + g(z_0)\dfrac{d}{dz}f(z_0)$

(iii) $\dfrac{d}{dz}\left[\dfrac{1}{f(z_0)}\right] = -\dfrac{f'(z_0)}{f^2(z_0)}, \quad f(z_0) \neq 0.$

Differentiability is a more restrictive property than continuity (just as in the real case). In fact, we have from Equation 3.15 that

$$|f(z_0 + h) - f(z_0)| < |h|(|A| + \epsilon), \tag{3.18}$$

which implies that $f(z)$ is continuous at $z = z_0$. If we introduce the notation

$$\Delta w = f(z_0 + h) - f(z_0),$$

then we can also deduce from Equation 3.15 that

$$\Delta w = f'(z_0)h + \eta h, \tag{3.19}$$

where η, a function of z_0 and h, $\eta = \eta(z_0, h)$, is an infinitesimal as h approaches zero. Thus, given any $\epsilon > 0$, we can find a $\delta > 0$ such that if $0 < |h| < \delta$, then $|\eta(z_0, h)| < \epsilon$. From Equation 3.19 one can define the *differential dw* as the principal part. That is,

$$dw = f'(z_0)h$$

by definition. [We can make $\eta(z_0, h)$ a continuous function of h by defining $\eta(z_0, 0)$ as zero.]

The important function-of-a-function rule may now be conveniently proved with the aid of the representation of Equation 3.19.

Theorem 6. Let $f(z)$ be defined and single-valued on an open region $\mathfrak{A}$ of the complex z-plane. Let $f(z)$ be differentiable at a point z_0 in $\mathfrak{A}$. Let $g(w)$ be defined and single-valued on an open region containing $f(z_0)$ and be differentiable at $w = f(z_0)$. Then at $z = z_0$,

$$\frac{d}{dz}g(f(z)) = \frac{d}{dw}g(w)\frac{d}{dz}f(z).$$

Proof: Since $g'(w)$ exists at $w_0 = f(z_0)$,

$$g(w_0 + \Delta w) - g(w_0) = g'(w_0)\Delta w + \epsilon \Delta w$$

by Equation 3.19 where ϵ is an infinitesimal as Δw approaches zero. Let $\Delta w = f(z_0 + \Delta z) - f(z_0)$. Now for $\Delta z \neq 0$,

$$\frac{g(w_0 + \Delta w) - g(w_0)}{\Delta z} = g'(w_0)\frac{\Delta w}{\Delta z} + \epsilon \frac{\Delta w}{\Delta z}.$$

But $\displaystyle\lim_{\Delta z \to 0} \frac{\Delta w}{\Delta z}$ exists and equals $f'(z_0)$ by hypothesis, while $\displaystyle\lim_{\Delta z \to 0} \epsilon = 0$, since $\displaystyle\lim_{\Delta z \to 0} \Delta w = 0$ by the continuity of $f(z)$ at z_0. We conclude therefore that

$$\lim_{\Delta z \to 0} \frac{g(w_0 + \Delta w) - g(w_0)}{\Delta z}$$

exists and equals $g'(f(z_0))f'(z_0)$.

3.9 The Cauchy-Riemann Conditions

From an inspection of the examples $f(z) = \bar{z}$ and $f(z) = |z|$ of the previous section one concludes that it is not necessarily an easy task to determine whether a given function of z does or does not have a derivative. We shall derive a convenient criterion to settle this question. These conditions are known as the *Cauchy-Riemann* equations; they are conditions on the real and imaginary parts of a complex function. If $w = f(z)$, where $z = x + iy$, then we may write $w = u + iv$ where u and v are functions of x and y, viz., $u = u(x,y)$, $v = v(x,y)$. We may thus write

$$w(z) = u(x,y) + i\, v(x,y),$$

where u and v are real functions of the *two* real variables x and y. Again this emphasizes our earlier remarks that in some respects the theory of functions of a single complex variable may be treated by considering real functions of *two* real variables.

We state the Cauchy-Riemann theorem in two parts.

Theorem 7: *(Cauchy-Riemann): Necessity.* Let $w = f(z) = u(x,y) + iv(x,y)$ be defined and single-valued on an open region $\mathfrak{A}$ of the complex plane. Let $z_0 = x_0 + iy_0$ be a point in $\mathfrak{A}$. Then a necessary condition that $f(z)$ have a derivative at z_0 is that:

(i) $u(x,y)$ and $v(x,y)$ be continuous at (x_0,y_0).

(ii) $\dfrac{\partial u}{\partial x}, \dfrac{\partial u}{\partial y}, \dfrac{\partial v}{\partial x}, \dfrac{\partial v}{\partial y}$ exist at (x_0, y_0).

(iii) $\dfrac{\partial u}{\partial x} = \dfrac{\partial v}{\partial y}$ and $\dfrac{\partial v}{\partial x} = -\dfrac{\partial u}{\partial y}$ at (x_0, y_0).

Proof: In other words, the theorem states that if $f(z)$ has a derivative at z_0, then the conclusions (i)—(iii) must be true. The equations expressed in (iii) are called the *Cauchy-Riemann* equations.

Since $f(z)$ has a derivative at z_0, the limit

$$\lim_{\Delta z \to 0} \frac{f(z_0 + \Delta z) - f(z_0)}{\Delta z}$$

must exist. This implies that both the limits

$$R_1 = \lim_{\substack{\Delta x \to 0 \\ \Delta y = 0}} \frac{f(z_0 + \Delta z) - f(z_0)}{\Delta z} \tag{3.20}$$

and

$$R_2 = \lim_{\substack{\Delta x = 0 \\ \Delta y \to 0}} \frac{f(z_0 + \Delta z) - f(z_0)}{\Delta z} \tag{3.21}$$

must exist and have the same value, $f'(z_0)$. Thus from Equation 3.20

$$f'(z_0) = R_1 = \lim_{\Delta x \to 0} \frac{u(x_0 + \Delta x, y_0) - u(x_0, y_0)}{\Delta x}$$
$$+ i \lim_{\Delta x \to 0} \frac{v(x_0 + \Delta x, y_0) - v(x_0, y_0)}{\Delta x}, \tag{3.22}$$

and from Equation 3.21

$$f'(z_0) = R_2 = \lim_{\Delta y \to 0} \frac{u(x_0, y_0 + \Delta y) - u(x_0, y_0)}{i\Delta y}$$
$$+ i \lim_{\Delta y \to 0} \frac{v(x_0, y_0 + \Delta y) - v(x_0, y_0)}{i\Delta y}. \tag{3.23}$$

The four limits on the right exist, which simply means that $\partial u/\partial x$, $\partial v/\partial x$, $\partial u/\partial y$ and $\partial v/\partial y$ exist at (x_0, y_0). Furthermore, since Equations 3.22 and 3.23 are equal, we have

$$\frac{\partial u}{\partial x} + i \frac{\partial v}{\partial x} = \frac{1}{i} \left(\frac{\partial u}{\partial y} + i \frac{\partial v}{\partial y} \right).$$

Equating real and imaginary parts we get the Cauchy-Riemann equations.

We have thus proved (ii) and (iii). It remains to prove (i). Since $f(z)$ has a derivative at $z = z_0$, it is continuous at z_0. Hence for $|\Delta z|$ sufficiently small,

$$|f(z_0 + \Delta z) - f(z_0)|$$

can be made less than any preassigned $\epsilon > 0$. But

$$|\Delta z| = \sqrt{\Delta x^2 + \Delta y^2}$$

and

$$|f(z_0 + \Delta z) - f(z_0)|$$
$$= \sqrt{[u(x_0 + \Delta x, y_0 + \Delta y) - u(x_0, y_0)]^2 + [v(x_0 + \Delta x, y_0 + \Delta y) - v(x_0, y_0)]^2}.$$

Since $|\Delta z|$ small implies and is implied by $|\Delta x|$ and $|\Delta y|$ small, and $|f(z_0 + \Delta z) - f(z_0)|$ small implies and is implied by $|u(x_0 + \Delta x, y_0 + \Delta y) - u(x_0, y_0)|$ and $|v(x_0 + \Delta x, y_0 + \Delta y) - v(x_0, y_0)|$ small, we infer that $u(x, y)$ and $v(x, y)$ are both jointly continuous at (x_0, y_0).

The converse of Theorem 7 is the following Theorem.

Theorem 8: (*Cauchy-Riemann*): *Sufficiency*. Let $w = f(z) = u(x, y) + iv(x, y)$ be defined and single-valued on an open region $\mathfrak{A}$ of the complex plane. Let $z_0 = x_0 + iy_0$ be a point of $\mathfrak{A}$. Then a sufficient condition that $f(z)$ have a derivative at z_0 is that:

(i) $u(x, y)$ and $v(x, y)$ be continuous at (x_0, y_0).

(ii) $\dfrac{\partial u}{\partial x}, \dfrac{\partial u}{\partial y}, \dfrac{\partial v}{\partial x}, \dfrac{\partial v}{\partial y}$ exist and be continuous in a neighborhood $\mathfrak{N}$ of (x_0, y_0).

(iii) $\dfrac{\partial u}{\partial x} = \dfrac{\partial v}{\partial y}$ and $\dfrac{\partial v}{\partial x} = -\dfrac{\partial u}{\partial y}$ at (x_0, y_0).

Proof: Note that (ii) of Theorem 8 requires the existence *and* continuity of the first partials in a *neighborhood* of (x_0, y_0). This is stronger than (ii) of Theorem 7. Of course, (i) and (iii) of Theorems 7 and 8 are identical. The existence and continuity of the partials makes (i) redundant, but we have put it down for the sake of symmetry. Actually, somewhat weaker conditions than those of (ii) would suffice for the proof of the theorem.

Consider

$$\Delta w = f(z_0 + \Delta z) - f(z_0) = \Delta u + i\,\Delta v$$

$$= \frac{\partial u}{\partial x}\,\Delta x + \frac{\partial u}{\partial y}\,\Delta y + \epsilon_1 \Delta x + \epsilon_2 \Delta y \tag{3.24}$$

$$+ i\left(\frac{\partial v}{\partial x}\,\Delta x + \frac{\partial v}{\partial y}\,\Delta y + \eta_1 \Delta x + \eta_2 \Delta y\right).$$

We have chosen $\Delta z = \Delta x + i\Delta y$ so small that all points z of the circle $|z_0 - z| \leqq |\Delta z|$ are in $\mathfrak{N}$. The representation of Δu and Δv in terms of the first partials then follows from Theorem 6 of Chapter 6 of *ARC*. The quantities ϵ_1, ϵ_2, η_1, η_2 are infinitesimals as Δx and Δy approach zero. The partial derivatives appearing in Equation 3.24 are, of course, evaluated at (x_0, y_0).

Now assuming the Cauchy-Riemann equations are valid (we have already used (i) and (ii) in deducing Equation 3.24), we are going to show that the derivative of $f(z)$ exists at z_0. Replacing $\partial u/\partial y$ by $-\partial v/\partial x$ and $\partial v/\partial y$ by $\partial u/\partial x$ in Equation 3.24 leads to

$$\Delta w = \frac{\partial u}{\partial x}(\Delta x + i\Delta y) + i\frac{\partial v}{\partial x}(\Delta x + i\Delta y) + \Delta x(\epsilon_1 + i\eta_1) + \Delta y(\epsilon_2 + i\eta_2)$$

and

$$\frac{\Delta w}{\Delta z} = \frac{\partial u}{\partial x} + i\frac{\partial v}{\partial x} + (\epsilon_1 + i\eta_1)\frac{\Delta x}{\Delta x + i\Delta y} + (\epsilon_2 + i\eta_2)\frac{\Delta y}{\Delta x + i\Delta y}.$$

But

$$\left|\frac{\Delta x}{\Delta x + i\Delta y}\right|^2 = \frac{\Delta x^2}{\Delta x^2 + \Delta y^2},$$

which is bounded. Similarly $|\Delta y/(\Delta x + i\Delta y)|$ is bounded. Thus since ϵ_1, ϵ_2, η_1, η_2 are infinitesimals as Δx and Δy (and hence Δz) approach zero,

$$\lim_{\Delta z \to 0} \frac{\Delta w}{\Delta z}$$

exists (and equals $\partial u/\partial x + i\partial v/\partial x$). Thus dw/dz exists.

Returning for a moment to the two functions $f(z) = \bar{z}$ and $f(z) = |z|$, we see that for $f(z) = \bar{z}$, $u = x$, $v = -y$, and for $f(z) = |z|$, $u = \sqrt{x^2 + y^2}$, $v = 0$; clearly the Cauchy-Riemann equations are not satisfied in either case.

To bring into prominence the importance of the Cauchy-Riemann equations we combine Theorems 7 and 8 in the following proposition.

Theorem 9. Let $w = f(z) = u(x,y) + i\,v(x,y)$ be defined and single-valued in an open region $\mathfrak{A}$ of the complex z-plane. Let $z_0 = x_0 + iy_0$ be a point in $\mathfrak{A}$. Let $\partial u/\partial x$, $\partial u/\partial y$, $\partial v/\partial x$, $\partial v/\partial y$ exist and be continuous in a neighborhood of (x_0, y_0). Then a necessary and sufficient condition that $f(z)$ have a derivative at $z = z_0$ is that the Cauchy-Riemann equations

$$\frac{\partial u}{\partial x} = \frac{\partial v}{\partial y}$$

$$\frac{\partial v}{\partial x} = -\frac{\partial u}{\partial y}$$

be satisfied at (x_0, y_0).

Let us use Theorem 9 to show that certain "expected" functions are differentiable and actually compute their derivatives. As a first example, consider

$$w = e^z.$$

Since $e^z = e^x(\cos y + i \sin y)$, we have in the notation of Theorems 7, 8, 9 that

$$u(x,y) = e^x \cos y, \qquad v(x,y) = e^x \sin y.$$

We easily see that

$$\frac{\partial u}{\partial x} = e^x \cos y = \frac{\partial v}{\partial y}$$

and

$$\frac{\partial v}{\partial x} = e^x \sin y = -\frac{\partial u}{\partial y}$$

and that these partials are continuous for all x and y. Hence e^z is differentiable at any point z of the complex plane and

$$\frac{dw}{dz} = \frac{\partial u}{\partial x} + i \frac{\partial v}{\partial x} = e^x \cos y + ie^x \sin y = e^x(\cos y + i \sin y) = e^z.$$

One can also easily show that

$$\frac{d}{dz} e^{\alpha z} = \alpha e^{\alpha z}, \tag{3.25}$$

where α is any complex constant.

Consider $w = \sin z$. Since

$$\sin z = \frac{1}{2i} e^{iz} - \frac{1}{2i} e^{-iz},$$

we have from Theorem 5 and Equation 3.25 that

$$\frac{d \sin z}{dz} = \frac{1}{2} e^{iz} + \frac{1}{2} e^{-iz} = \cos z$$

for any z.   One could also write

$$\sin z = \sin (x + iy) = \sin x \cosh y + i \cos x \sinh y$$

and hence .

$$u(x,y) = \sin x \cosh y, \qquad v(x,y) = \cos x \sinh y.$$

The Cauchy-Riemann equations are satisfied since

$$\frac{\partial u}{\partial x} = \cos x \cosh y = \frac{\partial v}{\partial y},$$

$$\frac{\partial v}{\partial x} = - \sin x \sinh y = - \frac{\partial u}{\partial y},$$

and

$$\frac{d}{dz} \sin z = \frac{\partial u}{\partial x} + i \frac{\partial v}{\partial x} = \cos x \cosh y - i \sin x \sinh y$$

$$= \cos (x + iy)$$

$$= \cos z.$$

The function $w = \log z$ is also single-valued and differentiable for $z \neq 0$ if we specify the branch.   Let us write

$$\log z = \log |z| + i(\Theta + 2n_0\pi),$$

where n_0 is an integer fixed for the discussion.   Thus we have picked a branch (which is not necessarily the principal value).   In this case,

$$u = \log |z| = \frac{1}{2} \log (x^2 + y^2),$$

$$v = \Theta + 2n_0\pi = \arctan \frac{y}{x} + 2n_0\pi.$$

(Note that from the trigonometry of real functions

$$\arctan \xi = \text{Arctan } \xi + n\pi$$

where Arctan ξ is the principal value, $-\tfrac{1}{2}\pi < \text{Arctan } \xi < \tfrac{1}{2}\pi$.)   From the Cauchy-Riemann equations,

$$\frac{\partial u}{\partial x} = \frac{x}{x^2 + y^2} = \frac{\partial v}{\partial y}$$

$$\frac{\partial v}{\partial x} = \frac{-y}{x^2 + y^2} = - \frac{\partial u}{\partial y}$$

and $\log z$ is differentiable.   Its derivative is

$$\frac{d}{dz} \log z = \frac{\partial u}{\partial x} + i \frac{\partial v}{\partial x} = \frac{x - iy}{x^2 + y^2} = \frac{\bar{z}}{z\bar{z}} = \frac{1}{z},$$

as anticipated.

Theorem 6 now allows us to compute the derivative of z^α where α is any complex number. By definition

$$z^\alpha = e^{\alpha \log z},$$

and specifying a branch of z^α makes the function single-valued. Thus

$$\frac{dw}{dz} = e^{\alpha \log z}\left[\alpha \frac{d}{dz}\log z\right] = z^\alpha\left[\alpha \frac{1}{z}\right] = \alpha z^{\alpha-1}.$$

In general, any derivative formula such as $\dfrac{d}{dx}f(x) = F(x)$ which is valid when x is real will also be true if x is replaced by the complex variable z.

3.10 Analyticity

Let $f(z)$ be defined and single-valued in an open region $\mathfrak{A}$ of the complex plane. Let z_0 be a point in $\mathfrak{A}$ such that for every z in a neighborhood of z_0 (including z_0) $f(z)$ has a derivative. Then we say $f(z)$ is *analytic* at $z = z_0$. Analyticity at a point is therefore equivalent to differentiability on a neighborhood of the point. Thus, for example, α, z, z^2, e^z, $\sin z$, $\cos z$ are analytic at every point of the complex plane. On the other hand, $\bar{z}$ and $|z|$ are not analytic. The function z^α where α is unrestricted is analytic in any open region of the slit plane not containing the origin. That is, each branch of z^α is analytic. On its Riemann surface, z^α is analytic at every point, except possibly for the origin. The function $z^{3/2}$ is differentiable at $z = 0$ but is not analytic at $z = 0$.

The sum, product, and quotient (provided the denominator is unequal to zero) of analytic functions are analytic. Also, with the usual statements about the domain and range, an analytic function of an analytic function is analytic. These results follow from Theorems 5 and 6. If $f(z)$ is analytic at every point of a region $\mathfrak{B}$, we say $f(z)$ is *analytic on* $\mathfrak{B}$, or *holomorphic* in $\mathfrak{B}$. If $f(z)$ is analytic throughout the whole complex plane, we say $f(z)$ is an *integral function* or an *entire function*. The exponential, sine, cosine, and polynomials are entire functions.

We have often mentioned "single-valued" in our precise statement of various theorems. Now in future theorems we shall often use the term *single-valued analytic functions*. This phraseology is not entirely redundant. Consider, for example, the function $f(z) = \sqrt{z}$ defined in the ring $\mathfrak{R}:\{1 < |z| < 2\}$. The region is connected but not simply connected (see Fig. 3.13). Now around every point z_0 in $\mathfrak{R}$ we can draw a circle $C:\{|z - z_0| = \delta\}$ which lies entirely in $\Re$. Any such circle can be considered to lie on only one sheet of the Riemann surface of $\sqrt{z}$, and clearly $f(z)$ is analytic at z_0. Thus $f(z)$ is analytic in $\Re$, but it is not single-valued. We refer to such functions as multi-valued analytic functions or *multiform* functions. Therefore one sometimes calls single-valued analytic functions by the name *uniform* functions.

We recall that a function continuous on a bounded perfect set was *uniformly* continuous (see Theorem 3 of Chapter 3). That is, there was

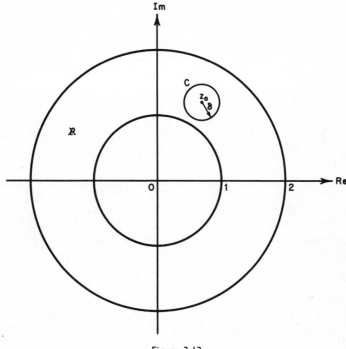

Figure 3.13

a certain "uniformity" of approach of $f(z)$ to $f(z_0)$ as z approached z_0. In the next theorem we shall show that a similar state of affairs exists for the derivative. That is, there is a certain "uniformity" of approach of the difference quotient to its derivative. This result will be crucial in our proof of the fundamental Cauchy integral theorem of the next chapter.

Theorem 10. Let $f(z)$ be single-valued and analytic on an open set $\mathfrak{A}$ and let E be a bounded perfect set interior to $\mathfrak{A}$. Then, given an

$\epsilon > 0$, there exists in E a finite number of points $\zeta_1, \zeta_2, \cdots, \zeta_N$ with the property that for every z in E there exists a ζ_k such that

$$f(z) - f(\zeta_k) = f'(\zeta_k)(z - \zeta_k) + \eta_k(z - \zeta_k),$$

where $\eta_k = \eta(\zeta_k, z)$ is in modulus less than ϵ.

Proof: Since $f(z)$ is differentiable at every point z_0 of E, we may write

$$f(z) - f(z_0) = f'(z_0)(z - z_0) + \eta(z_0, z)(z - z_0),$$

where η is an infinitesimal as z approaches z_0 (see Equation 3.19).

Now let $\epsilon > 0$ be assigned. Choose a neighborhood $|z_0 - z| \leqq \delta$ of z_0 so small that $|\eta(z_0, z)| < \epsilon$. By the Heine-Borel theorem a finite number of these neighborhoods suffices to cover every point of E. Let $\zeta_1, \zeta_2, \cdots, \zeta_N$ be the centers of this finite collection. Then if z is any point in E it must be in a closed neighborhood associated with some ζ_k. Thus

$$f(z) - f(\zeta_k) = f'(\zeta_k)(z - \zeta_k) + \eta(\zeta_k, z)(z - \zeta_k),$$

where $|\eta(\zeta_k, z)| < \epsilon$.

We have developed many theorems for the complex calculus which are natural extensions of those for the real differential calculus. An important theorem in the real calculus was the Law of the Mean. Unfortunately no such theorem exists for analytic functions. For example, if

$$f(z) = 1 - e^{2\pi i z}$$

then $f(0) = 0 = f(1)$, yet clearly no value of z (real or complex) makes $f'(z) = -2\pi i e^{2\pi i z}$ vanish. However, there is a useful result that we can develop without using such a theorem. We state it as a formal result.

Theorem 11. Let $f(z)$ be single-valued and analytic on a connected open set $\mathfrak{A}$. Then if $f'(z) = 0$, the function must be a constant.

Proof: If we write $f(z) = u(x,y) + i\, v(x,y)$, then by the Cauchy-Riemann equations

$$\frac{d}{dz} f(z) = \frac{\partial u}{\partial x} + i\frac{\partial v}{\partial x} = \frac{\partial v}{\partial y} - i\frac{\partial u}{\partial y}.$$

Since $f'(z) = 0$, this implies

$$\frac{\partial u}{\partial x} = \frac{\partial v}{\partial x} = \frac{\partial v}{\partial y} = \frac{\partial u}{\partial y} = 0.$$

But by the Law of the Mean for real variables, $\partial u/\partial x = 0 = \partial u/\partial y$ implies that u is a constant, say k_1, and applied to $\partial v/\partial x = 0 = \partial v/\partial y$ it implies that v is a constant, say k_2. Thus $f(z) = k_1 + ik_2$, that is, $f(z)$ is a (complex) constant.

Another useful result from real variable theory that also holds in the complex domain is *l'Hospital's rule.*

Theorem 12. Let $f(z)$ and $g(z)$ be single-valued and analytic in an open region $\mathfrak{A}$. Let z_0 be a point in $\mathfrak{A}$ at which $f(z_0) = 0$, $g(z_0) = 0$ and $g'(z_0) \neq 0$. Then

$$\lim_{z \to z_0} \frac{f(z)}{g(z)} = \frac{f'(z_0)}{g'(z_0)}.$$

Proof: By definition,

$$g'(z_0) = \lim_{h \to 0} \frac{g(z_0 + h) - g(z_0)}{h} \neq 0.$$

Thus for $|h|$ sufficiently small, $\frac{1}{h}[g(z_0 + h) - g(z_0)] \neq 0$. Since $g(z_0) = 0$ and $h \neq 0$, this implies $g(z_0 + h) \neq 0$.

From Equation 3.19 we may write

$$f(z_0 + h) = f(z_0) + f'(z_0)h + \eta_1(z_0,h)h,$$

$$g(z_0 + h) = g(z_0) + g'(z_0)h + \eta_2(z_0,h)h,$$

where η_1 and η_2 are infinitesimals as h approaches zero. Thus

$$\lim_{z \to z_0} \frac{f(z)}{g(z)} = \lim_{h \to 0} \frac{f(z_0 + h)}{g(z_0 + h)} = \lim_{h \to 0} \frac{f(z_0) + f'(z_0)h + \eta_1 h}{g(z_0) + g'(z_0)h + \eta_2 h}$$

$$= \lim_{h \to 0} \frac{f'(z_0) + \eta_1}{g'(z_0) + \eta_2},$$

since $f(z_0) = 0 = g(z_0)$. But $g'(z_0) \neq 0$ and η_1 and η_2 are infinitesimals as h approaches zero. An application of Theorem 1 completes the demonstration.

3.11 Mappings

Before turning to an intensive study of integration in the next chapter let us devote a section or two to the geometric interpretation of analytic functions. We mentioned in Section 3.2 that the equation $w = f(z)$ could be considered as a *mapping* of one region into another. Thus if we choose a point $z_0 = x_0 + iy_0$ in the complex z-plane, then

$w_0 = f(z_0) = f(x_0 + iy_0) = u(x_0,y_0) + i\,v(x_0,y_0)$ determines a point $w_0 = u_0 + iv_0$ [where $u_0 = u(x_0,y_0)$, $v_0 = v(x_0,y_0)$] in the complex w-plane. We shall call w_0 the *image* of z_0 under the mapping (or *transformation*) f. A simple illustration is given in Fig. 3.1 for the function $w = f(z) = 3z^2 + 1 + i$, where z is restricted to the unit circle. Thus while a function of a real variable, say $y = f(x)$, can be geometrically represented on a single plane (abscissa and ordinate), a complex function such as $w = f(z)$ needs *four* real variables (x, y, u, v) and hence requires a four-dimensional space. More conveniently, we use two planes. Returning to Fig. 3.1 again, we see that if we label a point z_0 in the z-plane, then the mapping $w = 3z^2 + 1 + i$ transforms it into a point w_0 in the w-plane. For example, the origin goes into the point $1 + i$. Now an interesting problem is to determine the image of a given subset of points in the domain of the function f. Of particular importance is the delineation of the image of a curve in the z-plane. Let us consider a few simple illustrations.

Suppose we consider the mapping

$$w = f(z) = z^2,$$

where the domain of f is the whole complex z-plane. Then if we write $z = x + iy$,

$$w = (x + iy)^2 = x^2 - y^2 + i\,2xy$$

and in our usual notation $w = u(x,y) + i\,v(x,y)$, we have

$$u = x^2 - y^2, \qquad v = 2xy.$$

Thus if (x_1,y_1) are the coordinates of a point in the z-plane, $(x_1^2 - y_1^2, 2x_1y_1)$ are the coordinates of its image in the w-plane. Now consider a straight line parallel to the x-axis,* say

$$y = a \qquad (a \text{ real}).$$

Then the image of this line will be the locus of points (u,v) in the w-plane, where

$$u = x^2 - a^2, \qquad v = 2ax.$$

If we eliminate the parameter x, we find that

$$4a^2u = v^2 - 4a^4, \tag{3.26}$$

which defines a parabola symmetrical about the u-axis with vertex

---

* It will be convenient to call the real axis of the z-plane the x-axis, the imaginary axis of the z-plane the y-axis, the real axis of the w-plane the u-axis, the imaginary axis of the w-plane the v-axis.

$u = -a^2$ and with the origin as focus (see Fig. 3.14b). Thus lines parallel to the x-axis are mapped into confocal parabolas with vertices on the negative u-axis.

Similarly, if we consider a line parallel to the y-axis, then the image of

$$x = b$$

is the set of points

$$u = b^2 - y^2, \qquad v = 2by,$$

which becomes

$$4b^2 u = 4b^4 - v^2$$

on eliminating the parameter y. This curve is plotted as the dashed curve in Fig. 3.14b. Its vertex is at $u = b^2$ and its focus is again at the origin. Thus the coordinate lines (that is, lines parallel to the x- and y-axes) are mapped into a family of confocal parabolas. One could, of course, consider the image of other curves in the z-plane; for example, the circle $|z - 1| = 1$ is mapped into a cardioid whose equation is $P = 2(1 + \cos \Theta)$ where $u = P \cos \Theta, v = P \sin \Theta$.

As a second example, consider

$$w = f(z) = e^z,$$

where the domain of f is the whole z-plane. In terms of real and imaginary parts,

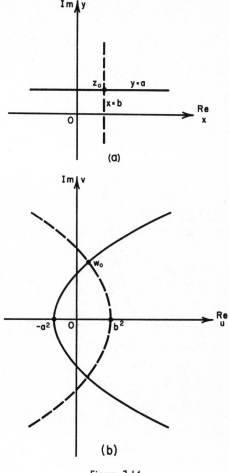

(a)

(b)

Figure 3.14

$$u = e^x \cos y, \qquad v = e^x \sin y,$$

and, for example, the line $x = b$ in the z-plane is mapped into the set of points (u,v), where

$$u = e^b \cos y, \qquad v = e^b \sin y.$$

If we eliminate y,

$$u^2 + v^2 = e^{2b}.$$

Thus the line $x = b$ is mapped into a circle in the w-plane of radius e^b with center at the origin (see Fig. 3.15b). Similarly, the image of the line $y = a$ is the set of points $(e^x \cos a, \ e^x \sin a)$, which yields the locus

$$v = (\tan a)u.$$

This is a ray with slope $\tan a$ (see Fig. 3.15b).

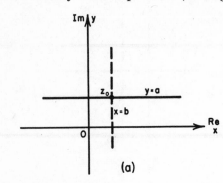

(a)

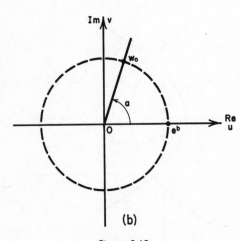

(b)

Figure 3.15

Before temporarily leaving this geometric approach, we would like to point out one more fact. The curves of Fig. 3.14b intersect at the points $(b^2 - a^2, \ \pm 2ab)$, and if we compute the slopes to both parabolas at these points we find them perpendicular—just as the lines $y = a$ and $x = b$ are at their point of intersection z_0. A similar remark applies to Fig. 3.15b where the orthogonality is obvious by inspection. We shall show in Chapter 8 that this is not a coincidence. In fact, if two curves C_1 and C_2 intersect at the point z_0 in the z-plane and make an angle θ with each other, then the images of C_1 and C_2 under the analytic mapping $w = f(z)$ (with $f'(z_0) \neq 0$) intersect at the point $w_0 = f(z_0)$ in the w-plane with the same angle. This leads to the following definition: If $f(z)$ is single-valued and analytic in some open region $\mathfrak{A}$ and $f'(z) \neq 0$, then we shall call $f(z)$ a *conformal mapping* or a *conformal transformation*. In Chapter 8 we shall delve more deeply into the study of conformal mappings.

3.12 Laplace's Equation

Let us digress for a moment and consider a problem which seems remote from our previous discussions. However, an intimate connection between them will be shown before the end of this section.

We refer to a problem in partial differential equations. It is shown in applied mathematics* that the steady-state temperature ψ in a thin two-dimensional plate insulated on its faces satisfies the partial differential equation

$$\frac{\partial^2\psi}{\partial x^2} + \frac{\partial^2\psi}{\partial y^2} = 0, \tag{3.27}$$

where of course ψ is a function of x and y. Suppose the plate is a rectangle such as illustrated in Fig. 3.16. Suppose further that the temperature on the boundaries of the plate have been specified as

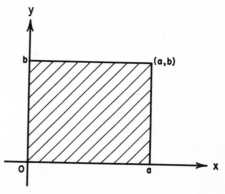

$$\psi(0,y) = 0$$
$$\psi(a,y) = 0$$
$$\psi(x,b) = 0 \tag{3.28}$$
$$\psi(x,0) = T \quad \text{(a constant)}.$$

These are called, appropriately enough, *boundary conditions*. The problem is then to find a function $\psi(x,y)$ which satisfies

Figure 3.16

Equation 3.27 *and* the boundary conditions of Equations 3.28. It can be shown† that in this case

$$\psi(x,y) = -\frac{4T}{\pi} \sum_{n=1,3,5,\cdots}^{\infty} \frac{\sin\dfrac{n\pi x}{a} \sinh\dfrac{n\pi}{a}(y-b)}{n \sinh\dfrac{n\pi b}{a}}$$

is the desired function.

Equation 3.27 is called *Laplace's equation* and is frequently written as $\nabla^2\psi = 0$. A solution of Laplace's equation is called a *harmonic function*. One can show that the potential functions of gravitational, electrostatic, and magnetostatic theory also satisfy Laplace's equation. An important problem in the theory of partial differential equations is to solve Laplace's equation in regions bounded by various closed curves and subject to a variety of boundary conditions.

How can complex variable theory help us solve such problems? Let $w = f(z) = u + iv$ be a single-valued analytic function defined

---

* See, for example, K. S. Miller, *Partial Differential Equations in Engineering Problems*, Prentice-Hall, Inc., 1953, chap. 1.

† *Ibid.*, chap. 3.

in an open region $\mathfrak{A}$. Let us suppose that u and v satisfy the additional requirements* that u and v have continuous second partials in $\mathfrak{A}$. Then since w is analytic it satisfies the Cauchy-Riemann equations,

$$\frac{\partial u}{\partial x} = \frac{\partial v}{\partial y}, \qquad \frac{\partial u}{\partial y} = -\frac{\partial v}{\partial x}. \tag{3.29}$$

Differentiating, we obtain

$$\frac{\partial^2 u}{\partial x^2} = \frac{\partial^2 v}{\partial x\,\partial y}, \qquad \frac{\partial^2 u}{\partial y^2} = -\frac{\partial^2 v}{\partial y\,\partial x}.$$

Since $\partial^2 v/\partial x\,\partial y$ and $\partial^2 v/\partial y\,\partial x$ are continuous, they are equal (see, for example, Theorem 4 of Chapter 6 of *ARC*). Thus

$$\frac{\partial^2 u}{\partial x^2} + \frac{\partial^2 u}{\partial y^2} = 0$$

and, similarly, differentiating the first of Equations 3.29 with respect to y and the second with respect to x leads to

$$\frac{\partial^2 v}{\partial x^2} + \frac{\partial^2 v}{\partial y^2} = 0.$$

Thus we see that the real and imaginary parts of an analytic function are harmonic functions. In particular, we often call the pair u,v *conjugate harmonic functions*.

It is not surprising, in view of the above manipulations, that there exists a close relationship between analytic functions and Laplace's equation. One important property is the following. Suppose $w = f(z) = u + i\,v$ is a conformal transformation and that the independent variables x and y of Laplace's equation are subject to the transformation

$$u = u(x,y)$$
$$v = v(x,y).$$

Then it is an easy exercise in the calculus (using the Cauchy-Riemann equations and the fact that u and v also satisfy Laplace's equation) to show that

$$\frac{\partial^2 \psi}{\partial x^2} + \frac{\partial^2 \psi}{\partial y^2} = |f'(z)|^2 \left(\frac{\partial^2 \psi}{\partial u^2} + \frac{\partial^2 \psi}{\partial v^2} \right).$$

Since $f'(z) \neq 0$ if $f(z)$ is conformal, we see that any solution of $\nabla^2 \psi = 0$ with x and y as the independent variables is also a solution of

---

* Actually this is a consequence of the analyticity of $f(z)$, as will be shown in Section 4.5.

$\nabla^2\psi = 0$ with u and v as the independent variables. Thus, under a conformal transformation, solutions of Laplace's equation remain solutions of Laplace's equation. These remarks underlie the reason for the great practical importance of studying the theory of conformal transformations.

EXERCISES

3.1. Let the domain of f be the strip bounded by the parallel lines $y = a$, $y = b$ in the complex z-plane where $a > 0$ and $b < 0$. If $f(z) = e^{iz}$, determine the range of f.

3.2. Let $f(z)$ be continuous on a bounded perfect set E. In Theorem 4 we saw that $f(z)$ was bounded on E. Let M be the least upper bound of $|f(z)|$ on E. Show that there exists a point ζ in E such that $|f(\zeta)| = M$.

3.3. Using the definition $E(x)$ of Equation 3.6 for the exponential e^x, show that it is a strictly monotonically increasing function of the real variable x.

3.4. Let

$$P(z) = a_n z^n + a_{n-1} z^{n-1} + \cdots + a_s z^s, \qquad a_n \neq 0 \neq a_s,$$

where $0 \leq s \leq n$, be a polynomial of degree n. Show that for all z on a circle of radius $R > 0$ with center at the origin that

$$\frac{1}{2} R^n |a_n| < |P(z)| < 2R^n |a_n|$$

for all R sufficiently large and

$$\frac{1}{2} R^s |a_s| < |P(z)| < 2R^s |a_s|$$

for all R sufficiently small.

3.5. Establish the following formulas for complex hyperbolic trigonometry:

(i) $\cosh^2 z - \sinh^2 z = 1$

(ii) $\sinh (z + \zeta) = \sinh z \cosh \zeta + \cosh z \sinh \zeta$

(iii) $\cosh (z + \zeta) = \cosh z \cosh \zeta + \sinh z \sinh \zeta$.

3.6. If $w = \cos z$, show that

$$z = \arccos w = -i \log (w + \sqrt{w^2 - 1}).$$

One then defines arcsin w by the equation

$$\arcsin w = \frac{\pi}{2} - \arccos w.$$

3.7. Let a be any positive number. Show that $f(z) = \tan z$ is bounded in the half plane Im $[z] > a$.

3.8. Let

$$x = y^3 - 3y + 3$$

define y as a real function of x. Determine the Riemann axis for y and the explicit values of the branches on their respective rays.

3.9. Discuss the Riemann surface of $w = \sqrt{(z - \alpha)(z - \beta)}$ for $\alpha \neq \beta$. What can you say if $\alpha = \beta$?

3.10. Let $f(z)$ be analytic in and on the unit circle. Show that there exists an $\epsilon > 0$ such that $f(z)$ is analytic in and on a circle of radius $1 + \epsilon$ with center at the origin.

3.11. Under the mapping $w = \sin z$, determine the image in the w-plane of lines parallel to the real and imaginary axes of the z-plane.

3.12. Consider the *linear fractional* or *bilinear* transformation

$$w = f(z) = \frac{\alpha z + \beta}{\gamma z + \delta},$$

where α, β, γ, δ are complex numbers with $\alpha\delta - \beta\gamma \neq 0$. Show that f always transforms circles into circles or straight lines.

CHAPTER 4

Contour Integrals

4.1 Introduction

The results clustered around the concept of *integral* play a distinguished role. Many of the theorems we shall derive are analogous to theorems we proved for integrals of functions of real variables. In fact, we shall take pains to point out these analogies because, despite the many similarities, there are certain striking divergences (witness the Cauchy integral formula of Section 4.5) which has no immediate parallel in the real domain. Perhaps by emphasizing the similarities at the beginning of the chapter we shall make the complex integral appear as a natural extension, rather than as a bizarre offshoot, of the ordinary Riemann integral.

The simplest extension of the real integral is to *complex-valued* functions of a *real* variable. Let $f(x) = f_1(x) + if_2(x)$ be such a function where x takes on real values on the closed (real) interval $[a,b]$, and $f_1(x)$ and $f_2(x)$ are real-valued functions. We shall say $f(x)$ is *continuous* if $f_1(x)$ and $f_2(x)$ are continuous. We shall say $f(x)$ is *differentiable* if $f_1(x)$ and $f_2(x)$ are differentiable and define the derivative $f'(x)$ of $f(x)$ by the equation

$$f'(x) = f_1'(x) + i f_2'(x).$$

Similarly, if $f_1(x)$ and $f_2(x)$ are integrable on $[a,b]$ we shall say $f(x)$ is *integrable* on $[a,b]$ and define its integral by the equation

$$\int_a^b f(x)\, dx = \int_a^b f_1(x)\, dx + i \int_a^b f_2(x)\, dx. \tag{4.1}$$

Using this definition we can show that $f(x)$ enjoys most of the properties assumed by real integrals (see, for example, Chapter 4 of *ARC*).

For instance, it is easy to show that

$$\int_a^b \gamma f(x)\, dx = \gamma \int_a^b f(x)\, dx, \tag{4.2}$$

where γ is a complex constant. For, let $\gamma = c_1 + ic_2$. Then

$$\int_a^b \gamma f(x)\, dx = \int_a^b (c_1 + ic_2)[f_1(x) + if_2(x)]\, dx$$

$$= \int_a^b \{[c_1 f_1(x) - c_2 f_2(x)] + i[c_2 f_1(x) + c_1 f_2(x)]\}\, dx$$

$$= \int_a^b [c_1 f_1(x) - c_2 f_2(x)]\, dx + i \int_a^b [c_2 f_1(x) + c_1 f_2(x)]\, dx$$

by Equation 4.1. On the other hand,

$$\gamma \int_a^b f(x)\, dx = (c_1 + ic_2)\left[\int_a^b f_1(x)\, dx + i \int_a^b f_2(x)\, dx\right]$$

$$= c_1 \int_a^b f_1(x)\, dx - c_2 \int_a^b f_2(x)\, dx$$

$$+ i[c_2 \int_a^b f_1(x)\, dx + c_1 \int_a^b f_2(x)\, dx].$$

The linearity of the real integral then establishes Equation 4.2. A similar simple argument will show that

$$\int_a^b [f(x) + g(x)]\, dx = \int_a^b f(x)\, dx + \int_a^b g(x)\, dx,$$

where $g(x)$ is also a complex-valued integrable function defined on $[a,b]$.

If $f(x)$ is integrable on $[a,b]$, then so is $|f(x)|$. For,

$$|f(x)| = \sqrt{f_1^2(x) + f_2^2(x)},$$

and it is easy to see that the right-hand side of this expression is a (real) integrable function of x. A slightly more difficult result is

$$\left| \int_a^b f(x)\, dx \right| \leq \int_a^b |f(x)|\, dx. \tag{4.3}$$

To prove this proposition we recall that if α is any complex number, then

$$\text{Re}\, [\alpha] \leq |\alpha|.$$

Thus if θ is a real number,

$$\mathrm{Re}\left[e^{i\theta}\int_a^b f(x)\,dx\right] = \int_a^b \mathrm{Re}\,[e^{i\theta}f(x)]\,dx \leqq \int_a^b |f(x)|dx,$$

with $e^{i\theta}f(x)$ playing the role of α. Now $\int_a^b f(x)\,dx$ is itself a complex number, say,

$$\int_a^b f(x)\,dx = r\,e^{i\phi}$$

If we let $\theta = -\phi$, then

$$\mathrm{Re}\left[e^{i\theta}\int_a^b f(x)\,dx\right] = r = \left|\int_a^b f(x)\,dx\right|,$$

which under the tacit assumption $b > a$ establishes Equation 4.3.

4.2 Contour Integrals

We now wish to extend our theory of integration to complex-valued functions of the complex variable z defined along curves in the complex z-plane. Let C,

$$C:\begin{cases} x = x(t) \\ y = y(t) \end{cases} \quad \alpha \leqq t \leqq \beta,$$

be a simple curve (and hence, according to the terminology of Chapter 2, also a continuous curve), which we may represent as

$$z = x + iy. \tag{4.4}$$

That is, the complex numbers z defined by Equation 4.4 are the points of the curve.

Now let $f(z)$ be a single-valued function of z defined along C. Let π be a *partition* of $[\alpha,\beta]$,

$$\alpha = t_0 < t_1 < \cdots < t_n = \beta.$$

Then to every t_k there will correspond a unique point, say z_k, of the curve:

$$z_k = z(t_k) = x(t_k) + i\,y(t_k) \equiv x_k + i\,y_k.$$

In each subinterval $[t_{k-1},t_k]$ choose an arbitrary point t_k',

$$t_{k-1} \leqq t_k' \leqq t_k$$

and let $z'_k = z(t'_k)$. Thus π now becomes a *marked partition*, π'. Consider the *approximating sum*,

$$\sigma = \sum_{k=1}^{n} f(z'_k)\Delta z_k$$

where $\Delta z_k = z_k - z_{k-1}$. Let $\Delta = \max_k |\Delta z_k|$ be the *norm* of the z_k-partition and $\nu = \max_k (t_k - t_{k-1})$ be the norm of π. Since C is continuous, Δ approaches zero as ν approaches zero.

We now give a formal definition of the integral.

Definition: Let $f(z)$ be a single-valued function defined along the simple curve C. Let π' be a marked partition of $[\alpha,\beta]$ of norm ν and let σ be an approximating sum for this partition. Then if there exists a complex number I such that given any $\epsilon > 0$ there exists a $\delta > 0$ such that

$$|\sigma - I| < \epsilon$$

whenever $\nu < \delta$ and for all markings of the partition, then we shall say $f(z)$ is *integrable along* C and write

$$I = \int_C f(z)\,dz = \lim_{\nu \to 0} \sum_{k=1}^{n} f(z'_k)\,\Delta z_k.$$

The similarity between this definition and that for the Riemann integral (see, for example, p. 56 of *ARC*) is too obvious to require further elucidation. Without laboring the point, the reader can see that if γ is any complex number, and $f(z)$ is integrable along C, then

$$\int_C \gamma f(z)\,dz = \gamma \int_C f(z)\,dz.$$

If $g(z)$ is also integrable along C, then

$$\int_C [f(z) + g(z)]\,dz = \int_C f(z)\,dz + \int_C g(z)\,dz.$$

If C' is a continuous curve which is inversely equivalent to C (for example, the points of C' could be $\zeta = x(-t) + iy(-t)$ where $-\beta \le t \le -\alpha$), then we write symbolically $C' = -C$ and have the result that

$$\int_C f(z)\,dz = -\int_{C'} f(z)\,dz.$$

Also, if t_0 is any point of $[\alpha,\beta]$ and we let C_1 be the curve defined for t in $[\alpha,t_0]$ and C_2 be the curve defined in $[t_0,\beta]$, then we again write symbolically

$$C = C_1 + C_2,$$

and have the result

$$\int_C f(z)\, dz = \int_{C_1} f(z)\, dz + \int_{C_2} f(z)\, dz.$$

The proofs of these and similar results analogous to the real case will be left for the reader. We also note that the above discussions can be easily modified to take care of the case where C is not necessarily simple. Integrals along curves are spoken of as *contour integrals* or *curvilinear integrals* or *line integrals*.

Another immediate consequence of the definition of the integral is that an integrable function is *bounded*.

Theorem 1. Let $f(z)$ be integrable along a continuous curve C. Then $f(z)$ is bounded on C.

Proof: We must show that there exists a real number M such that $M \geqq |f(z)|$ for all z on C. Let $I = \int_C f(z)\, dz$. Since $f(z)$ is integrable, we know that there exists a $\delta > 0$ such that if π' is any marked partition of norm less than δ, then

$$|\sigma - I| < 1, \tag{4.5}$$

where

$$\sigma = \sum_{k=1}^{n} f(z_k')\varDelta z_k \tag{4.6}$$

is the approximating sum constructed for π'.

Suppose now that $f(z)$ is not bounded. Then there must be at least one interval, say $t_j - t_{j-1}$, on which it is not bounded. Thus we may choose a point t_j'' in $[t_{j-1}, t_j]$ such that $|f(z_j'')|$ is arbitrarily large. In particular, for the new marked partition π'' of π employing the markings

$$z_1', z_2', \cdots, z_{j-1}', z_j'', z_{j+1}', \cdots, z_n',$$

we can choose z_j'' such that $|\sigma|$ exceeds $|I| + 1$. This contradicts Equation 4.5.

Theorem 1 can be used to prove the important inequality expressed in the next theorem. This result will be frequently used in subsequent sections of this chapter.

Theorem 2. Let $f(z)$ be integrable along the simple rectifiable curve C. Then

$$\left| \int_C f(z)\, dz \right| \leq ML$$

where $M \geq |f(z)|$ on C and L is the length of C.

Proof: Consider any approximating sum

$$\sigma = \sum f(z'_k)\Delta z_k$$

for $\int_C f(z)\, dz$. Then

$$|\sigma| \leq \sum |f(z'_k)| \cdot |\Delta z_k| \leq M \sum |\Delta z_k| \leq ML, \qquad (4.7)$$

since $\sum |\Delta z_k|$ is the length of a polygon inscribed in C. Thus we have our theorem, for if $\left| \int_C f(z)\, dz \right|$ exceeded ML, then there would exist an approximating sum σ^* so close to $\int_C f(z)\, dz$ that Equation 4.7 would be violated for this σ^*.

From the proof of the theorem one can also easily see the truth of the formula,

$$\left| \int_C f(z)\, dz \right| \leq \int_C |f(z)| \cdot |dz|.$$

4.3 Integrability of a Continuous Function

Let C,

$$C: \begin{cases} x = x(t) \\ y = y(t) \end{cases} \qquad \alpha \leq t \leq \beta,$$

be a continuous curve. Suppose further that $x(t)$ and $y(t)$ have continuous derivatives on $[\alpha, \beta]$. Then we shall call C a *differentiable curve*. By Theorem 6 and the corollary to Theorem 5 of Chapter 2, we see that this implies the rectifiability of C. Now let $f(z)$ be single-valued and continuous along C. We shall prove the important result:

Theorem 3. If $f(z)$ is single-valued and continuous along a differentiable curve C, then $f(z)$ is integrable along C.

Proof: Let π' be a marked partition of $[\alpha, \beta]$. Then, in obvious notation, we may consider the approximating sum

$$\sigma = \sum f(z'_k)\Delta z_k = \sum f(z(t'_k))[z(t_k) - z(t_{k-1})].$$

Now

$$z(t_k) - z(t_{k-1}) = [x(t_k) - x(t_{k-1})] + i[y(t_k) - y(t_{k-1})]$$
$$= x'(\tau_k)\Delta t_k + i\, y'(\tau_k^*)\Delta t_k$$

by the Law of the Mean for real variables where

$$t_{k-1} < \tau_k < t_k, \qquad t_{k-1} < \tau_k^* < t_k,$$

and $\Delta t_k = t_k - t_{k-1}$. Thus

$$\sigma = \sum f(z(t_k')) x'(\tau_k)\, \Delta t_k + i \sum f(z(t_k')) y'(\tau_k^*)\, \Delta t_k$$
$$= \sum f(z(t_k')) z'(t_k')\, \Delta t_k + \sum f(z(t_k'))[x'(\tau_k) - x'(t_k')]\, \Delta t_k \qquad (4.8)$$
$$+ i \sum f(z(t_k'))[y'(\tau_k^*) - y'(t_k')]\, \Delta t_k.$$

Since $f(z(t))\, z'(t)$ is a continuous function of t (complex-valued function of the real variable t), the integral

$$\int_\alpha^\beta f(z(t))\, z'(t)\, dt$$

exists.

Thus, given an $\epsilon > 0$, there exists a partition π of $[\alpha,\beta]$ of norm δ such that

$$\left| \int_\alpha^\beta f(z(t))\, z'(t)\, dt - \sum f(z(t_k'))\, z'(t_k')\, \Delta t_k \right| < \frac{\epsilon}{2}$$

for all approximating sums of smaller norm. We may also choose δ so small that the inequalities

$$|x'(\tau_k) - x'(t_k')| < \frac{\epsilon}{4M(\beta - \alpha)},$$

$$|y'(\tau_k^*) - y'(t_k')| < \frac{\epsilon}{4M(\beta - \alpha)},$$

are satisfied where $M > |f(z(t))|$ on C. This is possible since $x'(t)$ and $y'(t)$ are uniformly continuous on $[\alpha,\beta]$, and $f(z)$ is continuous on the perfect set C. Thus from Equation 4.8 we have

$$\left| \sigma - \int_\alpha^\beta f(z(t))\, z'(t)\, dt \right| \leq \left| \sum f(z(t_k'))\, z'(t_k')\, \Delta t_k - \int_\alpha^\beta f(z(t))\, z'(t)\, dt \right|$$
$$+ M \sum |x'(\tau_k) - x'(t_k')|\, \Delta t_k$$
$$+ M \sum |y'(\tau_k^*) - y'(t_k')|\, \Delta t_k$$
$$< \frac{\epsilon}{2} + \frac{\epsilon}{4} + \frac{\epsilon}{4} = \epsilon.$$

We have therefore not only shown that $f(z)$ is integrable along C, but have the additional result that

$$\int_C f(z)\, dz = \int_\alpha^\beta f(z(t))\, z'(t)\, dt. \qquad (4.9)$$

Equation 4.9 is sometimes taken as a starting point in defining the contour integral $\int_C f(z)\, dz$. However, our approach, we believe, lends a more physical interpretation to the integral and at the same time parallels the well-known development for the real Riemann integral.

If C is not differentiable but can be broken up into a finite number of curves each of which *is* differentiable, then we say C is *piece-wise* differentiable. Clearly the results of this section can be extended to piece-wise differentiable curves without complications.

Another useful fact that can be extracted from Equation 4.9 is the function-of-a-function rule. Let $t = t(\tau)$ be a monotonic increasing continuously differentiable function defined on the real τ-interval $[a,b]$ and having the property that $\alpha = t(a)$ and $\beta = t(b)$. Then from Equation 4.9,

$$\int_C f(z)\, dz = \int_\alpha^\beta f(z(t))\, z'(t)\, dt = \int_a^b f(z(t(\tau)))\, z'(t(\tau))\, t'(\tau)\, d\tau, \quad (4.10)$$

by the function-of-a-function rule for Riemann integrals extended to complex-valued functions (see, for example, Theorem 19, p. 72 of *ARC*). Another interpretation of this equation is that the curve C is independent of the parameter t. That is, the value of the integral is the same whether the points z of the curve C are represented by $z = x(t) + i\, y(t)$ with t as parameter, or by $z = x(t(\tau)) + i\, y(t(\tau))$ with τ as parameter (see Section 2.5).

Let us consider a few applications to concrete curves and functions. Let C be an arc of a circle with parametric equations,

$$C: \begin{cases} x = \cos t \\ y = \sin t \end{cases} \qquad 0 \le t \le \theta$$

(see Fig. 4.1). Let us evaluate the integral of $f(z) = z$ along C. From Equation 4.9,

$$\int_C z\, dz = \int_0^\theta (\cos t + i \sin t)(-\sin t + i \cos t)\, dt$$

$$= -\int_0^\theta 2 \sin t \cos t\, dt + i \int_0^\theta (\cos^2 t - \sin^2 t)\, dt \qquad (4.11)$$

$$= \frac{1}{2}(\cos 2\theta - 1) + i\frac{1}{2}(\sin 2\theta) = \frac{1}{2}[e^{2i\theta} - 1].$$

Thus if $\theta = \frac{1}{4}\pi$,

$$\int_C z \, dz = -\frac{1}{2} + \frac{i}{2}.$$

If $\theta = \frac{1}{2}\pi$,

$$\int_C z \, dz = -1.$$

If $\theta = \pi$ or 2π,

$$\int_C z \, dz = 0.$$

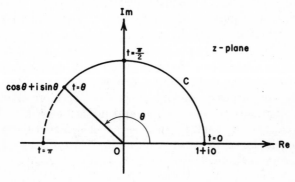

Figure 4.1

As a second example, let us calculate $\int_C dz/z$ over the same contour. Certainly $1/z$ is single-valued and continuous along C. We have

$$\int_C \frac{1}{z} \, dz = \int_0^\theta \frac{1}{\cos t + i \sin t} (-\sin t + i \cos t) \, dt$$

$$= i \int_0^\theta dt = i \, \theta.$$

If, in particular, $\theta = 2\pi$, then C becomes the complete circle and

$$\int_C \frac{dz}{z} = 2\pi i.$$

An identical argument shows that

$$\int_C \frac{dz}{z - \alpha} = 2\pi i \tag{4.12}$$

where α is any complex number and C is a circle of arbitrary radius and center at α.

In the present and forgoing sections we have considered properties of the integral defined over various types of contours. We have used, for example, such descriptive phrases as *continuous curve*, *simple curve*, *closed curve*, *rectifiable curve*, *differentiable curve*, *piece-wise differentiable curve*, *Jordan arc*, etc. Actually, some of our results are valid for slightly more general types of contours than we have specified. For example, Theorem 3 would have been true even if merely the continuity (and not the differentiability) of C had been assumed. However, in this case we would not have Equation 4.9. To avoid a complicated terminology, let us introduce one more definition—that of a *smooth curve*. We shall call a continuous curve a *smooth curve* if it is simple and piece-wise differentiable. This, of course, implies that it is rectifiable. Actually, some of the theorems we shall prove will be valid for a more general contour than a smooth curve. In most cases it will be clear when the hypotheses can be so generalized, and in what direction (say, for example, to non-simple curves). However, for most of our purposes, smooth curves will be more than adequate. The only other adjective we shall append is "closed." Thus by a *closed smooth curve* we shall mean a simple closed curve which is piece-wise differentiable.

In the next section we shall need the following result.

Theorem 4. Let C be a closed smooth curve. Then

$$\int_C K\,dz = 0 \qquad \text{and} \qquad \int_C z\,dz = 0,$$

where K is a constant.

Proof: Let C be a smooth curve with initial point a and terminal point b. Let π be a partition of the interval on which the parameter describing C is defined. Let

$$a = z_0, z_1, \cdots, z_n = b$$

be the corresponding points of C. Then

$$\sigma = \sum_{j=1}^{n} K(z_j - z_{j-1}) = K(z_n - z_0) = K(b - a)$$

is an approximating sum for $\int_C K\,dz$. Since σ is independent of the partition,

$$\int_C K\,dz = K(b - a). \tag{4.13}$$

Note that the integral depends only on the end points of C and not on the path of integration used to get from a to b. We shall exhibit later (Theorem 7) general conditions under which the integral of a function is independent of the path. If, in particular, C is a closed curve, then $b = a$ and Equation 4.13 yields the result announced in the theorem.

To prove the second formula of Theorem 4, consider the two approximating sums

$$\sigma_1 = \sum_{j=1}^{n} z_j(z_j - z_{j-1})$$

and

$$\sigma_2 = \sum_{j=1}^{n} z_{j-1}(z_j - z_{j-1}).$$

If we add them,

$$\sigma_1 + \sigma_2 = z_n^2 - z_0^2 = b^2 - a^2. \tag{4.14}$$

Since $\int_C z\,dz$ exists by Theorem 3,

$$\lim_{\delta \to 0} \sigma_1 = \lim_{\delta \to 0} \sigma_2 = \int_C z\,dz$$

where δ is the norm of the partition π. But $b^2 - a^2$ is independent of the partition. Thus Equation 4.14 implies

$$2 \int_C z\,dz = b^2 - a^2$$

or

$$\int_C z\,dz = \frac{1}{2}(b^2 - a^2),$$

and again the integral is independent of the path. (This result generalizes Equation 4.11.) If C is *closed*, $b = a$ and the above equation becomes

$$\int_C z\,dz = 0,$$

as we wanted to prove.

4.4 The Cauchy Integral Theorem

One of the most famous and important theorems in the calculus of the complex variable is the Cauchy-Goursat theorem, stated in Theorem 5 below. It is also often called *Cauchy's fundamental theorem* or *Cauchy's first integral theorem* or as we shall prefer to call it, *the*

Cauchy integral theorem (CIT). In the next section we shall prove an equally important theorem (Theorem 10), which we shall call the *Cauchy integral formula* (CIF). It is also called *Cauchy's fundamental formula* or *Cauchy's second integral theorem*.

The present section will be devoted to a proof of the CIT and to some of the consequences which stem from it.

Theorem 5: *(CIT)*. Let $f(z)$ be single-valued and analytic in an open region $\mathfrak{A}$. Let C be a closed smooth curve which together with its interior is in $\mathfrak{A}$. Then

$$\int_C f(z)\, dz = 0.$$

Proof: Let L be the length of C. Let $\mathfrak{F}$ denote the interior of C (an open set) and let us use the symbolic notation $C + \mathfrak{F}$ to indicate the points interior to or on C. Since $\mathfrak{F}$ is bounded, there exists a square $\mathfrak{R}$ with sides parallel to the real and imaginary axes such that $C + \mathfrak{F}$ is contained in $\mathfrak{R}$. (It is immaterial whether $\mathfrak{R}$ is entirely contained in $\mathfrak{A}$ or not.) Let λ be the length of a side of the square $\mathfrak{R}$ and let

$$M = \sqrt{2}(4\lambda^2 + \lambda L).$$

We are now going to show that

$$\left| \int_C f(z)\, dz \right| < \epsilon$$

for any $\epsilon > 0$. This, of course, proves our theorem.

Let $\epsilon > 0$ be assigned. About every point ζ_0 in $C + \mathfrak{F}$ we can draw a square $\mathfrak{R}_0$ entirely contained in $\mathfrak{A}$ with sides parallel to the real and imaginary axes and with center at ζ_0 such that

$$f(z) - f(\zeta_0) = f'(\zeta_0)(z - \zeta_0) + \eta(\zeta_0, z)(z - \zeta_0) \qquad (4.15)$$

where $|\eta(\zeta_0, z)| < \epsilon/M$ for all z in $\mathfrak{R}_0$ or on the boundary B_0 of $\mathfrak{R}_0$. Now imagine that by drawing parallels to the real and imaginary axes we subdivide $\mathfrak{R}$ into smaller squares. Some of the squares will be entirely contained in $C + \mathfrak{F}$. We shall call these *regular squares*. Others will contain points belonging to both $C + \mathfrak{F}$ and its complement. In this case, let us agree to consider only those points belonging to $C + \mathfrak{F}$ and call these squares *irregular squares*. Other squares may lie entirely in the complement of $C + \mathfrak{F}$. We shall ignore them. By virtue of Theorem 10 of Chapter 3 there exists a finite subdivision of $\mathfrak{R}$ of this form such that if $\mathfrak{R}_k$, $k = 1, 2, \cdots, n$ are the regular or irregular squares in $C + \mathfrak{J}$, then Equation 4.15 is satisfied for every $\mathfrak{R}_k$ with ζ_k in the interior of $\mathfrak{R}_k$.

The integral around $\mathfrak{R}_k$ may be written

$$\int_{B_k} f(z)\, dz = \int_{B_k} [f(\zeta_k) + f'(\zeta_k)(z - \zeta_k) + \eta(\zeta_k,z)(z - \zeta_k)]\, dz$$

$$= f(\zeta_k) \int_{B_k} dz + f'(\zeta_k) \int_{B_k} z\, dz - f'(\zeta_k)\zeta_k \int_{B_k} dz \qquad (4.16)$$

$$+ \int_{B_k} \eta(\zeta_k,z)(z - \zeta_k)\, dz,$$

where B_k is the boundary of $\mathfrak{R}_k$. Now $\lim\limits_{z \to \zeta_k} \eta(\zeta_k,z) = 0$. Thus if we define $\eta(\zeta_k,\zeta_k)$ as zero, it is clear from Equation 4.15 that $\eta(\zeta_k,z)$ is a continuous function of z in $\mathfrak{R}_k$. Thus the last integral of Equation 4.16 is well defined. From Theorem 4 we see that $\int_{B_k} dz = 0 = \int_{B_k} z\, dz$. Thus Equation 4.16 may be written as

$$\int_{B_k} f(z)\, dz = \int_{B_k} \eta(\zeta_k,z)(z - \zeta_k)\, dz. \qquad (4.17)$$

If λ_k is the length of a side of the square $\mathfrak{R}_k$, then

$$|z - \zeta_k| \leq \sqrt{2}\lambda_k,$$

since z is on B_k. Also $|\eta(\zeta_k,z)| < \epsilon/M$ by construction of the $\mathfrak{R}_k$. Thus

$$|\eta(\zeta_k,z)(z - \zeta_k)| < \frac{\epsilon\sqrt{2}\lambda_k}{M}.$$

The length of the contour B_k is less than or equal to $4\lambda_k + L_k$, where L_k is the length of that part of C which belongs to $\mathfrak{R}_k$. If $\mathfrak{R}_k$ is a regular square, $L_k = 0$. Theorem 2 then asserts that

$$\left| \int_{B_k} f(z)\, dz \right| \leq \frac{\epsilon\sqrt{2}\lambda_k}{M} (4\lambda_k + L_k). \qquad (4.18)$$

Now the integral along C may be replaced by the sum of integrals around B_k where each integral is taken in a counterclockwise sense. This is true since all the sides of the regular or irregular squares in $\mathfrak{J}$ are traversed twice—once in each direction—and since $f(z)$ is single-valued, their integrals cancel (see Fig. 4.2). Thus only the integrals along C contribute to the sum. Hence

$$\left| \int_C f(z)\, dz \right| = \left| \sum_{k=1}^{n} \int_{B_k} f(z)\, dz \right| \leq \frac{\epsilon \sqrt{2}}{M} \sum_{k=1}^{n} (4\lambda_k^2 + \lambda_k L_k)$$

by Equation 4.18. But

$$\sum_{k=1}^{n} \lambda_k^2 \leq \lambda^2 \qquad \text{and} \qquad \lambda_k < \lambda.$$

Thus

$$\left| \int_C f(z)\, dz \right| \leq \frac{\epsilon \sqrt{2}}{M}\left[4\lambda^2 + \lambda \sum_{k=1}^{n} L_k \right] = \frac{\epsilon \sqrt{2}}{M}(4\lambda^2 + \lambda L) = \frac{\epsilon}{M} M = \epsilon.$$

Our first extension of the CIT will be to non-simply connected regions. Let C_1 be a closed smooth curve and let C_2 be another closed smooth curve which together with its interior lies in the interior of C_1. Then $C_1 + C_2$ is the boundary of the ring-shaped region A of Fig. 4.3a. (This region is connected but not simply connected.) We define the integral of $f(z)$ over the boundary of A as

$$\int_{C_1 + C_2} f(z)\, dz,$$

where C_1 is positively sensed and C_2 is negatively sensed.

We now have the following amplification of Theorem 5.

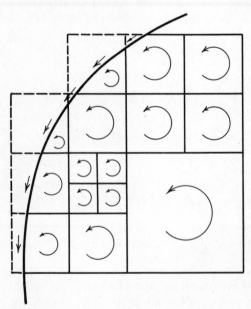

Figure 4.2

Theorem 6. Let $f(z)$ be single-valued and analytic in an open region $\mathfrak{A}$. Let C_1 be a closed smooth curve which lies in $\mathfrak{A}$. Let C_2 be another smooth curve which lies in the interior of C_1. Let $C = C_1 + C_2$, where C_1 is taken counterclockwise and C_2 clockwise. Let the open region bounded by C lie in $\mathfrak{A}$. Then

$$\int_C f(z)\, dz = 0.$$

Proof: Join C_1 to C_2 by a smooth curve Γ in $\mathfrak{A}$ such that every point of Γ except the terminal points are interior to C_1 and exterior to C_2 (see Fig. 4.3b). Then by Theorem 5,

$$\int_{C_1} f(z)\, dz + \int_{\Gamma} f(z)\, dz + \int_{C_2} f(z)\, dz + \int_{-\Gamma} f(z)\, dz = 0.$$

But $\int_{-\Gamma} f(z)\, dz = -\int_{\Gamma} f(z)\, dz$ since $f(z)$ is single-valued. Therefore the above equation reduces to the statement in the theorem.

Corollary. Let $C_2, C_3, \cdots, C_n$ be closed smooth curves which lie in the interior of C_1 but exterior to each other. Let $C = C_1 + C_2 +$

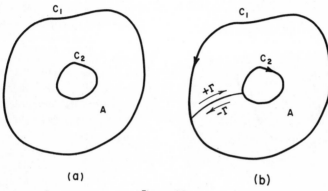

(a)   (b)

Figure 4.3

$\cdots + C_n$, where C_1 is positively sensed and C_i, $i = 2, 3, \cdots, n$ are negatively sensed. Let the open region bounded by C lie in $\mathfrak{A}$. Then

$$\int_C f(z)\, dz = 0.$$

We are now in a position to prove a very useful theorem which gives precise conditions under which an integral is independent of its path, that is, depends only upon the initial and terminal points. This in turn will lead to the fundamental theorem of the integral calculus which enables us to handle complex integrals in exactly the same manner as real integrals.

Theorem 7. Let $f(z)$ be single-valued and analytic in a simply connected open region $\mathfrak{A}$. Let C be a smooth curve lying in $\mathfrak{A}$. Let α be the initial point of C and β the terminal point of C. Then $\int_C f(z)\, dz$ depends only on α and β, that is, it is independent of the path C.

Proof: Let C' be a smooth curve drawn from β to α, sensed as in Fig. 4.4 and such that $\Gamma = C + C'$ is a simple closed curve. Then by Theorem 5,

$$\int_\Gamma f(z)\,dz = \int_C f(z)\,dz + \int_{C'} f(z)\,dz = 0$$

or

$$\int_C f(z)\,dz = -\int_{C'} f(z)\,dz = \int_{-C'} f(z)\,dz,$$

which proves our theorem.

Another way of looking at this result is to imagine that C has been continuously deformed into the contour $-C'$. Note that the simple connectedness of $\mathfrak{A}$ was essential, otherwise Theorem 5 would not be applicable to every Γ.

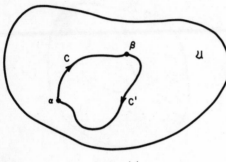

Figure 4.4

These results enable us to prove the fundamental theorem of the integral calculus. We saw in Equation 4.11 that

$$\int_C z\,dz = \frac{1}{2}(e^{2i\theta} - 1),$$

where C was the arc of a circle. Now if we formally integrate,

$$\int_C z\,dz = \frac{1}{2}z^2 \Big|_1^{e^{i\theta}} = \frac{1}{2}(e^{2i\theta} - 1),$$

we get the same result. Of course, we have tacitly assumed that the integral was independent of the path (see also Theorem 4). Theorem 8 states precise conditions under which the "fundamental theorem of the integral calculus" holds. Clearly, in these cases the evaluation of integrals is amenable to the same techniques used in the real calculus. By virtue of this theorem we no longer have to reduce our problem to the level of considering the parametric representation of C.

Theorem 8. Let $f(z)$ be single-valued and analytic in a simply connected open region $\mathfrak{A}$. Let C be a smooth curve in $\mathfrak{A}$ with initial point α and terminal point β. Then, if $G(z)$ is any single-valued function such that $G'(z) = f(z)$,

$$\int_C f(z)\,dz = G(\beta) - G(\alpha).$$

Proof: Let z be any point on C and let $C(z)$ represent the curve from α to z. By Theorem 7,

$$F(z) = \int_{C(z)} f(z)\, dz$$

is independent of the path. Thus we may write (see Fig. 4.5)

$$F(z) = \int_{\alpha}^{z} f(\zeta)\, d\zeta.$$

Clearly $F(\alpha) = \int_{\alpha}^{\alpha} f(\zeta)\, d\zeta = 0$. We wish to show that $F'(z) = f(z)$. Towards this end consider the difference

$$F(z + h) - F(z) = \int_{\alpha}^{z+h} f(\zeta)\, d\zeta - \int_{\alpha}^{z} f(\zeta)\, d\zeta.$$

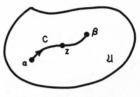

Figure 4.5

Since the integrals are independent of path we may choose the curve connecting z to $z + h$ to be a straight line segment and write

$$F(z + h) - F(z) = \int_{z}^{z+h} f(\zeta)\, d\zeta. \tag{4.19}$$

Now, since $f(z)$ is continuous, $\lim_{\zeta \to z} f(\zeta) = f(z)$. Thus we may write

$$f(\zeta) = f(z) + \eta(\zeta),$$

where η is an infinitesimal as ζ approaches z. Thus, given an $\epsilon > 0$, we can choose a $\delta > 0$ such that $|\eta(\zeta)| < \epsilon$ whenever $|\zeta - z| < \delta$. Using the above result in Equation 4.19 leads to

$$F(z + h) - F(z) = \int_{z}^{z+h} f(z)\, d\zeta + \int_{z}^{z+h} \eta(\zeta)\, d\zeta. \tag{4.20}$$

But

$$\int_{z}^{z+h} f(z)\, d\zeta = f(z) \int_{z}^{z+h} d\zeta = f(z)h$$

by Equation 4.13, and by Theorem 2

$$\left| \int_{z}^{z+h} \eta(\zeta)\, d\zeta \right| \le \epsilon |h|$$

for $|h| < \delta$. Thus we may write Equation 4.20 as

$$\left| \frac{F(z + h) - F(z)}{h} - f(z) \right| \le \epsilon$$

whenever $0 < |h| < \delta$. This proves that $F(z)$ is differentiable and that $F'(z) = f(z)$. In particular,

$$F(\beta) = \int_{\alpha}^{\beta} f(\zeta)\, d\zeta. \tag{4.21}$$

If $G(z)$ is any single-valued function with the property that $G'(z) = f(z)$, then by Theorem 11 of Chapter 3,

$$G(z) = F(z) + K \tag{4.22}$$

where K is a constant. But $G(\alpha) = F(\alpha) + K = K$ since $F(\alpha) = 0$. Equations 4.21 and 4.22 then imply that

$$G(\beta) - G(\alpha) = \int_{C} f(z)\, dz = \int_{\alpha}^{\beta} f(z)\, dz,$$

as we wanted to prove.

Immediate applications of this theorem are

$$\int_{\alpha}^{\beta} z^n\, dz = \frac{1}{n+1}[\beta^{n+1} - \alpha^{n+1}],$$

where n is a positive integer,

$$\int_{\alpha}^{\beta} \sin az\, dz = \frac{1}{a}[\cos a\alpha - \cos a\beta], \qquad a \neq 0,$$

$$\int_{\alpha}^{\beta} \cos az\, dz = \frac{1}{a}[\sin a\beta - \sin a\alpha], \qquad a \neq 0,$$

$$\int_{\alpha}^{\beta} e^{az}\, dz = \frac{1}{a}[e^{a\beta} - e^{a\alpha}], \qquad a \neq 0.$$

In all cases, $\mathfrak{A}$ can be any open region in the complex z-plane and the integration is performed along any smooth curve connecting α to β. If $\alpha = \beta$, then C is a closed curve and all the above integrals vanish, as is obvious by the CIT.

If $\mathfrak{A}$ is any simply connected region *not* containing the origin, then a particular branch of z^s (where s is an arbitrary complex number) may be specified. Thus z^s is single-valued in $\mathfrak{A}$ and

$$\int_{\alpha}^{\beta} z^s\, dz = \frac{1}{s+1}[\beta^{s+1} - \alpha^{s+1}], \qquad s \neq -1, \tag{4.23}$$

$$\int_{\alpha}^{\beta} \frac{dz}{z} = \log \beta - \log \alpha, \tag{4.24}$$

where the integration is performed along any smooth curve joining α to β. Again, from the above formulas or by an application of the CIT, both integrals are zero if $\alpha = \beta$, that is, if C is closed.

Let us now extend Theorem 8 to the case where the region $\mathfrak{A}$ is *not* simply connected. In this case, there is no guarantee that

$$F(z) = \int_{\alpha}^{z} f(\zeta) \, d\zeta$$

is single-valued. Let us therefore choose a branch $F_1(z)$ of $F(z)$ which is single-valued in some open subset $\mathfrak{A}'$ of $\mathfrak{A}$. In general, this subset $\mathfrak{A}'$ will be simply connected. The analysis of Theorem 8 is therefore applicable to $F_1(z)$ in $\mathfrak{A}'$. Another point of view is to consider the Riemann surface of $F(z)$. Then $F(z)$ is certainly single-valued on its Riemann surface and no complications arise.

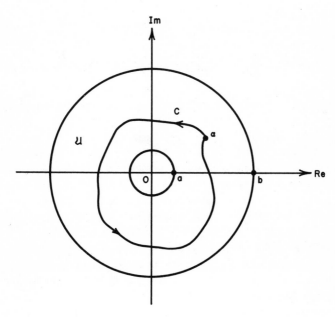

Figure 4.6

As an example, let $\mathfrak{A}$ be a ring around the origin, say defined by $a < |z| < b$ (see Fig. 4.6). This region is not simply connected. Consider the function $1/z$. It is certainly single-valued in $\mathfrak{A}$, yet the function $\log z$ whose derivative is $1/z$ is not single-valued in $\mathfrak{A}$. In any simply connected subset of $\mathfrak{A}$, Equation 4.24 holds. However, suppose

C is a closed smooth curve as in Fig. 4.6. Then it *might* appear that

$$\int_C \frac{dz}{z} = \log \alpha - \log \alpha = 0.$$

But this is not correct.   The important point to note is that while the curve C is closed in the z-plane, it is *not* closed on the Riemann surface of $\log z$.   Thus as we integrate around C we should write

$$\int_C \frac{dz}{z} = \log \alpha^{**} - \log \alpha^*,$$

where $\log \alpha^*$ is the value of $\log z$ on some sheet of the Riemann surface and log α^{**} is its value on the next sheet.   Thus if

$$\log \alpha^* = \log |\alpha| + [\theta + 2n\pi]i,$$

then

$$\log \alpha^{**} = \log |\alpha| + [\theta + 2(n + 1)\pi]i,$$

and

$$\int_C \frac{dz}{z} = \log \alpha^{**} - \log \alpha^* = 2\pi i.$$

(A special case where C was a circle was demonstrated in Equation 4.12.)

We have used the phrase "$f(z)$ analytic and single-valued in a simply connected open set $\mathfrak{A}$."   Actually, this is redundant, for if $f(z)$ is analytic in a *simply* connected open set it must be single-valued. For suppose it were not single-valued.   Then there would have to be a branch point of $f(z)$ in $\mathfrak{A}$.   But a function is not analytic at a branch point—a contradiction of the statement that $f(z)$ is analytic in $\mathfrak{A}$. However, we shall continue to use for emphasis the phrase "analytic and single-valued in a simply connected open set."   This is on a par with the frequently used statement "$f(x)$ is defined and continuous on $[a,b]$," used in real variables.   If $f(x)$ is continuous, it must *a fortiori* be defined.   Again we use both terms for emphasis.

The next logical theorem after Theorem 8 would seem to be a proof of the statement that we can make a change of variable in contour integrals analogous to the situation in real variables.   In this connection we have the following result.

Theorem 9.   Let $f(z)$ be single-valued and analytic in a simply connected open region $\mathfrak{A}$.   Let C be a smooth curve in $\mathfrak{A}$ with α as its initial point and β as its terminal point.   Let $z = g(\zeta)$ be a function of

ζ single-valued and analytic in a simply connected open region $\mathfrak{A}'$. Let C' be a smooth curve in $\mathfrak{A}'$ with initial point α' and terminal point β'. Furthermore, let $g(\zeta)$ have a single-valued inverse, $\zeta = g^{-1}(z)$ such that as z traces out the points of C from α to β, ζ traces out the points of C' from α' to β'. Let $g'(\zeta)$ be analytic.* Then

$$\int_C f(z) \, dz = \int_{C'} f(g(\zeta)) \, g'(\zeta) \, d\zeta.$$

Proof: Since $g(\zeta)$ is continuous, so is $f(g(\zeta))$. Also $g'(\zeta)$ is continuous and hence $f(g(\zeta)) \, g'(\zeta)$ is continuous, and therefore integrable by Theorem 3. Let

$$G(\zeta) = \int_{\alpha'}^{\zeta} f(g(\zeta)) \, g'(\zeta) \, d\zeta. \qquad (4.25)$$

By Theorem 7, $G(\zeta)$ is independent of the path from α' to ζ and by Theorem 8,

$$G'(\zeta) = f(g(\zeta)) \, g'(\zeta).$$

Similarly

$$F(z) = \int_{\alpha}^{z} f(z) \, dz$$

is independent of path, and by Theorem 6 of Chapter 3,

$$\frac{dF}{d\zeta} = \frac{dF}{dz} \frac{dg}{d\zeta}. \qquad (4.26)$$

From Equations 4.25 and 4.26 we conclude that

$$\frac{dF}{d\zeta} = \frac{dG}{d\zeta},$$

and by Theorem 11 of Chapter 3,

$$F(g(\zeta)) = G(\zeta) + K,$$

where K is a constant. But

$$F(g(\alpha')) = F(\alpha) = 0$$

and $G(\alpha') = 0$. Thus $K = 0$ and

$$\int_{\alpha'}^{\zeta} f(g(\zeta)) \, g'(\zeta) \, d\zeta = \int_{\alpha}^{g(\zeta)} f(z) \, dz.$$

If we let $\zeta = \beta'$, $g(\beta') = \beta$ and our theorem is proved.

---

* This part of the hypothesis is superfluous, as will be seen in Theorem 11.

After considering so many theoretical consequences of the Cauchy integral theorem it would perhaps not be amiss to consider a non-trivial practical application.　Thus we are going to evaluate the integral

$$\int_0^\infty \frac{\sin x}{x}\,dx \tag{4.27}$$

by use of the CIT.　This integral occurs in many places in pure and applied mathematics, for example, in the mathematical theory of Fourier series.　(There are, of course, other ways to evaluate this integral: see, for example, Chapter 6 of *ARC*.)

We start by considering the integral

$$\int_C \frac{e^{iz}}{z}\,dz,$$

where C, the contour illustrated in Fig. 4.7, consists of a semicircle Γ of radius R, a semicircle γ of radius r, and the straight line segments

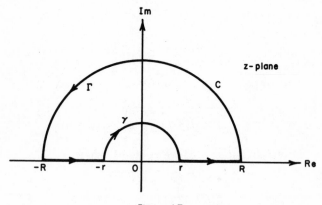

Figure 4.7

$-R$ to $-r$ and r to R.　Clearly $z^{-1}e^{iz}$ is single-valued and analytic in and on this closed smooth curve.　Hence by the Cauchy integral theorem

$$\int_C \frac{e^{iz}}{z}\,dz = 0. \tag{4.28}$$

Furthermore, this equation is valid for any positive R (no matter how large) and any positive r (no matter how small).　In expanded form Equation 4.28 becomes

$$\int_{-R}^{-r} \frac{e^{ix}}{x}\,dx + \int_\gamma \frac{e^{iz}}{z}\,dz + \int_r^R \frac{e^{ix}}{x}\,dx + \int_\Gamma \frac{e^{iz}}{z}\,dz = 0, \tag{4.29}$$

where we have replaced z by x in the first and third integrals since on the real axis, $z = x + i0$. If we replace x by $-x$ in the first integral, we may write, after some trivial manipulations,

$$\int_{-R}^{-r} \frac{e^{ix}}{x}\, dx + \int_{r}^{R} \frac{e^{ix}}{x}\, dx = 2i \int_{r}^{R} \frac{\sin x}{x}\, dx.$$

On γ, write $z = r\, e^{i\theta}$. Then by Equation 4.10,

$$\int_{\gamma} \frac{e^{iz}}{z}\, dz = i \int_{\pi}^{0} e^{ir(\cos\theta + i\sin\theta)}\, d\theta = -i \int_{0}^{\pi} e^{-r\sin\theta + ir\cos\theta}\, d\theta.$$

Since γ is *clockwise* (see Fig. 4.7), the integration is from π to 0 rather than from 0 to π. Also, if we let $z = R\, e^{i\phi}$ on Γ, we have

$$\int_{\Gamma} \frac{e^{iz}}{z}\, dz = i \int_{0}^{\pi} e^{-R\sin\phi + iR\cos\phi}\, d\phi.$$

Using these results in Equation 4.29 leads to

$$\int_{r}^{R} \frac{\sin x}{x}\, dx = \frac{1}{2} \int_{0}^{\pi} e^{-r\sin\theta + ir\cos\theta}\, d\theta - \frac{1}{2} \int_{0}^{\pi} e^{-R\sin\phi + iR\cos\phi}\, d\phi$$

and

$$\int_{0}^{\infty} \frac{\sin x}{x}\, dx = \lim_{\substack{R\to\infty \\ r\to 0}} \int_{r}^{R} \frac{\sin x}{x}\, dx = \frac{1}{2} \lim_{r\to 0} \int_{0}^{\pi} e^{-r\sin\theta + ir\cos\theta}\, d\theta$$

$$\tag{4.30}$$

$$- \frac{1}{2} \lim_{R\to\infty} \int_{0}^{\pi} e^{-R\sin\phi + iR\cos\phi}\, d\phi.$$

It remains to evaluate the two limits on the right which are actually complex-valued functions of the real variables r and R respectively. Now

$$\left| \int_{0}^{\pi} e^{-R\sin\phi + iR\cos\phi}\, d\phi \right| \leqq \int_{0}^{\pi} e^{-R\sin\phi}\, d\phi = 2 \int_{0}^{\pi/2} e^{-R\sin\phi}\, d\phi.$$

For ϕ between 0 and $\frac{1}{2}\pi$ it is easy to see that

$$\sin\phi \geqq \frac{2\phi}{\pi},$$

and hence

$$\int_{0}^{\pi/2} e^{-R\sin\phi}\, d\phi \leqq \int_{0}^{\pi/2} e^{-2R\phi/\pi}\, d\phi = \frac{\pi}{2R}\left(1 - e^{-R}\right).$$

This expression approaches zero as R increases without limit. Thus Equation 4.30 reduces to

$$\int_0^\infty \frac{\sin x}{x}\, dx = \frac{1}{2} \lim_{r \to 0} g(r), \qquad (4.31)$$

where

$$g(r) = \int_0^\pi e^{-r\sin\theta + ir\cos\theta}\, d\theta.$$

It is an easy exercise in real variable theory to show that $g(r)$ is continuous at $r = 0$. Hence

$$\lim_{r \to 0} g(r) = g(0) = \int_0^\pi d\theta = \pi.$$

Substituting in Equation 4.31 yields the desired result, namely,

$$\int_0^\infty \frac{\sin x}{x}\, dx = \frac{\pi}{2}. \qquad (4.32)$$

4.5 The Cauchy Integral Formula

Of all the formulas in the theory of functions of a complex variable the best known and most widely used is undoubtedly the Cauchy integral formula (CIF). It is our privilege in this section to derive this formula and related results. Additional generalizations with both theoretical and practical implications will be considered in subsequent chapters.

Theorem 10: (CIF). Let $f(z)$ be single-valued and analytic in an open region $\mathfrak{A}$. Let A be an open region interior to $\mathfrak{A}$, bounded by a finite number of closed smooth curves $C_1, C_2, \cdots, C_n$. Let $C = C_1 + C_2 + \cdots + C_n$, and let z be a point in A. Then

$$f(z) = \frac{1}{2\pi i} \int_C \frac{f(\zeta)}{\zeta - z}\, d\zeta.$$

Proof: When we say A is bounded by a finite number of closed smooth curves we mean in the sense of the corollary to Theorem 6 (see also Fig. 4.8).

The function $\dfrac{1}{\zeta - z}$ is not analytic in $\mathfrak{A}$; in fact, it is not even continuous. However, it *is* analytic in any region not containing z. Let us therefore draw a negatively sensed circle Γ of radius r about z, taking care that Γ and its interior lie in A. Let $\mathscr{C} = C + \Gamma$. Then in the region bounded by $\mathscr{C}$ the function $(\zeta - z)^{-1}f(\zeta)$ is single-valued and analytic.   Hence the CIT applies,

$$\int_{\mathscr{C}} \frac{f(\zeta)}{\zeta - z}\, d\zeta = 0,$$

or

$$\int_{C} \frac{f(\zeta)}{\zeta - z}\, d\zeta = \int_{-r} \frac{f(\zeta)}{\zeta - z}\, d\zeta. \qquad (4.33)$$

This equation is true for any $r > 0$ (provided only that Γ and its interior are in A).

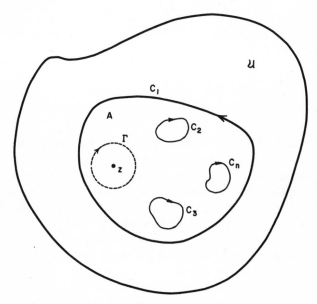

Figure 4.8

Since $f(\zeta)$ is analytic we may write

$$f(\zeta) = f(z) + f'(z)(\zeta - z) + \eta(z,\zeta)(\zeta - z), \qquad (4.34)$$

where $\eta(z,\zeta)$ is an infinitesimal as ζ approaches z.   If we define $\eta(z,z)$ as zero, then $\eta(z,\zeta)$ is a continuous function of ζ in a neighborhood of z.   Using this result in Equation 4.33, we have

$$\int_{C} \frac{f(\zeta)}{\zeta - z}\, d\zeta = f(z) \int_{-r} \frac{d\zeta}{\zeta - z} + f'(z) \int_{-r} d\zeta + \int_{-r} \eta(z,\zeta)\, d\zeta. \quad (4.35)$$

But $\displaystyle\int_{-r} \frac{d\zeta}{\zeta - z} = 2\pi i$ by Equation 4.12 and $\displaystyle\int_{-r} d\zeta = 0$ by Theorem 4.

Equation 4.35 may therefore be written as

$$\int_C \frac{f(\zeta)}{\zeta - z} \, d\zeta - 2\pi i \, f(z) = -\int_\Gamma \eta(z,\zeta) \, d\zeta. \qquad (4.36)$$

We are now going to show that $\left| \int_\Gamma \eta d\zeta \right|$ can be made arbitrarily small. Let $\epsilon > 0$ be assigned. Choose a $\delta > 0$ so small that $|\eta(z,\zeta)| < \epsilon/2\pi$ whenever $|z - \zeta| < \delta$. Now if we choose r (the radius of Γ) less than the minimum of 1 and δ, we have

$$\left| \int_\Gamma \eta(z,\zeta) \, d\zeta \right| < \frac{\epsilon}{2\pi} \, 2\pi r \leqq \epsilon$$

by Theorem 2. Thus Equation 4.36 implies

$$\left| \int_C \frac{f(\zeta)}{\zeta - z} \, d\zeta - 2\pi i \, f(z) \right| < \epsilon.$$

Since $\epsilon > 0$ is arbitrary, our theorem is established.

The remarkable fact about this theorem is that it specifies the value of an analytic function at any interior point provided only that we know the values of the function on the boundary. In other words, if it is known that a function is single-valued and analytic in an open region $\mathfrak{A}$ and if we are merely given the values that $f(z)$ assumes on some closed smooth curve C (which together with its interior lies in $\mathfrak{A}$), then the values of $f(z)$ are uniquely specified at every interior point of C!

As a practical application of the Cauchy integral formula let us compute the real infinite integral

$$I = \int_0^\infty \frac{\cos x}{1 + x^2} \, dx. \qquad (4.37)$$

The integral converges absolutely and hence I is a well-defined number. However, we cannot find an elementary function $f(x)$ such that $f'(x) = (\cos x)/(1 + x^2)$. Hence the fundamental theorem of the integral calculus is not of much use.

We shall start by considering the slightly more general integral

$$\int_C \frac{e^{i\zeta}}{\zeta^2 + 1} \, d\zeta$$

where C, the contour illustrated in Fig. 4.9, consists of a semicircle Γ of radius R and the straight line segment from $-R$ to R.

Now

$$\zeta^2 + 1 = (\zeta + i)(\zeta - i)$$

and

$$\frac{e^{i\zeta}}{\zeta^2 + 1} = \frac{e^{i\zeta}}{\zeta + i}\left(\frac{1}{\zeta - i}\right) = \frac{f(\zeta)}{\zeta - i},$$

where $f(\zeta) = e^{i\zeta}/(\zeta + i)$ is single-valued and analytic in and on C. Thus by the CIF,

$$f(i) = \frac{1}{2\pi i}\int_C \frac{f(\zeta)}{\zeta - i}\,d\zeta, \qquad (4.38)$$

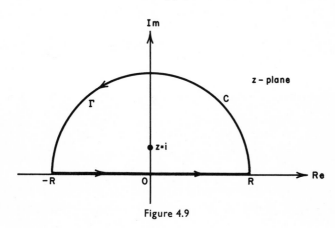

Figure 4.9

and this formula is valid for any $R > 1$. Since

$$f(i) = \frac{e^{i^2}}{i + i} = \frac{e^{-1}}{2i},$$

we may write Equation 4.38 as

$$\frac{1}{2ie} = \frac{1}{2\pi i}\int_C \frac{f(\zeta)}{\zeta - i}\,d\zeta = \frac{1}{2\pi i}\int_C \frac{e^{i\zeta}}{\zeta^2 + 1}\,d\zeta$$

or

$$\int_C \frac{e^{i\zeta}}{\zeta^2 + 1}\,d\zeta = \frac{\pi}{e}.$$

Since

$$\int_C = \int_\Gamma + \int_{-R}^R,$$

we have

$$\int_{-R}^R \frac{e^{i\zeta}}{\zeta^2 + 1}\,d\zeta = \frac{\pi}{e} - \int_\Gamma \frac{e^{i\zeta}}{\zeta^2 + 1}\,d\zeta.$$

On the real axis ζ is real, so we may write the above equation as

$$\int_{-\infty}^{\infty} \frac{e^{ix}}{x^2 + 1}\, dx = \lim_{R \to \infty} \int_{-R}^{R} \frac{e^{ix}}{x^2 + 1}\, dx = \frac{\pi}{e} - \lim_{R \to \infty} \int_{\Gamma} \frac{e^{i\zeta}}{\zeta^2 + 1}\, d\zeta.$$

$$(4.39)$$

Our problem is therefore reduced to a study of

$$\int_{\Gamma} \frac{e^{i\zeta}}{\zeta^2 + 1}\, d\zeta$$

for large R. For ζ on Γ we may write

$$\zeta = R\, e^{i\theta}, \qquad 0 \leq \theta \leq \pi$$

and

$$\int_{\Gamma} \frac{e^{i\zeta}}{\zeta^2 + 1}\, d\zeta = iR \int_{0}^{\pi} \frac{e^{i\theta} e^{iR\,(\cos\theta + i\sin\theta)}}{R^2 e^{2i\theta} + 1}\, d\theta.$$

Now

$$\left| e^{i\theta}\, e^{iR\,(\cos\theta + i\sin\theta)} \right| = e^{-R\sin\theta} \leq 1 \qquad \text{for} \qquad 0 \leq \theta \leq \pi$$

and

$$\left| R^2 e^{2i\theta} + 1 \right| \geq \left| R^2 e^{2i\theta} \right| - |1| = R^2 - 1.$$

Thus

$$\left| \int_{\Gamma} \frac{e^{i\zeta}}{\zeta^2 + 1}\, d\zeta \right| \leq \frac{R}{R^2 - 1} \int_{0}^{\pi} d\theta = \frac{\pi R}{R^2 - 1},$$

which approaches zero as R approaches infinity.   Equation 4.39 then implies

$$\int_{-\infty}^{\infty} \frac{e^{ix}}{x^2 + 1}\, dx = \frac{\pi}{e}.$$

Taking real and imaginary parts, we have

$$\int_{-\infty}^{\infty} \frac{\cos x}{x^2 + 1}\, dx = \frac{\pi}{e}, \qquad \int_{-\infty}^{\infty} \frac{\sin x}{x^2 + 1}\, dx = 0.$$

From the first integral we have

$$\int_{0}^{\infty} \frac{\cos x}{x^2 + 1}\, dx = \frac{\pi}{2e}$$

(since the integrand is an even function), which evaluates the integral of Equation 4.37.

A word of caution.   If we have evaluated an infinite integral, say by the CIF, by considering the limit

$$\int_{-\infty}^{\infty} f(x)\, dx = \lim_{R \to \infty} \int_{-R}^{R} f(x)\, dx,$$

then it does not necessarily follow that the integral $\int_{-\infty}^{\infty} f(x)\, dx$ exists. (In our particular problem it *does* exist.)   We recall from the classical theory of real variables that for $\int_{-\infty}^{\infty} f(x)\, dx$ to exist both $\int_{a}^{\infty} f(x)\, dx$ and $\int_{-\infty}^{a} f(x)\, dx$ must exist.   Thus the definition of the doubly infinite integral (if it exists) is

$$\lim_{\substack{a \to -\infty \\ b \to \infty}} \int_{a}^{b} f(x)\, dx = \int_{-\infty}^{\infty} f(x)\, dx.$$

This is *not* the same as writing

$$\lim_{R \to \infty} \int_{-R}^{R} f(x)\, dx = \int_{-\infty}^{\infty} f(x)\, dx.$$

For this latter limit may exist while the former may not.   As an illustration,

$$\lim_{R \to \infty} \int_{-R}^{R} x\, dx = \lim_{R \to \infty} \left[\frac{x^2}{2} \right]\Big|_{-R}^{R} = \lim_{R \to \infty} \left[\frac{R^2}{2} - \frac{R^2}{2} \right] = 0,$$

yet $\int_{-\infty}^{\infty} x\, dx$ does not exist in the classical sense since neither $\int_{0}^{\infty} x\, dx$ nor $\int_{-\infty}^{0} x\, dx$ exists.   To emphasize this particular method of taking a limit we frequently write

$$\lim_{R \to \infty} \int_{-R}^{R} f(x)\, dx = \text{P.V.} \int_{-\infty}^{\infty} f(x)\, dx,$$

where P.V. stands for "principal value."   We then say that $\int_{-\infty}^{\infty} f(x)\, dx$ exists as a *Cauchy principal value*.   Thus while $\int_{-\infty}^{\infty} f(x)\, dx$ may not exist in the classical sense, it may exist as a Cauchy principal value. If it *does* exist in the classical sense, then *a fortiori* it exists as a Cauchy principal value.*

---

* The term is also applied to improper integrals.   Suppose $f(x)$ has an infinite discontinuity at a point c in the interval $[a,b]$.   Then, if the limit

$$\lim_{\substack{\epsilon \to 0 \\ \epsilon > 0}} \left[\int_{a}^{c-\epsilon} f(x)\, dx + \int_{c+\epsilon}^{b} f(x)\, dx \right]$$

exists, we call $\int_{a}^{b} f(x)\, dx$ a *Cauchy principal value*.   For example, $\int_{-1}^{1} x^{-3}\, dx$ does not exist in the classical sense, but since

$$\lim_{\substack{\epsilon \to 0 \\ \epsilon > 0}} \left[\int_{-1}^{-\epsilon} x^{-3}\, dx + \int_{\epsilon}^{1} x^{-3}\, dx \right] = \lim_{\substack{\epsilon \to 0 \\ \epsilon > 0}} \frac{1}{2} \left[-\epsilon^{-2} + 1 - 1 + \epsilon^{-2} \right] = 0$$

exists, P.V. $\int_{-1}^{1} x^{-3}\, dx$ exists and equals zero.

In Chapter 6 we shall return to this interesting topic of evaluating integrals.

Let us now consider a theoretical application of the CIF. We shall show in Theorem 11 that if a function is analytic, then all of its derivatives exist and are analytic functions. This is quite a departure from the real variable case where the existence (and even the continuity) of the first derivative of a function did not imply even the existence of the second derivative. This result is perhaps the most striking difference between the theory of functions of a real variable and the complex calculus.

Theorem 11. Let $f(z)$ be single-valued and analytic in an open region $\mathfrak{A}$. Let C be a closed smooth curve which together with its interior lies in $\mathfrak{A}$ and let z be any point in the interior of C. Then

$$f^{(n)}(z) = \frac{n!}{2\pi i} \int_C \frac{f(\zeta)\, d\zeta}{(\zeta - z)^{n+1}}.$$

Proof: By the Cauchy integral formula we have

$$f(z) = \frac{1}{2\pi i} \int_C \frac{f(\zeta)}{\zeta - z}\, d\zeta. \tag{4.40}$$

Of course, $f'(z)$ exists since $f(z)$ is analytic by hypothesis. We shall first show that $f'(z)$ may be expressed as

$$f'(z) = \frac{1}{2\pi i} \int_C \frac{f(\zeta)}{(\zeta - z)^2}\, d\zeta, \tag{4.41}$$

which is exactly what one would obtain by formally differentiating Equation 4.40 under the integral sign.

Since the interior $\mathfrak{I}$ of C is an open set, we can draw a circle about z which is entirely in $\mathfrak{I}$. If r is the radius of such a circle and ζ is any point on C, then

$$|\zeta - z| > r.$$

Hold r fixed for the remainder of the discussion. Now by definition of derivative

$$f'(z) = \lim_{h \to 0} \frac{f(z + h) - f(z)}{h}.$$

Let $0 < |h| < \tfrac{1}{2}r$ and consider

$$\frac{f(z + h) - f(z)}{h} = \frac{1}{h 2\pi i} \int_C f(\zeta) \left[\frac{1}{\zeta - (z + h)} - \frac{1}{\zeta - z} \right] d\zeta$$

$$= \frac{1}{2\pi i} \int_C \frac{f(\zeta)}{(\zeta - z - h)(\zeta - z)}\, d\zeta.$$

We shall show that for $|h|$ sufficiently small,

$$\left| \frac{f(z+h) - f(z)}{h} - \frac{1}{2\pi i} \int_C \frac{f(\zeta)}{(\zeta - z)^2} \, d\zeta \right|$$

can be made less than any preassigned $\epsilon > 0$. This will then imply the validity of Equation 4.41.

Now

$$\frac{f(z+h) - f(z)}{h} - \frac{1}{2\pi i} \int_C \frac{f(\zeta)}{(\zeta - z)^2} \, d\zeta = \frac{h}{2\pi i} \int_C \frac{f(\zeta) \, d\zeta}{(\zeta - z)^2(\zeta - z - h)}.$$

Since $f(\zeta)$ is continuous on C, it is bounded. Let $M \geq |f(\zeta)|$ on C. Also $|\zeta - z| > r$ and $|\zeta - z - h| > \frac{1}{2}r$ for $|h| < \frac{1}{2}r$. Thus

$$\left| \int_C \frac{f(\zeta) \, d\zeta}{(\zeta - z)^2(\zeta - z - h)} \right| < \frac{M}{r^2 \left(\dfrac{r}{2}\right)} L = \frac{2ML}{r^3},$$

where L is the length of the rectifiable curve C. Let $\epsilon > 0$ be assigned and let

$$\delta = \min\left(\frac{r}{2}, \frac{\pi r^3}{ML} \epsilon\right).$$

Then, for $0 < |h| < \delta$,

$$\left| \frac{f(z+h) - f(z)}{h} - \frac{1}{2\pi i} \int_C \frac{f(\zeta)}{(\zeta - z)^2} \, d\zeta \right| \leq \frac{|h|}{2\pi}\left(\frac{2ML}{r^3}\right) < \frac{\delta ML}{\pi r^3} \leq \epsilon,$$

as we wanted to prove.

Of course, this result was not unexpected. We knew that $f(z)$ had a derivative. Our only contribution was to show that it had the explicit representation of Equation 4.41. The deep part of the theorem is to prove the existence of the higher derivatives.

We shall prove our formula by induction. Suppose

$$f^{(n)}(z) = \frac{n!}{2\pi i} \int_C \frac{f(\zeta) \, d\zeta}{(\zeta - z)^{n+1}} \tag{4.42}$$

is true for $n = k$. The result has been established for $n = 1$. Thus we need only show it true for $n = k + 1$. By definition,

$$f^{(k+1)}(z) = \lim_{h \to 0} \frac{f^{(k)}(z+h) - f^{(k)}(z)}{h}.$$

From Equation 4.42

$$f^{(k)}(z + h) - f^{(k)}(z) = \frac{k!}{2\pi i} \int_C f(\zeta) \left[\frac{1}{(\zeta - z - h)^{k+1}} - \frac{1}{(\zeta - z)^{k+1}} \right] d\zeta,$$

and by some simple algebraic manipulations we determine that

$$\frac{f^{(k)}(z + h) - f^{(k)}(z)}{h} - \frac{(k + 1)!}{2\pi i} \int_C \frac{f(\zeta)\, d\zeta}{(\zeta - z)^{k+2}}$$

$$= \frac{h(k + 2)!}{4\pi i} \int_C f(\zeta) \frac{P(\zeta - z, h)}{(\zeta - z)^{k+2}(\zeta - z - h)^{k+1}} d\zeta,$$

where $P(\lambda, h)$ is a polynomial in λ and h, whose leading term is λ^k. Since $f(\zeta) P(\zeta - z, h)$ is analytic in and on C, there exists an M such that $M \geq |f(\zeta) P(\zeta - z, h)|$ on C. Thus if L is the length of C,

$$\left| \frac{f^{(k)}(z + h) - f^{(k)}(z)}{h} - \frac{(k + 1)!}{2\pi i} \int_C \frac{f(\zeta)\, d\zeta}{(\zeta - z)^{k+2}} \right|$$

$$\leq |h| \frac{(k + 2)!}{4\pi} \frac{ML}{r^{k+2} \left(\dfrac{r}{2}\right)^{k+1}},$$

which approaches zero as $|h|$ approaches zero.

This theorem, as just proved, will be a useful tool in treating sequences and series of functions (to be taken up in the next chapter). However, let us complete this chapter by giving a proof of a converse of Cauchy's integral *theorem*, attributed to Morera. The proof invokes the previous theorem.

Theorem 12: (*Morera*). Let $f(z)$ be single-valued and continuous on an open region $\mathfrak{A}$ of the z-plane. Let $\int_C f(z)\, dz = 0$ for every closed smooth curve in $\mathfrak{A}$. Then $f(z)$ is analytic in $\mathfrak{A}$.

Proof: By hypothesis

$$F(z) = \int_\alpha^z f(\zeta)\, d\zeta$$

is independent of the path from α to z. Thus the proof used in Theorem 8 implies $F'(z)$ exists and equals $f(z)$ for all z in $\mathfrak{A}$. (Note that in the proof of Theorem 8 only the *continuity* of $f(z)$ was used to establish this result.) Thus $F(z)$ is an analytic function. But by the previous theorem, the derivative of an analytic function is also analytic. Since $F'(z) = f(z)$, we infer that $f(z)$ is analytic.

EXERCISES

4.1. In Theorem 3 we showed that if $f(z)$ were single-valued and continuous along a *differentiable* curve C, then $\int_C f(z)\, dz$ existed. Assuming merely that C is a *continuous* rectifiable curve, prove that $f(z)$ is integrable along C.

4.2. Show that a necessary and sufficient condition that a function $f(z)$ be integrable along a smooth curve C is: Given an $\epsilon > 0$ there exists a $\delta > 0$ such that if σ and σ' are any two approximating sums constructed for partitions of norm less than δ, then

$$|\sigma - \sigma'| < \epsilon.$$

4.3. Let $f(z)$ and $g(z)$ be single-valued and continuous along a smooth curve C. Prove that

$$\left| \int_C f(z)\overline{g(z)}\, dz \right|^2 \leq \left| \left[\int_C |f(z)|^2\, dz \right]\left[\int_C |g(z)|^2\, dz \right] \right|.$$

This is known as the *Cauchy-Schwarz* inequality.

4.4. Let $f(z)$ and $g(z)$ be single-valued and analytic in an open region $\mathfrak{A}$. Let C be a smooth curve in $\mathfrak{A}$. Prove that

$$\int_C f(z)g'(z)\, dz = f(z)g(z)\Big|_C - \int_C g(z)f'(z)\, dz.$$

(By $f(z)g(z)|_C$ we mean the difference between the value of $f(z)g(z)$ at the terminal point of C arrived at by traversing C, and its value at the initial point of C.)

4.5. Prove that

$$\int_{-\infty}^{\infty} \frac{z^2 + 4 - 3i}{(z + 2i)^4}\, dz = 0.$$

4.6. Let C be a circle with center at the origin. If n is a positive or negative integer, show that

$$\int_C z^{n-1}\, dz = 0.$$

4.7. Let $f(z)$ be single-valued and analytic in and on a circle C of radius $R > 0$ with center at the origin. Then by the CIF

$$f(z) = \frac{1}{2\pi i} \int_C \frac{f(\zeta)}{\zeta - z}\, d\zeta$$

for all z interior to C. Making the substitution $\zeta = R\, e^{i\theta}$, $z = r\, e^{i\phi}$, show that

$$f(z) = \frac{1}{2\pi} \int_0^{2\pi} f(R\, e^{i\theta}) \frac{R^2 - r^2}{R^2 + r^2 - 2Rr \cos(\theta - \phi)}\, d\theta.$$

This is *Poisson's formula.* If $f(z) = u + iv$, show that

$$u(r,\phi) = \frac{1}{2\pi} \int_0^{2\pi} \frac{u(R,\theta)(R^2 - r^2)}{R^2 + r^2 - 2Rr \cos(\theta - \phi)} \, d\theta.$$

4.8. Let $f(z)$ be single-valued and analytic in an open region $\mathfrak{A}$. Let α be a point in $\mathfrak{A}$. By using the CIF show that

$$f(z) = f(\alpha) + f'(\alpha)(z - \alpha) + f''(a)\frac{(z - \alpha)^2}{2!} + \cdots + f^{(n)}(\alpha)\frac{(z - \alpha)^n}{n!}$$
$$+ f_{n+1}(z)(z - \alpha)^{n+1},$$

where $f_{n+1}(z)$ is analytic in $\mathfrak{A}$.

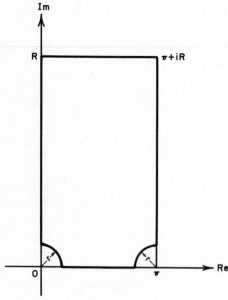

Figure 4.10

4.9. Let $f(z)$ be single-valued and analytic in a simply connected open set $\mathfrak{A}$. Let C be a circle of radius R with center at a point α in $\mathfrak{A}$ such that C lies entirely in $\mathfrak{A}$. Prove that

$$\left| f^{(n)}(\alpha) \right| \leqq \frac{M \, n!}{R^n},$$

$$n = 0, 1, 2, \cdots,$$

where $M = \max |f(z)|$ for all z on C. This is called *Cauchy's inequality.*

4.10. By integrating the function $\log(-2ie^{iz} \sin z)$ over the contour illustrated in Fig. 4.10, applying the CIT and then letting R approach infinity and r approach zero, show that

$$\int_0^\pi \log \sin x \, dx = -\pi \log 2.$$

4.11. Show that the integral

$$\int_0^\infty x^{a-1} e^{-x} \, dx$$

converges where x is real and $\operatorname{Re}[\alpha] > 0$. Students of applied mathematics will recognize this integral as the *Gamma function,* $\Gamma(\alpha)$.

CHAPTER 5

Sequences and Series

5.1 Introduction

The reader has probably already noticed that our development of complex variable theory closely paralleled the development for the real case. He is also aware of certain striking differences, particularly the results associated with the CIT of the previous chapter. In the present chapter this duality will be continued further. Since by now the reader has gained some experience in the handling of proofs for the complex case, we shall develop that portion of the theory of sequences and series which is analogous to the real variable case with the minimum of detail. We shall do this because the proofs are invariably word for word the same as in the real case. All proofs which we dispose of in this manner may be found, for example, in Chapter 5 of *ARC*. This, of course, is no excuse for treating the whole subject in a cavalier fashion. Every theorem will be precisely stated in the appropriate form for the complex case, and only when the proofs are truly identical with the real case will they be omitted. Occasionally we shall include such a proof just to convince the reader of this fact. This method of approach will allow us more time and space to consider certain facets of the theory which could have been—but perhaps were not—treated in detail in real variable theory, as well as those proofs and theorems (mainly relating to analytic functions and the use of the CIF) which have no immediate real counterpart.

5.2 Series of Complex Numbers

In Chapter 1 we considered sequences of complex numbers. A sequence $\{\sigma_n\}$ of complex numbers was said to converge to σ if given any $\epsilon > 0$ there existed an N such that for all $n > N$,

$$|\sigma_n - \sigma| < \epsilon.$$

Now let us consider a sequence of complex numbers $\{\alpha_n\}$ and the "sum,"

$$\alpha_1 + \alpha_2 + \cdots + \alpha_n + \cdots = \sum_{n=1}^{\infty} \alpha_n. \qquad (5.1)$$

Equation 5.1 is called an *infinite series*. In order to define precisely the terms *convergence of a series* and *sum of a series* we proceed as in the real case. Let

$$\sigma_n = \alpha_1 + \alpha_2 + \cdots + \alpha_n, \qquad n = 1, 2, \cdots$$

be the nth partial sum of the series of Equation 5.1. Then if the sequence $\{\sigma_n\}$ converges we shall say that the infinite series of Equation 5.1 *converges*. If $\{\sigma_n\}$ converges to σ, we shall say that the *sum* of the series is σ. Thus the convergence of series is referred back to the more basic question of the convergence of sequences. If the sequence of partial sums does *not* converge, we shall say that the infinite series *diverges*.

Conversely, if we are given a *sequence* such as $\{\sigma_n\}$ we can convert it to a series by writing

$$\sigma_1 + (\sigma_2 - \sigma_1) + (\sigma_3 - \sigma_2) + \cdots + (\sigma_n - \sigma_{n-1}) + \cdots .$$

Thus we see that once we have established a property for sequences we can readily infer the comparable theorem for series and vice versa. For instance, the fundamental Cauchy convergence theorem, worded in terms of series, becomes the following theorem.

Theorem I. Let

$$\sum_{n=1}^{\infty} \alpha_n$$

be a series of complex numbers. A necessary and sufficient condition that the series converge is: Given an $\epsilon > 0$, there exists an N such that

$$|\alpha_{n+1} + \alpha_{n+2} + \cdots + \alpha_{n+p}| < \epsilon$$

for all $n > N$ and all $p > 0$.

Proof: Let

$$\sigma_n = \sum_{k=1}^{n} \alpha_k$$

be the nth partial sum. Then

$$\sigma_{n+p} - \sigma_n = \alpha_{n+1} + \cdots + \alpha_{n+p}.$$

The theorem now follows by Theorem 4 of Chapter 1.

If the infinite series

$$\sum_{n=1}^{\infty} \alpha_n$$

has the property that the series of moduli

$$\sum_{n=1}^{\infty} |\alpha_n|$$

converges, then we shall say that $\sum \alpha_n$ converges *absolutely*. Again, this is the natural extension of the term as applied to real series. We immediately infer the following theorem.

Theorem 2. If a sequence converges absolutely, it converges.

The proof is identical with the real case.

An important property of absolutely convergent real series was that the terms could be rearranged at will and the new series would still converge to the sum of the original series. The same situation prevails in the complex case, and the proof is identical with the real case. Precisely stated, we have the following theorem.

Theorem 3. Let

$$\sum_{n=1}^{\infty} \alpha_n$$

converge absolutely. Then

$$\sum_{i=1}^{\infty} \alpha_{n_i},$$

where $n_1, n_2, \cdots$ is a rearrangement of the integers $1, 2, \cdots$, converges absolutely and its sum is the same as that of $\sum \alpha_n$.

If

$$\sum_{n=1}^{\infty} \alpha_n \qquad \text{and} \qquad \sum_{n=1}^{\infty} \beta_n$$

are two series, then their *product* is defined as the sum

$$\sum_{n=2}^{\infty} \gamma_n,$$

where

$$\gamma_n = \alpha_1\beta_{n-1} + \alpha_2\beta_{n-2} + \cdots + \alpha_{n-1}\beta_1, \qquad n = 2, 3, \cdots .$$

The convergence of $\sum \alpha_n$ and $\sum \beta_n$ does not imply the convergence of $\sum \gamma_n$. However, we do have the following theorem.

Theorem 4.　Let

$$\alpha = \sum_{n=1}^{\infty} \alpha_n \qquad \text{and} \qquad \beta = \sum_{n-1}^{\infty} \beta_n$$

be two convergent series and let at least one of them converge absolutely.　Then their product,

$$\sum_{n=2}^{\infty} \gamma_n,$$

where

$$\gamma_n = \sum_{k=1}^{n-1} \alpha_k \beta_{n-k},$$

converges and

$$\sum_{n=2}^{\infty} \gamma_n = \alpha\beta.$$

Again the proof is identical with the real case.　Theorem 4 does not insure the *absolute* convergence of $\sum \gamma_n$.　However, we do have the following corollary.

Corollary.　Let

$$\alpha = \sum_{n=1}^{\infty} \alpha_n \qquad \text{and} \qquad \beta = \sum_{n=1}^{\infty} \beta_n$$

both converge absolutely.　Then their product

$$\sum_{n=2}^{\infty} \gamma_n,$$

where

$$\gamma_n = \sum_{k=1}^{n-1} \alpha_k \beta_{n-k},$$

converges *absolutely*.

Proof: By Theorem 4, $\sum \gamma_n$ converges to $\alpha\beta$.　It remains to show that $\sum |\gamma_n|$ converges.　Now

$$(\sum |\alpha_n|)(\sum |\beta_n|) = \sum \delta_n,$$

where

$$\delta_n = \sum_{k=1}^{n-1} |\alpha_k||\beta_{n-k}|,$$

and $\sum \delta_n$ converges, since $\sum |\alpha_n|$ and $\sum |\beta_n|$ both converge absolutely. Also, since $|\gamma_n| \leq \delta_n$,

$$\left| |\gamma_{n+1}| + |\gamma_{n+2}| + \cdots + |\gamma_{n+p}| \right| \leq \delta_{n+1} + \delta_{n+2} + \cdots + \delta_{n+p},$$

which for n sufficiently large and $p > 0$ can be made less than any preassigned $\epsilon > 0$. Hence $\sum |\gamma_n|$ converges by the Cauchy convergence criterion (Theorem 1).

5.3 Sequences and Series of Functions

Let $\{u_n(z)\}$ be a sequence of single-valued *functions* of the complex variable z, all of which are defined in some region $\mathfrak{B}$ of the complex plane. The sequence $\{u_n(z)\}$ is said to converge at the point $z = z_0$ in $\mathfrak{B}$ if the sequence of *numbers* $\{u_n(z_0)\}$ converges. As in the theory of functions of a real variable, the notion of *uniform convergence* plays a fundamental role. The definition is the same as for real functions.

Definition. Let $\{u_n(z)\}$ be a sequence of single-valued functions defined on a set $\mathfrak{B}$. If there exists a function $u(z)$, also defined on $\mathfrak{B}$, such that, given any $\epsilon > 0$, there exists an N such that for all $n > N$ and all z in $\mathfrak{B}$,

$$|u_n(z) - u(z)| < \epsilon,$$

then we shall say that $\{u_n(z)\}$ *converges uniformly* to $u(z)$ on $\mathfrak{B}$.

An immediate consequence of this definition is Theorem 5. The proof parallels the real case.

Theorem 5. A necessary and sufficient condition that the sequence of functions $\{u_n(z)\}$ converge uniformly to $u(z)$ is: Given an $\epsilon > 0$, there exists an N such that for all $n > N$ and all $p > 0$,

$$|u_{n+p}(z) - u_n(z)| < \epsilon$$

for all z in $\mathfrak{B}$.

Two other important theorems follow.

Theorem 6. Let $\{u_n(z)\}$ be a sequence of single-valued functions defined and continuous on a smooth curve C. Let $\{u_n(z)\}$ converge uniformly to $u(z)$ on C. Then $u(z)$ is continuous on C.

Theorem 7. Let $\{u_n(z)\}$ be a sequence of single-valued functions defined and continuous on a smooth curve C. Let $\{u_n(z)\}$ converge uniformly to $u(z)$ on C. Then $\left\{ \int_C u_n(z)\, dz \right\}$ converges to $\int_C u(z)\, dz$.

The proofs of these theorems are again identical with the proofs for the real case.

The convergence of an infinite series of functions is defined in the expected way. Let $\{u_n(z)\}$ be a sequence of functions defined on a set $\mathfrak{B}$. Consider the infinite series

$$\sum_{n=1}^{\infty} u_n(z).$$

We say that this series converges at $z = z_0$ (a point in $\mathfrak{B}$) if the sequence of partial sums $\{\sigma_n(z)\}$, where

$$\sigma_n(z) = \sum_{k=1}^{n} u_k(z)$$

converges at $z = z_0$. The definition of uniform convergence, as well as the statements of Theorems 5, 6, and 7, can be worded in terms of series. We leave this to the reader.

For series we also have the Weierstrass M-test.

Theorem 8. Let

$$\sum_{n=1}^{\infty} M_n$$

be a convergent series of non-negative real numbers. Let

$$\sum_{n=1}^{\infty} u_n(z)$$

be a series of functions defined on some region $\mathfrak{B}$ such that for all z in $\mathfrak{B}$,

$$|u_n(z)| \leq M_n, \qquad n = 1, 2, \cdots.$$

Then

$$\sum_{n=1}^{\infty} u_n(z)$$

converges uniformly and absolutely on $\mathfrak{B}$.

5.4 Sequences of Analytic Functions

Because of the great importance of analytic functions, we shall devote a section to the proof of certain fundamental theorems regarding sequences of analytic functions. A powerful tool now at our disposal is the CIF.

It will be convenient to preface our treatment with two lemmas.

Lemma 1. Let $f(\zeta)$ be single-valued and continuous on a closed smooth curve C. Let z be any point in the interior of C. Then

$$\int_C \frac{f(\zeta)}{\zeta - z}\, d\zeta$$

is an analytic function of z on the interior of C.

Proof: Write

$$F(z) = \int_C \frac{f(\zeta)}{\zeta - z}\, d\zeta.$$

Then

$$\frac{F(z + h) - F(z)}{h} = \int_C \frac{f(\zeta)\, d\zeta}{(\zeta - z - h)(\zeta - z)}.$$

In the proof of Theorem 11 of Chapter 4 we showed that

$$\lim_{h \to 0} \frac{1}{2\pi i} \int_C \frac{f(\zeta)\, d\zeta}{(\zeta - z - h)(\zeta - z)} = \frac{1}{2\pi i} \int_C \frac{f(\zeta)}{(\zeta - z)^2}\, d\zeta,$$

merely using the continuity of $f(\zeta)$ on C. Thus

$$F'(z) = \lim_{h \to 0} \frac{F(z + h) - F(z)}{h}$$

exists.

An immediate corollary is

$$F^{(n)}(z) = n! \int_C \frac{f(\zeta)\, d\zeta}{(\zeta - z)^{n+1}}.$$

Lemma 2. Let $\{u_n(z)\}$ be a sequence of functions defined and single-valued on an open region $\mathfrak{A}$. Let $\{u_n(z)\}$ converge uniformly to $u(z)$ on $\mathfrak{A}$. Let C be a closed smooth curve which, together with its interior, lies in $\mathfrak{A}$. Let z be a point in the interior of C, and let p be any fixed positive integer. Then the sequence

$$\{u_n(\zeta)(\zeta - z)^{-p}\}$$

converges uniformly to $u(\zeta)/(\zeta - z)^p$ for all ζ on C.

Proof: Let Γ be a circle of radius r with center at z such that Γ and its interior lie in the interior of C. Then $|\zeta - z| > r$ for ζ on C. Let $\epsilon > 0$ be assigned. By the Cauchy convergence theorem (Theorem 5) there exists an N such that, for all $n > N$, $m > 0$, and ζ on C,

$$|u_{n+m}(\zeta) - u_m(\zeta)| < \epsilon\, r^p.$$

Thus

$$\left| \frac{u_{n+m}(\zeta)}{(\zeta - z)^p} - \frac{u_n(\zeta)}{(\zeta - z)^p} \right| < \frac{|u_{n+m}(\zeta) - u_n(\zeta)|}{r^p} < \epsilon$$

for all $n > N$, $m > 0$, and ζ on C.

Our first major theorem follows.

Theorem 9. Let $\{u_n(z)\}$ be a sequence of analytic functions defined and single-valued on an open set $\mathfrak{A}$. Let $\{u_n(z)\}$ converge uniformly to $u(z)$ on $\mathfrak{A}$. Then $u(z)$ is analytic on $\mathfrak{A}$.

Proof: Let z_0 be any point in $\mathfrak{A}$ and let C be a circle with center at z_0 such that C and its interior lie in $\mathfrak{A}$. We shall show that $u(z)$ is analytic in C and hence at z_0.

Let z be any point in the interior of C. Then the sequence

$$\left\{ \frac{u_n(\zeta)}{\zeta - z} \right\}$$

converges uniformly to $\dfrac{u(\zeta)}{\zeta - z}$ for ζ on C by Lemma 2. Since $\dfrac{u_n(\zeta)}{\zeta - z}$ is continuous for all ζ on C, it follows from Theorem 6 that $\dfrac{u(\zeta)}{\zeta - z}$ is continuous and hence

$$\left\{ \int_C \frac{u_n(\zeta)}{\zeta - z} \, d\zeta \right\} \to \int_C \frac{u(\zeta)}{\zeta - z} \, d\zeta,$$

by Theorem 7. Lemma 1 now implies that $\displaystyle\int_C \frac{u(\zeta)}{\zeta - z} \, d\zeta$ is analytic. But $u_n(z) = \dfrac{1}{2\pi i} \displaystyle\int_C \frac{u_n(\zeta)}{\zeta - z} \, d\zeta$ by the CIF. Thus

$$u(z) = \frac{1}{2\pi i} \int_C \frac{u(\zeta)}{\zeta - z} \, d\zeta, \tag{5.2}$$

which implies that $u(z)$ is analytic for all z interior to C.

We shall now consider the sequence of *derivatives* $\{u_n'(z)\}$ of the sequence $\{u_n(z)\}$ considered in Theorem 9. It is, of course, a sequence of analytic functions. Hence $\{u_n'(z)\}$ converges to some function, say $v(z)$, which is analytic in $\mathfrak{A}$. The important result we shall prove in Theorem 10 is that $v(z) = u'(z)$ and that the convergence is *uniform* in C. This immediately implies the uniform convergence of the sequence of mth derivatives, $\{u_n^{(m)}(z)\}$ to $u^{(m)}(z)$ in C.

Theorem 10.   Let $\{u_n(z)\}$ be a sequence of analytic functions defined and single-valued on an open set $\mathfrak{A}$.   Let $\{u_n(z)\}$ converge uniformly to $u(z)$ on $\mathfrak{A}$.   Then the sequence of derivatives $\{u_n'(z)\}$ converges to $u'(z)$ on $\mathfrak{A}$.   If C is a circle which, together with its interior, lies in $\mathfrak{A}$, then the convergence of $\{u_n'(z)\}$ to $u'(z)$ is *uniform* in and on C.

Proof: Let z be any point in $\mathfrak{A}$ and C a circle about z which together with its interior lies in $\mathfrak{A}$.   Then from Equation 5.2

$$u'(z) = \frac{1}{2\pi i} \int_C \frac{u(\zeta)\,d\zeta}{(\zeta - z)^2}.$$

But

$$u_n'(z) = \frac{1}{2\pi i} \int_C \frac{u_n(\zeta)}{(\zeta - z)^2}\,d\zeta,$$

and the sequence $\{u_n(\zeta)(\zeta - z)^{-2}\}$ converges uniformly to $\{u(\zeta)(\zeta - z)^{-2}\}$ for all ζ on C by Lemma 2.   Thus by Theorem 7 the sequence

$$\left\{ \int_C \frac{u_n(\zeta)}{(\zeta - z)^2}\,d\zeta \right\}$$

converges to $\int_C u(\zeta)(\zeta - z)^{-2}\,d\zeta$, or what is the same thing, $\{u_n'(z)\}$ converges to $u'(z)$ for all z in C.   Hence for every z in $\mathfrak{A}$ the sequence of derivatives $\{u_n'(z)\}$ converges to $u'(z)$.   This establishes the first part of the theorem.   We must now show that the convergence is uniform in any circle interior to $\mathfrak{A}$.

Let C and C' be any circles which, together with their interiors, lie in $\mathfrak{A}$.   Let r be the radius of C.   Let C' be a circle of radius $r + \delta$ concentric with C.   Since $\mathfrak{A}$ is open it is possible to find such a C' with $\delta > 0$.   Choose any such δ and hold it fixed for the remainder of the discussion.   Let $\epsilon > 0$ be assigned.   Since $\{u_n(\zeta)\}$ converges uniformly to $u(\zeta)$ by hypothesis, there exists an N such that for all $n > N$

$$|u(\zeta) - u_n(\zeta)| < \frac{\epsilon \delta^2}{r + \delta}$$

for all ζ on C'.   Now for $n > N$ and z in or on C, we have $|\zeta - z| \geq \delta$.   Since the length of C' is $2\pi(r + \delta)$,

$$|u'(z) - u_n'(z)| = \left| \frac{1}{2\pi i} \int_{C'} \frac{u(\zeta) - u_n(\zeta)}{(\zeta - z)^2}\,d\zeta \right|$$

$$\leq \frac{1}{2\pi\delta^2} \int_{C'} |u(\zeta) - u_n(\zeta)||d\zeta|$$

$$< \frac{1}{2\pi\delta^2} \left(\frac{\epsilon\delta^2}{r + \delta} \right) 2\pi(r + \delta) = \epsilon$$

for all $n > N$ and all z in or on C. This establishes the uniformity of the convergence of the sequence of derivatives.

As a corollary to Theorem 10 we see that $\{u_n'(z)\}$ converges uniformly on any closed bounded set F interior to $\mathfrak{A}$. For about every point z_0 of F we can find a spherical neighborhood $C(z_0)$ such that there exists an $N(z_0)$ with the property that

$$\left| u'(z) - u_n'(z) \right| < \epsilon$$

for all $n > N(z_0)$ and all z in $C(z_0)$. By the Heine-Borel theorem a finite number of these circles (say those associated with the points $z_1, z_2, \cdots, z_k$) with the above property cover F. Let N be the maximum of the $N(z_j)$, $j = 1, 2, \cdots, k$. Then for $n > N$

$$\left| u'(z) - u_n'(z) \right| < \epsilon$$

for all z in F.

5.5 Power Series

Series of the form

$$S(z) = \sum_{n=0}^{\infty} c_n(z - \alpha)^n, \tag{5.3}$$

where α and the c_n are complex numbers, are called *power series*. Clearly $S(z)$ converges at $z = \alpha$. Suppose $S(z)$ converges at $z = z_0 \neq \alpha$, that is,

$$\sum_{n=0}^{\infty} c_n(z_0 - \alpha)^n$$

is a convergent series of complex numbers. We shall show that $S(z)$ converges uniformly and absolutely in any circle $|z - \alpha| \leq r$ where r is any number less than $|z_0 - \alpha|$.

Since $\sum c_n(z_0 - \alpha)^n$ is a convergent series of numbers, there exists an M independent of n such that

$$\left| c_n(z_0 - \alpha)^n \right| < M$$

for all n, $n = 0, 1, 2, \cdots$. Thus for $|z - \alpha| \leq r$,

$$\left| c_n(z - \alpha)^n \right| \leq \left| c_n \right| r^n = \left| c_n(z_0 - \alpha)^n \right| \left| \frac{r}{z_0 - \alpha} \right|^n < M \left| \frac{r}{z_0 - \alpha} \right|^n.$$

The series

$$\sum_{n=0}^{\infty} M \left| \frac{r}{z_0 - \alpha} \right|^n$$

is a convergent geometric series, since $|r/(z_0 - \alpha)| < 1$, and hence by the Weierstrass M-test (Theorem 8) the power series of Equation 5.3 converges uniformly and absolutely for all z such that $|z - \alpha| \leqq r$.

Clearly the partial sums of $S(z)$ are analytic functions. Hence Theorem 10 implies that term by term differentiation of Equation 5.3 is valid, namely, that

$$S^{(p)}(z) = \sum_{n=p}^{\infty} n(n - 1) \cdots (n - p + 1)c_n(z - \alpha)^{n-p},$$

and that $S^{(p)}(z)$ converges uniformly and absolutely in $|z - \alpha| \leqq r$.

Now it may be that there exists no value of z with the property that $S(z)$ converges when $|z - \alpha| > |z_0 - \alpha|$. In this case we say that $|z_0 - \alpha|$ is the *radius of convergence* of the power series, and call $|z - \alpha| = |z_0 - \alpha|$ the *circle of convergence*. Suppose, though, there exists a value of z, say z_1 with $|z_1 - \alpha| > |z_0 - \alpha|$, at which $S(z)$ converges. Then we see by a repetition of the above argument that $S(z)$ converges absolutely for all z with $|z - \alpha| < |z_1 - \alpha|$; and uniformly in and on any circle $|z - \alpha| \leqq r_1$ where $r_1 < |z_1 - \alpha|$. Continuing, there may exist a z_2 with $|z_2 - \alpha| > |z_1 - \alpha|$ and such that $S(z)$ converges at z_2. Two cases arise: either the numbers $|z_0 - \alpha|$, $|z_1 - \alpha|$, $|z_2 - \alpha|$, $\cdots$ increase indefinitely and there is no point at which $S(z)$ fails to converge, or else there *are* points for which $S(z)$ does not converge. In the first case we say that the radius of convergence of $S(z)$ is infinite. In the second case, since $|z_0 - \alpha|$, $|z_1 - \alpha|$, $|z_2 - \alpha|$, $\cdots$ is bounded from above, there exists a least upper bound, say R. Clearly R has the property that for all z with $|z - \alpha| < R$ the series converges and for all z with $|z - \alpha| > R$ the series diverges. We call R the radius of convergence of the power series. (If $z = \alpha$ is the only point at which $S(z)$ converges, then we say that the radius of convergence of $S(z)$ is zero.)

Thus we see that $S(z)$ converges absolutely at every point in the interior of its circle of convergence and diverges at every point exterior to its circle of convergence. On the circle of convergence it may converge at some points and diverge at others. If C is any circle with center at α and positive radius less than R, then $S(z)$ converges uniformly in and on C and represents an analytic function there.

5.6 Taylor's Expansion

We have seen that a power series represents an analytic function in its circle of convergence. We shall now prove the converse, namely, every analytic function can be uniquely expressed as a power series. This result is precisely formulated in Theorem 11.

Theorem 11. Let $f(z)$ be analytic and single-valued in an open region $\mathfrak{A}$. Let α be any point in $\mathfrak{A}$. Let C be a circle with center at α which together with its interior lies in $\mathfrak{A}$. Then at every point z in C the power series

$$f(\alpha) + f'(\alpha)(z - \alpha) + f''(\alpha)\frac{(z - \alpha)^2}{2!} + \cdots + f^{(n)}(\alpha)\frac{(z - \alpha)^n}{n!} + \cdots$$

converges to $f(z)$.

Proof: By the Cauchy integral formula

$$f(z) = \frac{1}{2\pi i} \int_C \frac{f(\zeta)}{\zeta - z} \, d\zeta \tag{5.4}$$

for all z in C. Now by a simple algebraic manipulation (see Exercise 1.4)

$$\frac{1}{\zeta - z} = \frac{1}{(\zeta - \alpha) - (z - \alpha)} = \frac{1}{\zeta - \alpha} + \frac{z - \alpha}{(\zeta - \alpha)^2} + \cdots$$

$$+ \frac{(z - \alpha)^n}{(\zeta - \alpha)^{n+1}} + \frac{(z - \alpha)^{n+1}}{(\zeta - \alpha)^{n+1}(\zeta - z)}. \tag{5.5}$$

Since

$$\frac{1}{2\pi i} \int_C f(\zeta)(\zeta - \alpha)^{-(k+1)} \, d\zeta = f^{(k)}(\alpha)/k!, \qquad k = 0, 1, 2, \cdots,$$

we have from Equations 5.4 and 5.5 that

$$f(z) = f(\alpha) + f'(\alpha)(z - \alpha) + f''(\alpha)\frac{(z - \alpha)^2}{2!} + \cdots$$

$$+ f^{(n)}(\alpha)\frac{(z - \alpha)^n}{n!} + R_n(z),$$

where

$$R_n(z) = \frac{(z - \alpha)^{n+1}}{2\pi i} \int_C \frac{f(\zeta) \, d\zeta}{(\zeta - \alpha)^{n+1}(\zeta - z)}$$

is the remainder. If we can show that

$$\lim_{n \to \infty} |R_n(z)| = 0$$

our theorem will be established.

If r is the radius of C, then $|z - \alpha| < r$ for any z in C and

$$|\zeta - z| = |(\zeta - \alpha) + (\alpha - z)| \geq |\zeta - \alpha| - |\alpha - z|$$

$$\geq r - |\alpha - z| > \delta > 0.$$

Also, since $f(z)$ is continuous in $\mathfrak{A}$, it is bounded on C.   Let $M \geq |f(z)|$ on C.   Then

$$|R_n(z)| \leq \frac{|z - \alpha|^{n+1}}{2\pi} \frac{M}{r^{n+1}\, \delta} L,$$

where $L = 2\pi r$ is the length of C.   Thus

$$|R_n(z)| \leq \frac{ML}{2\pi\delta} \left|\frac{z - \alpha}{r}\right|^{n+1}.$$

Since $|(z - \alpha)/r| < 1$, $\lim\limits_{n \to \infty} |R_n(z)| = 0$.

If $\alpha = 0$, we obtain

$$f(z) = f(0) + f'(0)z + f''(0)\frac{z^2}{2!} + \cdots + f^{(n)}(0)\frac{z^n}{n!} + \cdots,$$

which is generally called *Maclaurin's series*.

It remains but to show that the expansion we have obtained is unique.   Suppose

$$c_0 + c_1(z - \alpha) + c_2(z - \alpha)^2 + \cdots$$

represents $f(z)$ in a neighborhood of $z = \alpha$.   Then there exists a circle Γ with center at $z = \alpha$ such that the power series converges uniformly and absolutely for all z in and on Γ.   If $z = \alpha$,

$$f(\alpha) = c_0.$$

Since the power series converges uniformly,

$$f'(z) = c_1 + 2c_2(z - \alpha) + 3c_3(z - \alpha)^2 + \cdots$$

and

$$f'(\alpha) = c_1.$$

Repeated applications of this argument yield

$$f^{(n)}(\alpha) = n!c_n, \qquad n = 0, 1, 2, \cdots.$$

Thus the expansion of $f(z)$ in powers of $(z - \alpha)$ as given in Theorem 11 is unique.

5.7 The Root Test

We would like to give a "practical" test to determine the radius of convergence of a power series such as

$$\sum_{n=0}^{\infty} c_n(z - \alpha)^n.$$

One such test can be formulated by considering the *limit superior* of $\sqrt[n]{|c_n|}$ as n approaches infinity. Preliminary to proving this main theorem we shall first define and prove certain properties of the limit superior.

We recall that if $\{a_n\}$ is a bounded sequence of real numbers then the least upper bound and the greatest lower bound of $\{a_n\}$ always exist while $\lim\limits_{n \to \infty} a_n$ may or may not exist. For example, the sequence

$$2, \ -2, \ 1\frac{1}{2}, \ -1\frac{1}{2}, \ \cdots, \ 1 + \frac{1}{2^n}, \ -\left(1 + \frac{1}{2^n}\right), \cdots \tag{5.6}$$

has the l.u.b. of 2, the g.l.b. of -2, while the limit does not exist. If we consider the even terms of Equation 5.6 we see that these terms converge to -1 while an examination of the odd terms of Equation 5.6 leads to the conclusion that they converge to $+1$. It would seem, therefore, that the numbers $+1$ and -1 play a special role with regard to this sequence. Can we therefore define some type of "limit" which will bring these numbers into prominence? The answer is yes and is contained in the important definitions of *upper limit* and *lower limit*.

Definition. Let $\{a_n\}$ be a sequence of real numbers. If there exists a number β with the property that for every $\epsilon > 0$ an infinite number of the a_n exceed $\beta - \epsilon$, while only a finite number exceed $\beta + \epsilon$; then we call β the *upper limit* or *greatest limit* or *limit superior* of the sequence $\{a_n\}$. In symbols we write

$$\beta = \overline{\lim_{n \to \infty}} \ a_n$$

or

$$\beta = \lim_{n \to \infty} \sup a_n.$$

Similarly, if there exists a number α with the property that for every $\epsilon > 0$ an infinite number of the a_n are less than $\alpha + \epsilon$, while only a finite number are less than $\alpha - \epsilon$, then we call α the *lower limit* or *least limit* or *limit inferior* of the sequence $\{a_n\}$ and write

$$\alpha = \underline{\lim_{n \to \infty}} \ a_n$$

or

$$\alpha = \lim_{n \to \infty} \inf a_n.$$

It is clear that if $\{a_n\}$ is the sequence of Equation 5.6 then

$$\overline{\lim_{n \to \infty}} \ a_n = +1 \qquad \text{and} \qquad \underline{\lim_{n \to \infty}} \ a_n = -1.$$

We see therefore that with a given bounded sequence we can associate more than one type of limit. Unlike the "limit," the limit superior and limit inferior always exist.

Theorem 12. Let $\{a_n\}$ be a bounded sequence. Then the greatest limit and least limit always exist and are unique.

Proof: Let A be the totality of real numbers which have the property of being exceeded by an infinite number of the a_n. Since $\{a_n\}$ is bounded, A is bounded from above. Let $a = $ l.u.b. A. We assert that

$$a = \varlimsup_{n \to \infty} a_n.$$

Let $\epsilon > 0$ be assigned. Then $a - \epsilon$ is an element of A. By hypothesis, an infinite number of the a_n exceed $a - \epsilon$. But $a + \epsilon$ is not an element of A. Hence, at most, a finite number of the a_n exceed $a + \epsilon$.

We shall show that a is unique. Suppose a and a' with $a \neq a'$ are both upper limits. Without loss of generality, let $a' > a$ and choose an $\epsilon > 0$ such that

$$a + \epsilon = a' - \epsilon,$$

[that is, $\epsilon = \frac{1}{2}(a' - a)$]. Now an infinite number of the a_n exceed $a' - \epsilon$, and thus an infinite number exceed $a + \epsilon$. But by definition of greatest limit, only a finite number exceed $a + \epsilon$—a contradiction. The proof of the existence and uniqueness of $\varliminf a_n$ is similar.

Theorem 13. Let $\{a_n\}$ be a bounded sequence. Then

$$\varlimsup_{n \to \infty} a_n \geq \varliminf_{n \to \infty} a_n.$$

Proof: Let $\beta = \varlimsup a_n$ and $\alpha = \varliminf a_n$. We shall assume $\beta < \alpha$ and force a contradiction. Since β is the upper limit, only a finite number of the a_n exceed $\beta + \epsilon$ for any $\epsilon > 0$. Thus there exists an N' such that for all $n > N'$, $a_n \leq \beta + \epsilon$. Similarly, since α is the lower limit, only a finite number of the a_n are less than $\alpha - \epsilon$. Therefore there exists an N'' such that for all $n > N''$, $a_n \geq \alpha - \epsilon$. Hence there exists an a_N such that

$$\alpha - \epsilon \leq a_N \leq \beta + \epsilon.$$

Therefore

$$\alpha - \beta \leq 2\epsilon$$

for every $\epsilon > 0$. But if $\alpha > \beta$, let $\epsilon = \frac{1}{4}(\alpha - \beta)$. Then the above inequality implies

$$\alpha - \beta \leq \frac{1}{2}(\alpha - \beta),$$

which is absurd.

If the limit superior equals the limit inferior, then we have the following important result.

Theorem 14. Let $\{a_n\}$ be a bounded sequence of real numbers. Then $\lim_{n \to \infty} a_n$ exists if and only if

$$\overline{\lim_{n \to \infty}} \, a_n = \underline{\lim_{n \to \infty}} \, a_n$$

and in this case all three are equal.

Proof: Suppose $\overline{\lim} \, a_n = \underline{\lim} \, a_n$. Call their common value β. Since only a finite number of the a_n exceed $\beta + \epsilon$ and only a finite number of the a_n are less than $\beta - \epsilon$ for any $\epsilon > 0$, there exists an N such that for all $n > N$,

$$\beta - \epsilon \leq a_n \leq \beta + \epsilon,$$

or

$$|a_n - \beta| \leq \epsilon$$

for all $n > N$. Thus $\lim_{n \to \infty} a_n$ exists, by definition of limit of a sequence, and equals β.

Conversely, suppose $\lim_{n \to \infty} a_n$ exists. Call it a. Then, given an $\epsilon > 0$, there exists an N such that for all $n > N$,

$$-\epsilon < a_n - a < \epsilon.$$

Thus for all $n > N$,

$$a_n > a - \epsilon$$

and

$$a_n < a + \epsilon.$$

Thus only a finite number of the a_n are less than $a - \epsilon$ and greater than $a + \epsilon$. Hence a is both the upper limit and lower limit.

In the previous theorems we required that the sequence $\{a_n\}$ in question be bounded. If $\{a_n\}$ is *not* bounded from above, we shall say that the limit superior is plus infinity. This simply means that there are an infinite number of the a_n which exceed any finite number we may care to name.   Similarly, if $\{a_n\}$ is not bounded from below, we shall say that the limit inferior is minus infinity.

We are now in a position to state the *root test*.

Theorem 15: (*The Root Test*).   Let

$$f(z) = \sum_{n=1}^{\infty} c_n(z - \alpha)^n \qquad (5.7)$$

be a power series.   Let

$$L = \overline{\lim_{n \to \infty}} \sqrt[n]{|c_n|}.$$

Then $R = 1/L$ is the radius of convergence of the power series.

Proof: Let $z_0 \neq \alpha$ be any complex number such that $|z_0 - \alpha| < R$. Then

$$\frac{1}{|z_0 - \alpha|} > \frac{1}{R} = L.$$

Let a be a real number satisfying the inequalities

$$1 > a > |z_0 - \alpha|L.$$

Since

$$L = \overline{\lim_{n \to \infty}} \sqrt[n]{|c_n|} \qquad \text{and} \qquad \frac{a}{|z_0 - \alpha|} > L,$$

there exists only a finite number of the $\sqrt[n]{|c_n|}$ which exceed $a/|z_0 - \alpha|$. Hence there exists an N such that for all $n > N$,

$$\sqrt[n]{|c_n|} \leqq \frac{a}{|z_0 - \alpha|}$$

or

$$|c_n(z_0 - \alpha)^n| \leqq a^n.$$

Thus

$$\sum_{k=0}^{\infty} |c_k(z_0 - \alpha)^k| \leqq \sum_{k=0}^{N} |c_k(z_0 - \alpha)^k| + \sum_{k=N+1}^{\infty} a^k.$$

But $a < 1$ and hence

$$\sum_{k=N+1}^{\infty} a^k$$

is a convergent geometric series.   Thus $f(z)$ converges absolutely for all z with $|z - \alpha| = |z_0 - \alpha|$.

Now let z_0 be any complex number such that $|z_0 - \alpha| > R$.   Then

$$\frac{1}{|z_0 - \alpha|} < \frac{1}{R} = L,$$

and there exists an infinite number of the $\sqrt[n]{|c_n|}$ which exceed $|z_0 - \alpha|^{-1}$. Thus

$$\sqrt[n]{|c_n|} > \frac{1}{|z_0 - \alpha|}$$

or

$$|c_n(z_0 - \alpha)^n| > 1$$

for an infinite number of the n. Hence $\lim\limits_{n \to \infty} c_n(z_0 - \alpha)^n \neq 0$ and the power series of Equation 5.7 diverges for all z with $|z - \alpha| = |z_0 - \alpha|$.

Two special cases, namely $L = 0$ and $L = \infty$, require an additional word or two of elucidation. (i) If $L = 0$, then, following through the proof of Theorem 15, we see that $f(z)$ converges for every z_0. (ii) If the sequence $\{\sqrt[n]{|c_n|}\}$ is unbounded, then L is infinite. Thus an infinite number of the $\sqrt[n]{|c_n|}$ exceed $1/|z_0 - \alpha|$ for any $z_0 \neq \alpha$ and, as in the proof of Theorem 15, this implies that $f(z)$ diverges for all $z_0 \neq \alpha$.

For example, if

$$f_1(z) = 1 + z + z^2 + \cdots + z^n + \cdots,$$

then $c_n = 1$ and $\overline{\lim}\ \sqrt[n]{|c_n|} = 1$. Thus the radius of convergence of $f_1(z)$ is 1. If

$$f_2(z) = z - \frac{z^3}{3!} + \frac{z^5}{5!} - \cdots + (-1)^{n+1} \frac{z^{2n-1}}{(2n-1)!} + \cdots,$$

then $c_n = (-1)^{n+1}/(2n + 1)!$ and $\overline{\lim}\ \sqrt[n]{|c_n|} = 0$. Thus the radius of convergence of $f_2(z)$ is infinite. (Of course, $f_2(z) = \sin z$.) If

$$f_3(z) = 1 + z + 2!z^2 + \cdots + n!z^n + \cdots,$$

then $c_n = n!$ and $\overline{\lim}\ \sqrt[n]{|c_n|} = \infty$. Thus $f_3(z)$ converges only for $z = 0$.

5.8 Laurent Series

In the previous sections we considered power series, that is, series of functions of the form

$$\sum_{n=0}^{\infty} c_n(z - \alpha)^n.$$

Another type of series of analytic functions that plays a prominent role in the complex calculus is a series of *negative* powers of $(z - \alpha)$, viz.,

$$f_1(z) = c_{-1}(z - \alpha)^{-1} + c_{-2}(z - \alpha)^{-2} + \cdots$$

$$\text{(5.8)}$$

$$+ c_{-n}(z - \alpha)^{-n} + \cdots = \sum_{n=1}^{\infty} c_{-n}(z - \alpha)^{-n}.$$

If the series

$$\sum_{n=1}^{\infty} c_{-n}\zeta^n$$

has a positive radius of convergence R, then it will converge for $|\zeta| < R$ and diverge for $|\zeta| > R$. Thus the series of Equation 5.8 with $z - \alpha = 1/\zeta$ will converge for $|z - \alpha| > R^{-1}$ and diverge for $|z - \alpha| < R^{-1}$. In particular, if R is infinite, $f_1(z)$ will converge for all z exterior to any circle of positive radius with center at α.

Suppose now that

$$f_2(z) = \sum_{n=0}^{\infty} c_n(z - \alpha)^n$$

is a power series with a radius of convergence $S > R^{-1}$. Then $f_2(z)$ converges for $|z - \alpha| < S$ and diverges for $|z - \alpha| > S$. Thus

$$f(z) = f_1(z) + f_2(z)$$

$$\text{(5.9)}$$

$$= \sum_{n=1}^{\infty} c_{-n}(z - \alpha)^{-n} + \sum_{n=0}^{\infty} c_n(z - \alpha)^n = \sum_{n=-\infty}^{\infty} c_n(z - \alpha)^n$$

converges for all z such that

$$R^{-1} < |z - \alpha| < S.$$

The right-hand side of equation 5.9 is called a *Laurent series*. The series $f_1(z)$ of negative powers is called the *principal part* of the development. A Taylor series is a special case of a Laurent series where $c_n = 0, n = -1, -2 \cdots$.

The fundamental theorem regarding Laurent series is expressed in Theorem 16.

Theorem 16. Let C_1 and C_2 be concentric circles with centers at α and positive radii r_1 and r_2 respectively with $r_1 > r_2$. Let $f(z)$ be single-valued and analytic in the region $r_2 \leqq |z - \alpha| \leqq r_1$. Then $f(z)$ admits of a Laurent series development

$$f(z) = \sum_{n=-1}^{-\infty} c_n(z - \alpha)^n + \sum_{n=0}^{\infty} c_n(z - \alpha)^n,$$

which converges for all z in the open region $\mathfrak{A}$ between C_1 and C_2, and

$$c_n = \frac{1}{2\pi i} \int_{C_1} \frac{f(\zeta)\,d\zeta}{(\zeta - \alpha)^{n+1}}, \qquad n = 0, 1, 2, \cdots$$

$$c_{-n} = \frac{1}{2\pi i} \int_{C_2} \frac{f(\zeta)\,d\zeta}{(\zeta - \alpha)^{-n+1}}, \qquad n = 1, 2, 3, \cdots.$$

Proof: By the CIF

$$f(z) = \frac{1}{2\pi i} \int_{C_1} \frac{f(\zeta)}{\zeta - z}\,d\zeta - \frac{1}{2\pi i} \int_{C_2} \frac{f(\zeta)}{\zeta - z}\,d\zeta \tag{5.10}$$

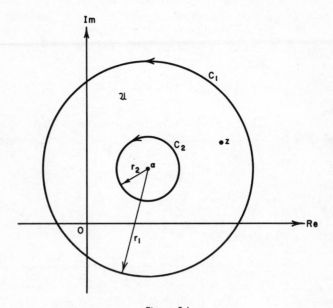

Figure 5.1

for all z in $\mathfrak{A}$ (see Fig. 5.1). Now we may express $\dfrac{1}{\zeta - z}$ by means of Equation 5.5, and interchanging the roles of ζ and z, we have

$$\frac{1}{z - \zeta} = \frac{1}{z - \alpha} + \frac{\zeta - \alpha}{(z - \alpha)^2} + \cdots + \frac{(\zeta - \alpha)^n}{(z - \alpha)^{n+1}} + \frac{(\zeta - \alpha)^{n+1}}{(z - \alpha)^{n+1}(z - \zeta)}.$$

$$\tag{5.11}$$

Replace $\dfrac{1}{\zeta - z}$ by Equation 5.5 in the first integral of Equation 5.10 and

$\dfrac{1}{z-\zeta}$ by Equation 5.11 in the second integral of Equation 5.10 to obtain

$$f(z) = c_0 + c_1(z - \alpha) + c_2(z - \alpha)^2 + \cdots + c_n(z - \alpha)^n + R_n(z)$$
$$+ c_{-1}(z - \alpha)^{-1} + c_{-2}(z - \alpha)^{-2} + \cdots + c_{-n}(z - \alpha)^{-n} + R_{-n}(z),$$

where

$$R_n(z) = \frac{(z - \alpha)^{n+1}}{2\pi i} \int_{C_1} \frac{f(\zeta)\, d\zeta}{(\zeta - \alpha)^{n+1}(\zeta - z)}$$

and

$$R_{-n}(z) = \frac{1}{2\pi i(z - \alpha)^{n+1}} \int_{C_2} \frac{(\zeta - \alpha)^{n+1} f(\zeta)}{z - \zeta}\, d\zeta.$$

If we can show that

$$\lim_{n \to \infty} |R_{\pm n}(z)| = 0,$$

our theorem will be established. The proof that

$$\lim_{n \to \infty} |R_n(z)| = 0$$

is identical with that given in Theorem 11. It therefore remains but to prove that $\lim_{n \to \infty} |R_{-n}(z)| = 0$.

Let $M \geq |f(z)|$ on C_2. Since $|\alpha - \zeta| = r_2$ and $r_2 < |z - \alpha| < r_1$ for any z in $\mathfrak{A}$,

$$|z - \zeta| = |(z - \alpha) + (\alpha - \zeta)| \geq |z - \alpha| - |\alpha - \zeta|$$
$$= |z - \alpha| - r_2 = \delta > 0.$$

Thus

$$|R_{-n}(z)| \leq \frac{1}{2\pi |z - \alpha|^{n+1}} \frac{M r_2^{n+1}}{\delta} L = \frac{ML}{2\pi\delta} \left| \frac{r_2}{z - \alpha} \right|^{n+1},$$

where $L = 2\pi r_2$ is the length of C_2. Since $|r_2/(z - \alpha)| < 1$, $\lim_{n \to \infty} |R_{-n}(z)| = 0$ and Theorem 16 is established.

If Γ is any circle with center at α and radius r with $r_2 < r < r_1$, then we easily see that the coefficients $c_{\pm n}$ of Theorem 16 may be expressed by the single formula

$$c_n = \frac{1}{2\pi i} \int_{\Gamma} \frac{f(\zeta)\, d\zeta}{(\zeta - \alpha)^{n+1}}, \qquad n = 0, \pm 1, \pm 2, \cdots. \qquad (5.12)$$

We now wish to show that the expansion we have obtained is unique. Suppose, then, that

$$f(z) = \sum_{n=1}^{\infty} b_{-n}(z - \alpha)^{-n} + \sum_{n=0}^{\infty} b_n(z - \alpha)^n$$

is a representation for $f(z)$ which converges for $r_2 \leq |z - \alpha| \leq r_1$. Then if m is any integer, positive, negative, or zero,

$$f(z)(z - \alpha)^m = \sum_{n=1}^{\infty} b_{-n}(z - \alpha)^{-n+m} + \sum_{n=0}^{\infty} b_n(z - \alpha)^{n+m} \quad (5.13)$$

and this series converges uniformly in $\mathfrak{A}$. As before, let Γ be a circle with center at α and radius r, $r_2 < r < r_1$. Then, since the series of Equation 5.13 converges uniformly on Γ, we may integrate term by term along Γ to obtain

$$\int_{\Gamma} f(z)(z-\alpha)^m \, dz = \sum_{n=1}^{\infty} b_{-n} \int_{\Gamma} (z-\alpha)^{-n+m} \, dz + \sum_{n=0}^{\infty} b_n \int_{\Gamma} (z-\alpha)^{n+m} \, dz.$$

But, for all integers p with $p \neq -1$,

$$\int_{\Gamma} f(z)(z - \alpha)^p \, dz = 0.$$

Thus

$$\int_{\Gamma} f(z)(z - \alpha)^m \, dz = b_{-(m+1)} \int_{\Gamma} \frac{dz}{z - \alpha} = 2\pi i \, b_{-(m+1)}$$

or

$$b_{-(m+1)} = \frac{1}{2\pi i} \int_{\Gamma} f(z)(z - \alpha)^m \, dz, \qquad m = 0, \pm 1, \pm 2, \cdots.$$

Letting $n = -(m + 1)$ reduces the above equation to Equation 5.12.

Expansions of the Laurent type will be useful in evaluating definite integrals by the method of residues. We shall give a detailed exposition of this fascinating theory in the next chapter.

5.9 Classification of Singularities

We have often used the "number" infinity when discussing various limiting processes, particularly those relating to sequences and series. It is convenient at this stage to adjoin to our complex number system a symbol ∞. This is somewhat analogous to our adjunction of the symbol i to the real numbers, thus obtaining the complex number system. By *definition* we lay down the following arithmetic rules which we require the symbol ∞ to obey:

(i) $\dfrac{\alpha}{\infty} = 0,$ α any finite complex number

(ii) $\dfrac{\alpha}{0} = \infty, \alpha \cdot \infty = \infty \cdot \alpha = \infty,$ α any non-zero complex number

(iii) $\dfrac{\infty}{\alpha} = \infty, \alpha \pm \infty = \infty \pm \alpha = \infty,$ α any complex number $\neq \infty$

We shall call the symbol ∞ a complex number. When we adjoin ∞ to the complex plane we call it the *extended* complex plane and use the term "point at infinity" to describe $z = \infty$. Note that no distinction is made between $+\infty$ and $-\infty$. The points of the extended complex plane may be mapped on a sphere (called the *Riemann sphere*) in a natural fashion. Consider a sphere of radius R placed on the z-plane with its south pole at the origin. Any line emanating from the north pole will intersect the z-plane and the Riemann sphere each in one, and only one, second point. This is our one to one correspondence. The south pole is mapped into the origin; the point at infinity is mapped onto the north pole. The equator is mapped onto the circle $|z| = R$ in the z-plane. The advantage of using the Riemann sphere rather than the z-plane is that in the former the point at infinity is in no way distinguished from any other point.

A *neighborhood* of ∞ is defined as the exterior of any circle. The statement $\lim_{z \to a} f(z) = \infty$ means that given any real number M, no matter how large, we can find a $\delta > 0$ such that $|f(\beta)| > M$ for all β such that $0 < |\alpha - \beta| < \delta$. We shall say that $f(z)$ is analytic at $z = \infty$ if $f(1/\zeta)$ is analytic at $\zeta = 0$. In general, the behavior of a function $f(z)$ in the neighborhood of ∞ is the same as the behavior of the function $f(1/\zeta)$ in the neighborhood of $\zeta = 0$. Let $f(z)$ be analytic in the exterior $\mathfrak{E}$ of some circle with center at the origin. Then $f(z)$ has a representation

$$f(z) = \sum_{n=1}^{\infty} c_{-n} z^{-n} + \sum_{n=0}^{\infty} c_n z^n$$

valid in $\mathfrak{E}$. We shall call this development the Laurent expansion of $f(z)$ about the point $z = \infty$. If $c_n = 0, n = 1, 2, \cdots$, then

$$f(z) = c_0 + c_{-1} z^{-1} + c_{-2} z^{-2} + \cdots$$

and we shall say $f(z)$ is *analytic at infinity*. Thus

$$f\left(\frac{1}{\zeta}\right) = c_0 + c_{-1}\zeta + c_{-2}\zeta^2 + \cdots$$

is analytic at $\zeta = 0$. The point $z = \infty$ is a *branch point* of $w = \sqrt{z}$, since if we circulate about a large circle with center at the origin we pass from one branch of $\sqrt{z}$ to the other. The point $z = \infty$ is *not* a branch point for $w = \sqrt{(z - \alpha)(z - \beta)}$, $(\alpha \neq \beta)$, since if we circulate about a large circle with center at the origin, w returns to its initial value.

The main purpose of this section is to discuss functions which are analytic in some region $\mathfrak{A}$ except, perhaps, at one point in $\mathfrak{A}$. For example, $\dfrac{1}{z - \alpha}$ is analytic in any circle with α as an interior point, except at α.

Let C be a circle of positive radius R with center at $z = \alpha$. Let $f(z)$ be single-valued and analytic in C except at $z = \alpha$. Then we shall say $z = \alpha$ is an *isolated singularity* of the function $f(z)$. We shall examine the character of isolated singularities in the next few paragraphs.

Suppose first that $f(z)$ is bounded in the open set $\mathfrak{A} : \{0 < |z - \alpha| < R\}$. That is, there exists a number M such that

$$|f(z)| \leq M$$

for all z in $\mathfrak{A}$. Since $f(z)$ is analytic in $\mathfrak{A}$ it has a Laurent expansion

$$f(z) = \sum_{n=1}^{\infty} c_{-n}(z - \alpha)^{-n} + \sum_{n=0}^{\infty} c_n(z - \alpha)^n$$

valid for any z in $\mathfrak{A}$, where

$$c_n = \frac{1}{2\pi i} \int_{\Gamma} \frac{f(\zeta)\, d\zeta}{(\zeta - \alpha)^{n+1}}, \qquad n = 0,\, \pm 1,\, \pm 2,\, \cdots$$

and Γ is any circle with center at α which lies in $\mathfrak{A}$. In particular, if n is positive,

$$c_{-n} = \frac{1}{2\pi i} \int_{\Gamma} f(\zeta)(\zeta - \alpha)^{n-1}\, d\zeta.$$

Let $r > 0$ be the radius of Γ. Then since $|f(z)| \leq M$ on $\mathfrak{A}$ by hypothesis,

$$|c_{-n}| \leq \frac{1}{2\pi} M r^{n-1} L = M r^n,$$

where $L = 2\pi r$ is the length of Γ. Since $n \geq 1$ and r can be taken arbitrarily small,

$$c_{-n} = 0, \qquad n = 1, 2, \cdots.$$

Thus

$$f(z) = c_0 + c_1(z - \alpha) + c_2(z - \alpha)^2 + \cdots$$

for z in $\mathfrak{A}$. Let us *define* $f(z)$ at $z = \alpha$ as c_0. Then $f(z)$ is analytic in the circle $|z - \alpha| < R$. In this case we call $z = \alpha$ a *removable singularity* of the function $f(z)$. For by defining (or possibly redefining) $f(\alpha)$ as c_0 we obtain a function analytic in the interior of C. For example, the function $z^{-1} \sin z$ has a removable singularity at the origin.

Now let us suppose that the Laurent expansion of $f(z)$ in $\mathfrak{A}$ actually contains negative powers. If the expansion contains only a *finite* number of negative powers, we shall call $z = \alpha$ a *pole* of $f(z)$. In particular, if $f(z)$ admits of the representation

$$f(z) = \frac{c_{-p}}{(z - \alpha)^p} + \frac{c_{-p+1}}{(z - \alpha)^{p-1}} + \cdots + \frac{c_{-1}}{z - \alpha} + \sum_{n=0}^{\infty} c_n(z - \alpha)^n,$$

where $c_{-p} \neq 0$, we say $f(z)$ has a *pole of order p* at $z = \alpha$. If $p = 1$, we say $f(z)$ has a *simple pole* at $z = \alpha$. On the other hand, if the expansion contains an infinite number of non-zero terms with negative exponents, we shall call α an *essential singularity* of $f(z)$. For example,

$$e^{1/z} = 1 + \frac{1}{z} + \frac{1}{2!z^2} + \cdots + \frac{1}{n!z^n} + \cdots$$

has an essential singularity at $z = 0$.

If $f(z)$ has a Laurent expansion in the exterior of some circle, then we shall say, when *positive* powers are actually present, that $f(z)$ has an *isolated singularity* at $z = \infty$. If only a finite number of terms with positive powers appear, we shall say $z = \infty$ is a *pole* of $f(z)$. If

$$f(z) = c_p z^p + c_{p-1} z^{p-1} + \cdots + c_1 z + \sum_{n=0}^{\infty} c_{-n} z^{-n}$$

and $c_p \neq 0$, then we say $f(z)$ has a *pole of order p* at $z = \infty$. If the expansion contains an infinite number of non-zero terms with positive exponents, then we shall call $z = \infty$ an *essential singularity* of $f(z)$. The series of positive terms of the Laurent development of $f(z)$ in the neighborhood of ∞ is called the *principal part* of the expansion.

EXERCISES

5.1. If

$$\sum_{n=0}^{\infty} z_n = \alpha \qquad \text{and} \qquad \sum_{n=0}^{\infty} \zeta_n = \beta,$$

prove that

$$\sum_{n=0}^{\infty} (z_n + \zeta_n) = \alpha + \beta.$$

5.2. Let $z_n = x_n + iy_n$, $n = 1, 2, \cdots$, be complex numbers. Show that

$$\sum_{n=1}^{\infty} z_n$$

converges if, and only if,

$$\sum_{n=1}^{\infty} x_n \quad \text{and} \quad \sum_{n=1}^{\infty} y_n$$

converge. Furthermore, if $\sum z_n = \sigma$, show that

$$\sum x_n = \text{Re}\,[\sigma], \qquad \sum y_n = \text{Im}\,[\sigma].$$

Conversely, if $\sum x_n = \sigma_1$ and $\sum y_n = \sigma_2$, show that

$$\sum z_n = \sigma_1 + i\sigma_2.$$

5.3. Prove that $\lim_{n \to \infty} \alpha_n = 0$ is a *necessary* condition that the series

$$\sum_{n=1}^{\infty} \alpha_n$$

converge.

5.4. Let $\{\alpha_n\}$ be a sequence of complex numbers with $\text{Re}\,[\alpha_n] \geq 0$, $n = 1, 2, 3, \cdots$. If both

$$\sum_{n=1}^{\infty} \alpha_n \quad \text{and} \quad \sum_{n=1}^{\infty} \alpha_n^2$$

converge, prove that

$$\sum_{n=1}^{\infty} |\alpha_n|^2$$

converges.

5.5. Let $\{a_n\}$ be a bounded sequence of real numbers. Show that

$$\lim_{n \to \infty} \text{l.u.b.}_{m \geq n} a_m = \overline{\lim_{n \to \infty}} a_n$$

and

$$\lim_{n \to \infty} \text{g.l.b.}_{m \geq n} a_m = \underline{\lim_{n \to \infty}} a_n.$$

5.6. Consider the series

$$\sum_{n=1}^{\infty} \alpha_n$$

of complex numbers. If there exists an N such that for all $n > N$,

$$\left| \frac{\alpha_{n+1}}{\alpha_n} \right| \geq 1,$$

show that the series *diverges*. If

$$\overline{\lim_{n \to \infty}} \left| \frac{\alpha_{n+1}}{\alpha_n} \right| < 1,$$

show that the series *converges*.

5.7. If $\{\alpha_n\}$ is a sequence of complex numbers, show that

$$\lim_{n \to \infty} \left| \frac{\alpha_{n+1}}{\alpha_n} \right| \leq \lim_{n \to \infty} \sqrt[n]{|\alpha_n|}$$

and

$$\overline{\lim_{n \to \infty}} \sqrt[n]{|\alpha_n|} \leq \overline{\lim_{n \to \infty}} \left| \frac{\alpha_{n+1}}{\alpha_n} \right|.$$

5.8. If $f(z)$ is single-valued and analytic in a neighborhood of a point $z = \alpha$ and has the Taylor series expansion

$$f(z) = c_p(z - \alpha)^p + c_{p+1}(z - \alpha)^{p+1} + \cdots,$$

where $c_p \neq 0$, then we say $f(z)$ *has a zero of order p at $z = \alpha$.* If $f(z)$ has a zero of order p at $z = \alpha$, show that $1/f(z)$ has a pole of order p at $z = \alpha$.

5.9. Let $f(z)$ have a pole of order p at the point $z = \alpha$. Show that for any $M > 0$, no matter how large, there exists a $\delta > 0$ such that $|f(z)| > M$ whenever $|z - \alpha| < \delta$.

5.10. Show that the function

$$f(z) = \frac{\csc \frac{\pi}{2} z}{z^2 + 2iz - 5}$$

has a Laurent expansion in powers of $(z - 4i)$ which is valid in a neighborhood of $z = 3$. Determine the region of convergence of the expansion.

5.11. Let $f(z)$ have an essential singularity at $z = \alpha$. If β is *any* complex number, then for any $\epsilon > 0$ and any $\delta > 0$ show that there exists a ζ such that $|f(\zeta) - \beta| < \epsilon$ *and* $|\zeta - \alpha| < \delta$.

CHAPTER 6

The Calculus of Residues

6.1 Introduction

The main purpose of this chapter is to show how various definite integrals may be evaluated by using the techniques of complex variable theory. We shall therefore consider some appropriate theorems which are easy consequences of our earlier work. Then we shall discuss large classes of definite (real) integrals which may be evaluated by using these results. We shall also consider integrals other than real integrals, namely the so-called loop and double loop integrals which occur in various branches of mathematics (see, for example, Chapter 9).

6.2 Theorems on Residues

Let $f(z)$ be single-valued and analytic in a simply connected open region $\mathfrak{A}$, except perhaps at some point $z = \alpha$ in $\mathfrak{A}$ where it has an isolated singularity (see Fig. 6.1). Let

$$f(z) = \sum_{n=1}^{\infty} c_{-n}(z - \alpha)^{-n} + \sum_{n=0}^{\infty} c_n(z - \alpha)^n \qquad (6.1)$$

be the Laurent expansion of $f(z)$, which is valid in an annular region A around α. Then the quantity c_{-1} is called the *residue* of $f(z)$ at α. Thus

$$c_{-1} = \frac{1}{2\pi i} \int_C f(z) \, dz,$$

where C is a positively sensed circle in A with center at α.

We therefore have a method which is frequently convenient for evaluating integrals around closed smooth curves. For example, let

C be a closed smooth curve about the origin and let us evaluate the integral

$$\int_C z^{-4} \sinh z \, dz.$$

Now the function $z^{-4} \sinh z$ has an isolated singularity at $z = 0$ and

$$\frac{1}{z^4} \sinh z = \frac{1}{z^4} \left(z + \frac{z^3}{3!} + \frac{z^5}{5!} + \cdots \right)$$

$$= \frac{1}{z^3} + \frac{1}{3!z} + \frac{z}{5!} + \cdots.$$

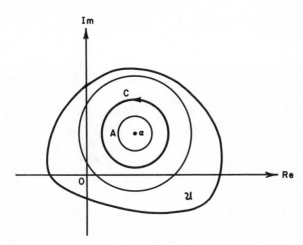

Figure 6.1

Thus $c_{-1} = 1/3!$ and

$$\frac{1}{2\pi i} \int_C z^{-4} \sinh z \, dz = \frac{1}{3!}$$

or

$$\int_C z^{-4} \sinh z \, dz = \frac{1}{3} \pi i.$$

We shall show in the next section how this technique can be used to evaluate definite real integrals.

If $f(z)$ is single-valued and analytic in the neighborhood of infinity with the Laurent expansion

$$f(z) = \sum_{n=1}^{\infty} c_{-n} z^{-n} + \sum_{n=0}^{\infty} c_n z^n,$$

then $-c_{-1}$ is the residue of $f(z)$ at $z = \infty$. Thus

$$c_{-1} = -\frac{1}{2\pi i} \int_C f(z)\, dz,$$

where C is a *positively* sensed circle.

The theorem that will be fundamental in our subsequent investigations is Theorem 1.

Theorem I. Let $f(z)$ be single-valued and analytic, except for isolated singularities in an open region $\mathfrak{A}$. Let C be a closed smooth

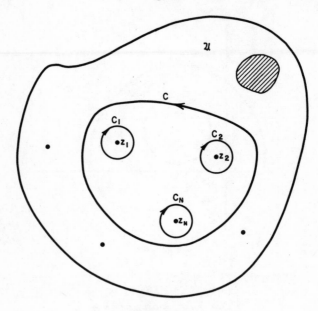

Figure 6.2

curve which together with its interior lies in $\mathfrak{A}$ and on which $f(z)$ is analytic. Let σ be the sum of the residues at the singular points of $f(z)$ which lie inside C. Then

$$\frac{1}{2\pi i} \int_C f(z)\, dz = \sigma.$$

Proof: Since C is rectifiable, the region interior to C is bounded and hence there can be at most a finite number of points at which $f(z)$ has singularities. Let these points be $z_1, z_2, \cdots, z_N$ (see Fig. 6.2).

Let C_k, $k = 1, 2, \cdots, N$ be circles with centers at z_k which lie interior to C and exterior to each other. Then by the CIT,

$$\int_C f(z)\, dz + \int_{\Sigma C_k} f(z)\, dz = 0$$

or

$$\int_C f(z)\, dz = -\sum_{k=1}^{N} \int_{C_k} f(z)\, dz.$$

But if σ_k is the residue of $f(z)$ at $z = z_k$, then

$$\sigma_k = -\frac{1}{2\pi i} \int_{C_k} f(z)\, dz$$

(since C_k is a negatively sensed circle). Thus

$$\int_C f(z)\, dz = 2\pi i(\sigma_1 + \sigma_2 + \cdots + \sigma_N) = 2\pi i \sigma.$$

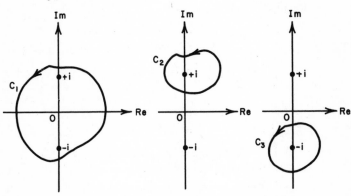

Figure 6.3

There are more general theorems than this (see Chapter 7), but we shall have no occasion to use them in this chapter.

As an application of Theorem 1, let us evaluate the integral

$$\int \frac{z + (2 + i)}{z^2 + 1}\, dz$$

over the various contours illustrated in Fig. 6.3. The curves C_1, C_2, C_3 are all supposed to be closed smooth curves.

The function

$$f(z) = \frac{z + (2 + i)}{z^2 + 1}$$

has isolated singularities (simple poles) at $z = \pm i$. Thus our first task is to compute the residues of $f(z)$ at $z = +i$ and $z = -i$. To compute the residue σ_i at $z = i$ we write

$$f(z) = \frac{z + (2 + i)}{z^2 + 1} = \frac{z + (2 + i)}{z + i} \frac{1}{z - i}$$

and expand $\dfrac{z + (2 + i)}{z + i}$ in a Taylor series about $z = i$. We obtain

$$\frac{z + (2 + i)}{z + i} = (1 - i) + \frac{1}{2}(z - i) + \frac{i}{4}(z - i)^2 + \cdots$$

and hence

$$f(z) = \frac{1 - i}{z - i} + \frac{1}{2} + \frac{i}{4}(z - i) + \cdots.$$

Therefore

$$\sigma_i = 1 - i.$$

Similarly the residue σ_{-i} at $z = -i$ is

$$\sigma_{-i} = i.$$

Thus

$$\int_{C_1} f(z)\, dz = 2\pi i(\sigma_i + \sigma_{-i}) = 2\pi i$$

$$\int_{C_2} f(z)\, dz = 2\pi i(\sigma_i) = 2\pi(1 + i)$$

$$\int_{C_3} f(z)\, dz = 2\pi i(\sigma_{-i}) = -2\pi.$$

A single-valued function which is analytic except for poles is called a *meromorphic* function. Thus every rational function is a meromorphic function. If $f(z)$ is meromorphic in some region of the complex z-plane and has a pole of order p at some point $z = \alpha$ in this region, then

$$\phi(z) = (z - \alpha)^p f(z)$$

has a removable singularity at $z = \alpha$. If $\phi(z)$ is appropriately defined, then it will be analytic in a neighborhood of $z = \alpha$. Thus it has a Taylor series expansion

$$\phi(z) = \phi(\alpha) + \phi'(\alpha)(z - \alpha) + \phi''(\alpha)\frac{(z - \alpha)^2}{2!} + \cdots$$

valid in a neighborhood of $z = \alpha$. The residue σ_α of $f(z)$ at $z = \alpha$ is therefore

$$\sigma_\alpha = \frac{\phi^{(p-1)}(\alpha)}{(p - 1)!}. \tag{6.2}$$

As an application of this simple result, let us find the residues of the function $f(z)$ considered earlier, viz.,

$$f(z) = \frac{z + (2 + i)}{z^2 + 1}$$

at $z = i$ and $z = -i$. Since $f(z)$ has a simple pole at $z = i$,

$$\phi(z) = (z - i)f(z) = \frac{z + (2 + i)}{z + i}$$

and Equation 6.2 becomes (with $p = 1$)

$$\sigma_i = \frac{i + (2 + i)}{i + i} = 1 - i.$$

Similarly for $z = -i$,

$$\phi(z) = (z + i)f(z) = \frac{z + (2 + i)}{z - i}$$

and

$$\sigma_{-i} = \frac{-i + (2 + i)}{-i - i} = i.$$

Certainly this is a more convenient method than the expansions used earlier, although this is not always the case. One can also often use l'Hospital's rule (see Theorem 12 of Chapter 3). For instance, if $z = i$,

$$\sigma_i = \lim_{z \to i} \frac{\dfrac{d}{dz}\left[(z - i)(z + 2 + i)\right]}{\dfrac{d}{dz}\left[z^2 + 1\right]} = \lim_{z \to i} \frac{2z + 2}{2z} = 1 - i.$$

The brief preliminaries of this section are adequate preparation for an intensive study of the calculus of residues.

6.3 Integrals Involving Rational Functions

A. Without more ado let us evaluate the real definite integral

$$I = \int_0^\infty \frac{x^2}{x^4 + x^2 + 1}\, dx$$

by residues. We start by considering the complex integral

$$\int_C \frac{z^2}{z^4 + z^2 + 1}\, dz$$

over some contour C to be described below. The integrand is a mero-morphic function with simple poles at $\alpha, \beta, \bar{\alpha}, \bar{\beta}$, as indicated in Fig. 6.4. Thus

$$\alpha = \frac{1}{2} + i\frac{\sqrt{3}}{2}, \qquad \beta = -\frac{1}{2} + i\frac{\sqrt{3}}{2}. \qquad (6.3)$$

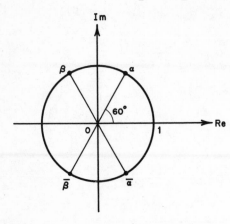

Figure 6.4

Let C be the contour illustrated in Fig. 6.5 consisting of a semi-circle Γ in the upper half plane and the straight line segment $[-R, R]$. Our general philosophy is as follows. If $R > 1$, then the poles of $f(z)$,

$$f(z) = \frac{z^2}{z^4 + z^2 + 1},$$

which occur at $z = \alpha$ and $z = \beta$ will be interior to the contour. No matter how large R becomes, the contour will never enclose any other singular points of $f(z)$. Thus for *any* $R > 1$,

$$\int_C f(z)\, dz = 2\pi i\sigma \qquad (6.4)$$

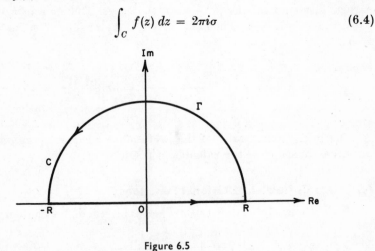

Figure 6.5

by Theorem 1, where σ is the sum of the residues of $f(z)$ at $z = \alpha$ and $z = \beta$. Now if we can show that

$$\lim_{R \to \infty} \int_\Gamma f(z)\, dz = 0,$$

we shall have

$$2\pi i\sigma = \lim_{R\to\infty} \int_C f(z)\,dz = \lim_{R\to\infty} \int_{-R}^{R} f(z)\,dz,$$

which evaluates I.

To carry out the above line of attack we first compute the residues of $f(z)$ at $z = \alpha$ and $z = \beta$. They are

$$\sigma_\alpha = \lim_{z\to\alpha} (z - \alpha)f(z) = \frac{\alpha}{4\alpha^2 + 2} = \frac{\alpha}{2i\sqrt{3}},$$

$$\sigma_\beta = \lim_{z\to\beta} (z - \beta)f(z) = \frac{\beta}{4\beta^2 + 2} = -\frac{\beta}{2i\sqrt{3}}.$$

Thus

$$\sigma = \sigma_\alpha + \sigma_\beta = \frac{1}{2i\sqrt{3}}(\alpha - \beta) = \frac{1}{2i\sqrt{3}} \tag{6.5}$$

and we have evaluated the integral of Equation 6.4.

Now

$$\int_C f(z)\,dz = \int_{-R}^{R} f(z)\,dz + \int_\Gamma f(z)\,dz, \tag{6.6}$$

and we wish to show that

$$\lim_{R\to\infty} \int_\Gamma f(z)\,dz = 0.$$

For any z

$$|z^4 + z^2 + 1| \geq |z^4| - |z^2 + 1| \geq |z^4| - |z^2| - 1,$$

which for z sufficiently large in modulus will be positive. Thus

$$\left| \int_\Gamma f(z)\,dz \right| \leq \int_\Gamma \frac{|z|^2|dz|}{|z|^4 - |z^2| - 1}.$$

Let $z = R\,e^{i\theta}$. Then for R sufficiently large

$$\left| \int_\Gamma f(z)\,dz \right| \leq \int_0^\pi \frac{R^2}{R^4 - R^2 - 1}\,R\,d\theta = \frac{\pi R^3}{R^4 - R^2 - 1},$$

which approaches zero as R increases without limit.

Equations 6.4 and 6.5 then imply that

$$2\pi i\sigma = \lim_{R\to\infty} \int_{-R}^{R} f(x)\,dx,$$

where we have replaced z by x in the integrand since, along the real axis, $z = x$. Recalling the value of σ in Equation 6.5,

$$2\pi i\left(\frac{1}{2i\sqrt{3}}\right) = \text{P.V.} \int_{-\infty}^{\infty} \frac{x^2}{x^4 + x^2 + 1}\, dx,$$

and we have evaluated I,

$$I = \int_0^{\infty} \frac{x^2}{x^4 + x^2 + 1}\, dx = \frac{\pi}{2\sqrt{3}}. \tag{6.7}$$

B. Let us see if we can generalize the result of the previous example. Consider therefore the integral

$$I = \int_{-\infty}^{\infty} \frac{P(x)}{Q(x)}\, dx,$$

where $P(x)$ and $Q(x)$ are relatively prime* polynomials in x of degrees p and q respectively. Let $q > p + 1$ and suppose that $Q(x)$ has no real zeros (for if it did, I would not be a proper integral). Consider, as in the earlier example,

$$\int_C \frac{P(z)}{Q(z)}\, dz,$$

where C is the contour illustrated in Fig. 6.5. Since $P(z)/Q(z)$ is a meromorphic function, its only singularities are poles. Let us suppose that R, the radius of Γ, exceeds in magnitude the moduli of the complex numbers at which P/Q has poles. Then if σ is the sum of the residues of P/Q in C,

$$\int_C \frac{P(z)}{Q(z)}\, dz = 2\pi i\sigma \tag{6.8}$$

by Theorem 1. Now we may write

$$\int_C \frac{P(z)}{Q(z)}\, dz = \int_{-R}^{R} \frac{P(x)}{Q(x)}\, dx + \int_{\Gamma} \frac{P(z)}{Q(z)}\, dz. \tag{6.9}$$

Let $z = R\,e^{i\theta}$. Then

$$\left|\int_{\Gamma} \frac{P(z)}{Q(z)}\, dz\right| = \left|i\int_0^{\pi} \frac{P(R\,e^{i\theta})}{Q(R\,e^{i\theta})}\, R\,e^{i\theta}\, d\theta\right| \leq R\int_0^{\pi} \frac{|P(R\,e^{i\theta})|}{|Q(R\,e^{i\theta})|}\, d\theta.$$

But from Exercise 3.4 of Chapter 3,

$$|P(R\,e^{i\theta})| < 2R^p|a_p|$$

and

$$|Q(R\,e^{i\theta})| > \frac{1}{2}\,R^q|b_q|$$

* That is, they have no common factors in x.

for R sufficiently large, where a_p is the coefficient of z^p in $P(z)$ and b_q is the coefficient of z^q in $Q(z)$.   Thus

$$\left| \int_\Gamma \frac{P(z)}{Q(z)} \, dz \right| < R \, \frac{2R^p|a_p|}{\frac{1}{2} R^q|b_q|} \int_0^\pi d\theta = 4\pi |a_p| |b_q^{-1}| R^{p+1-q}.$$

Since $q > p + 1$, the above expression approaches zero as R increases without limit.   Thus by virtue of Equations 6.8 and 6.9

$$2\pi i\sigma = \lim_{R \to \infty} \int_C \frac{P(z)}{Q(z)} \, dz = \text{P.V.} \int_{-\infty}^\infty \frac{P(x)}{Q(x)} \, dx.$$

Since the condition $q > p + 1$ implies the convergence of the real integral

$$\int_{-\infty}^\infty \frac{P(x)}{Q(x)} \, dx,$$

we can delete the "principal value" symbol P.V. before the integral.

Our results may be summarized by the following theorem.

Theorem 2.   Let $P(x)$ and $Q(x)$ be relatively prime polynomials where the degree of Q exceeds the degree of P by at least two.   Let $Q(z)$ have no real zeros.   Let σ be the sum of the residues of $P(z)/Q(z)$ at the zeros of $Q(z)$ which lie in the upper half plane.   Then

$$\int_{-\infty}^\infty \frac{P(x)}{Q(x)} \, dx = 2\pi i\sigma. \tag{6.10}$$

C. As a non-trivial application of this theorem let us evaluate the integral

$$I = \int_0^\infty \frac{x^{2m}}{1 + x^{2n}} \, dx,$$

where $n > m \geq 0$.   By Theorem 2,

$$I = \frac{1}{2} \int_{-\infty}^\infty \frac{x^{2m}}{1 + x^{2n}} \, dx = \frac{1}{2} \left(2\pi i\sigma \right) = \pi i\sigma, \tag{6.11}$$

where σ is the sum of the residues of $z^{2m}/(1 + z^{2n})$ in the upper half plane.   The poles of $z^{2m}/(1 + z^{2n})$ occur at the roots of $1 + z^{2n} = 0$. All the roots are simple and those in the upper half plane may be expressed as

$$\omega_k = e^{\frac{\pi i}{2n}(2k+1)} \qquad k = 0, 1, \cdots, n - 1. \tag{6.12}$$

Thus by l'Hospital's rule

$$\sigma = \sum_{k=0}^{n-1} \omega_k^{2m} \lim_{z \to \omega_k} \frac{z - \omega_k}{1 + z^{2n}} = \frac{1}{2n} \sum_{k=0}^{n-1} \omega_k^{2m-2n+1}.$$

Using the definition of ω_k in Equation 6.12, we may write

$$\omega_k^{2m-2n+1} = -\rho^{2k+1},$$

where $\rho = e^{\pi i \left(\frac{2m+1}{2n}\right)}$, and hence

$$\sigma = -\frac{1}{2n} \sum_{k=0}^{n-1} \rho^{2k+1}.$$

But this is a finite geometric series. Thus

$$\sigma = -\frac{1}{2n} \frac{\rho - \rho^{2n+1}}{1 - \rho^2} = -\frac{1}{2n} \frac{2\rho}{1 - \rho^2},$$

since $\rho^{2n} = -1$. If we write σ in the form

$$\sigma = \frac{1}{n(\rho - \rho^{-1})}$$

and recall the definition of ρ, we have

$$\sigma = \frac{1}{2ni \sin \dfrac{\pi(2m+1)}{2n}}.$$

Equation 6.11 then yields

$$\int_0^\infty \frac{x^{2m}}{1 + x^{2n}} \, dx = \frac{\pi}{2n} \csc \frac{\pi(2m+1)}{2n}, \qquad n > m \geq 0. \qquad (6.13)$$

D. As another example we consider the integral

$$I = \int_{-\infty}^\infty \frac{dx}{(x^2 + 1)^n},$$

whose integrand satisfies the conditions of Theorem 2. In this case the poles of the integrand are no longer simple. The only root of $(z^2 + 1)^n = 0$ in the upper half plane is $z = i$, and it is a root of multiplicity n. Thus if we set

$$\phi(z) = (z - i)^n \frac{1}{(z^2 + 1)^n},$$

the residue σ at $z = i$ is given by Equation 6.2 as

$$\sigma = \frac{\phi^{(n-1)}(i)}{(n-1)!}.$$

Now we may write $\phi(z)$ as

$$\phi(z) = \frac{(z - i)^n}{[(z - i)(z + i)]^n} = (z + i)^{-n}.$$

Hence

$$\phi^{(n-1)}(z) = (-1)^{n-1}n(n + 1)(n + 2)\cdots(n + n - 2)(z + i)^{-(n+n-1)}$$

and

$$\sigma = -\frac{i}{2^{2n-1}}\frac{(2n - 2)!}{(n - 1)!(n - 1)!}.$$

By Theorem 2

$$I = \int_{-\infty}^{\infty}\frac{dx}{(x^2 + 1)^n} = 2\pi i\sigma = \frac{\pi}{2^{2n-2}}\frac{(2n - 2)!}{[(n - 1)!]^2}. \tag{6.14}$$

Students of applied mathematics will recognize the right side of Equation 6.14 as the Beta function, $B(\frac{1}{2}, n - \frac{1}{2})$. Thus

$$\int_{-\infty}^{\infty}\frac{dx}{(x^2 + 1)^n} = B\left(\frac{1}{2}, n - \frac{1}{2}\right). \tag{6.15}$$

E. We turn now to integrals whose integrands involve trigonometric as well as rational functions. One such example was given in Chapter 4 to illustrate the CIF. There we showed that

$$\int_{0}^{\infty}\frac{\cos x}{1 + x^2}dx = \frac{\pi}{2e}. \tag{6.16}$$

A little reflection shows that the CIF is simply a special case of our residue theorem, corresponding to the case where the contour encloses just *one* singularity.

F. To evaluate the integral of Equation 6.16 we started by considering the complex integral

$$\int\frac{e^{iz}}{z^2 + 1}dz.$$

Let us now consider more general integrals of the form

$$\int_{-\infty}^{\infty}\frac{P(x)}{Q(x)}e^{i\omega x}dx = \int_{-\infty}^{\infty}\frac{P(x)}{Q(x)}\cos\omega x\,dx + i\int_{-\infty}^{\infty}\frac{P(x)}{Q(x)}\sin\omega x\,dx, \quad \omega > 0,$$

where $P(x)$ and $Q(x)$ are relatively prime polynomials of degrees p and q respectively. Let $q > p$ and suppose that $Q(x)$ has no real zeros. We begin by considering the integral

$$\int_{C}\frac{P(z)}{Q(z)}e^{i\omega z}dz$$

along the contour C of Fig. 6.5. Thus

$$\int_C \frac{P(z)}{Q(z)} e^{i\omega z} dz = \int_{-R}^{R} \frac{P(x)}{Q(x)} e^{i\omega x} dx + \int_\Gamma \frac{P(z)}{Q(z)} e^{i\omega z} dz. \qquad (6.17)$$

We shall show that the second integral on the right approaches zero as R increases without limit. Let $z = R\, e^{i\theta}$. Then

$$\int_\Gamma \frac{P(z)}{Q(z)} e^{i\omega z} dz = iR \int_0^\pi \frac{P(R\, e^{i\theta})}{Q(R\, e^{i\theta})} e^{i\omega R e^{i\theta}} e^{i\theta} d\theta. \qquad (6.18)$$

By Exercise 3.4 of Chapter 3

$$|P(R\, e^{i\theta})| < 2R^p |a_p|, \qquad |Q(R\, e^{i\theta})| > \frac{1}{2} R^q |b_q|$$

for R sufficiently large. We also recall from Section 4.4 that

$$\left| \int_0^\pi e^{i\omega R e^{i\theta}} d\theta \right| = \left| \int_0^\pi e^{i\omega R(\cos\theta + i\sin\theta)} d\theta \right|$$

$$\leq \int_0^\pi e^{-\omega R \sin\theta} d\theta = 2 \int_0^{\pi/2} e^{-\omega R \sin\theta} d\theta \leq 2 \int_0^{\pi/2} e^{-2\omega R\theta/\pi} d\theta$$

$$= \frac{\pi}{\omega R} (1 - e^{-\omega R}) < \frac{\pi}{\omega R}$$

for R sufficiently large. Equation 6.18 then becomes

$$\left| \int_\Gamma \frac{P(z)}{Q(z)} e^{i\omega z} dz \right| \leq 4\omega^{-1} \pi |a_p| |b_q^{-1}| R^{p-q}.$$

Since $q > p$, the above expression approaches zero as R approaches infinity. Thus from Equation 6.17 and Theorem 1

$$2\pi i\sigma = \int_C \frac{P(z)}{Q(z)} e^{i\omega z} dz = \text{P.V.} \int_{-\infty}^{\infty} \frac{P(x)}{Q(x)} e^{i\omega x} dx,$$

where σ is the sum of the residues of $\dfrac{P(z)}{Q(z)} e^{i\omega z}$ in the upper half plane.

This leads to the following theorem.

Theorem 3. Let $P(x)$ and $Q(x)$ be relatively prime polynomials where the degree of Q exceeds the degree of P. Let $Q(z)$ have no real zeros. Let σ be the sum of the residues of $\dfrac{P(z)}{Q(z)} e^{i\omega z}$ at the roots of $Q(z) = 0$ which lie in the upper half plane. Then

$$\int_{-\infty}^{\infty} \frac{P(x)}{Q(x)} e^{i\omega x} dx = 2\pi i\sigma, \qquad \omega > 0.$$

As an immediate consequence we may write, by taking real and imaginary parts of the above expression,

$$\int_{-\infty}^{\infty} \frac{P(x)}{Q(x)} \cos \omega x \, dx = \text{Re}\,[2\pi i\sigma] = -2\pi\,\text{Im}\,[\sigma] \qquad (6.19)$$

and

$$\int_{-\infty}^{\infty} \frac{P(x)}{Q(x)} \sin \omega x \, dx = \text{Im}\,[2\pi i\sigma] = 2\pi\,\text{Re}\,[\sigma]. \qquad (6.20)$$

One can sometimes relax the restriction that $Q(x)$ have no real zeros if at such a point $P(x)Q^{-1}(x) \sin \omega x$ or $P(x)Q^{-1}(x) \cos \omega x$ has a removable singularity (see the evaluation of $\int_0^{\infty} \frac{\sin x}{x} \, dx$ in Section 4 of Chapter 4).

If $\omega < 0$ we choose a semicircle in the lower half of the complex plane and let σ be the sum of the residues of $P(z)Q^{-1}(z)e^{i\omega z}$ which lie in the lower half plane.

G. As a non-trivial application of Theorem 3 let us evaluate the integral

$$I = \int_0^{\infty} \frac{\cos x}{1 + x^{2n}} \, dx.$$

From Theorem 3

$$\int_{-\infty}^{\infty} \frac{e^{ix}}{1 + x^{2n}} \, dx = 2\pi i\sigma,$$

where σ is the sum of residues of $e^{iz}/(1 + z^{2n})$ in the upper half plane. The roots of $1 + z^{2n} = 0$ are all simple and those in the upper half plane are

$$\omega_k = e^{\frac{\pi i}{2n}(2k+1)}, \qquad k = 0, 1, \cdots, n - 1. \qquad (6.21)$$

Thus, as in **C**,

$$\sigma = \sum_{k=0}^{n-1} e^{i\omega_k} \lim_{z \to \omega_k} \frac{z - \omega_k}{1 + z^{2n}} = \frac{1}{2n} \sum_{k=0}^{n-1} e^{i\omega_k} \omega_k^{-(2n-1)}.$$

$$= -\frac{1}{2n} \sum_{k=0}^{n-1} e^{i\omega_k} e^{\frac{\pi i}{2n}(2k+1)}.$$

Since

$$\omega_k = \cos \frac{(2k+1)}{2n} \pi + i \sin \frac{(2k+1)}{2n} \pi$$

by Equation 6.21, we may write

$$\sigma = -\frac{1}{2n} \sum_{k=0}^{n-1} e^{-\sin \lambda_k} [\cos (\cos \lambda_k) + i \sin (\cos \lambda_k)] \cdot [\cos \lambda_k + i \sin \lambda_k],$$

where

$$\lambda_k = \frac{2k + 1}{2n} \pi. \tag{6.22}$$

The imaginary part of σ is

$$\text{Im}\,[\sigma] = -\frac{1}{2n} \sum_{k=0}^{n-1} e^{-\sin \lambda_k} \left[\sin\,(\cos \lambda_k)\cos \lambda_k + \cos\,(\cos \lambda_k)\sin \lambda_k\right]$$

$$= -\frac{1}{2n} \sum_{k=0}^{n-1} e^{-\sin \lambda_k} \sin\,(\lambda_k + \cos \lambda_k).$$

By Equation 6.19

$$\int_{-\infty}^{\infty} \frac{\cos x}{1 + x^{2n}}\,dx = \frac{\pi}{n} \sum_{k=0}^{n-1} e^{-\sin \lambda_k} \sin\,(\lambda_k + \cos \lambda_k), \tag{6.23}$$

where λ_k is given by Equation 6.22.

H. Consider now

$$I = \int_0^{2\pi} \frac{d\theta}{a + \cos \theta}, \qquad a > 1,$$

an integral involving *only* trigonometric functions. This does not seem to be of the form previously studied, namely, integrals involving rational functions. However, if we make the change of variable

$$z = e^{i\theta},$$

$$I = -2i \int_C \frac{dz}{z^2 + 2az + 1}, \tag{6.24}$$

where C is the unit circle with center at the origin. Now Equation 6.24 represents the integral of a rational function. An immediate application of the residue theorem, Theorem 1, gives

$$I = -2i[2\pi i\sigma] = 4\pi\sigma,$$

where σ is the sum of the residues of $(z^2 + 2az + 1)^{-1}$ in C.

The poles of this function are simple and occur at

$$z = -a \pm \sqrt{a^2 - 1}.$$

Since $a > 1$, the root $-a - \sqrt{a^2-1}$ is always *exterior* to the unit circle while the root $\alpha = -a + \sqrt{a^2 - 1}$ is always *interior* to the unit circle. Thus, if σ_α is the residue of $(z^2 + 2az + 1)^{-1}$ at $z = \alpha$,

$$I = 4\pi\sigma_\alpha.$$

Now

$$\sigma_\alpha = \lim_{z \to \alpha} \frac{z - \alpha}{z^2 + 2az + 1} = \frac{1}{2\sqrt{a^2 - 1}}$$

and

$$\int_0^{2\pi} \frac{d\theta}{a + \cos \theta} = \frac{2\pi}{\sqrt{a^2 - 1}}, \qquad a > 1. \tag{6.25}$$

I. In general, then, consider

$$I = \int_0^{2\pi} f(\sin \theta, \cos \theta) \, d\theta,$$

where f is a rational function of its arguments.   Then under the substitution

$$\sin \theta = \frac{e^{i\theta} - e^{-i\theta}}{2i}, \qquad \cos \theta = \frac{e^{i\theta} + e^{-i\theta}}{2},$$

the integral becomes

$$I = \int_0^{2\pi} f\left(\frac{e^{i\theta} - e^{-i\theta}}{2i}, \frac{e^{i\theta} + e^{-i\theta}}{2}\right) d\theta.$$

Now, under the transformation $z = e^{i\theta}$,

$$I = -i \int_C \frac{1}{z} f\left(\frac{z^2 - 1}{2iz}, \frac{z^2 + 1}{2z}\right) dz,$$

where C is the unit circle with center at the origin.   Since a rational function of a rational function is a rational function, the integrand of the integral is a rational function of z.   Thus the techniques developed earlier in this section are applicable.

J. Consider the integral

$$I = \int_0^\infty \frac{\log x}{1 + x^2} \, dx.$$

It is easy to see that the integral converges, even though it is improper at $x = 0$.   We start with the complex integral

$$\int_C \frac{\log z}{1 + z^2} \, dz,$$

where C is the indented contour of Fig. 6.6. If $x > 0$, then $\log z = \log x$, while, if $x < 0$, $\log z = \log |x| + \pi i$.   Thus

$$\int_C \frac{\log z}{1 + z^2} \, dz = \int_r^R \frac{\log x}{1 + x^2} \, dx + \int_\Gamma \frac{\log z}{1 + z^2} \, dz$$

$$+ \int_{-R}^{-r} \frac{\log |x| + \pi i}{1 + x^2} \, dx + \int_\gamma \frac{\log z}{1 + z^2} \, dz. \tag{6.26}$$

Since the only pole of $\dfrac{\log z}{1 + z^2}$ in C is at $z = i$, the residue is

$$\sigma = \lim_{z \to i} \frac{(z - i) \log z}{z^2 + 1} = \frac{\log i}{i + i} = \frac{\log |i| + \dfrac{\pi}{2} i}{2i} = \frac{\pi}{4}.$$

Hence by Theorem 1

$$2\pi i \left(\frac{\pi}{4} \right) = \int_C \frac{\log z}{1 + z^2} \, dz = \int_r^R \frac{\log x}{1 + x^2} \, dx + \int_\Gamma \frac{\log z}{1 + z^2} \, dz$$

$$+ \int_r^R \frac{(\log x + \pi i)}{1 + x^2} \, dx + \int_\gamma \frac{\log z}{1 + z^2} \, dz, \qquad (6.27)$$

where we have replaced x by $-x$ in the third integral on the right of Equation 6.26.

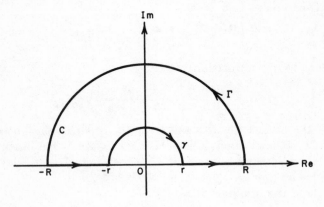

Figure 6.6

We shall show that the integral along Γ tends to zero as R increases without limit and that the integral along γ tends to zero as r approaches zero. Let $z = R\, e^{i\theta}$. Then for R sufficiently large

$$\left| \int_\Gamma \frac{\log z}{1 + z^2} \, dz \right| = \left| \int_0^\pi \frac{(\log R + i\theta)}{1 + R^2 \, e^{2i\theta}} \, iR \, e^{i\theta} \, d\theta \right|$$

$$\leq \frac{R \log R}{R^2 - 1} + \frac{R}{R^2 - 1} \int_0^\pi \theta \, d\theta,$$

which approaches zero as R increases without limit. Similarly if $z = r\, e^{i\theta}$, then for r sufficiently small

$$\left| \int_\gamma \frac{\log z}{1 + z^2} \, dz \right| = \left| \int_0^\pi \frac{(\log r + i\theta)}{1 + r^2 e^{2i\theta}} \, ir \, e^{i\theta} \, d\theta \right| \leq \frac{r \log r}{1 - r^2} + \frac{r}{1 - r^2} \int_0^\pi \theta \, d\theta,$$

which approaches zero as r approaches zero. Thus from Equation 6.27

$$\frac{i\pi^2}{2} = \lim_{\substack{R \to \infty \\ r \to 0}} \left[2 \int_r^R \frac{\log x}{1 + x^2}\, dx + \pi i \int_r^R \frac{dx}{1 + x^2} \right].$$

Since

$$\int_0^\infty \frac{dx}{1 + x^2} = \frac{1}{2}\pi,$$

we deduce from the above formula that

$$\int_0^\infty \frac{\log x}{1 + x^2}\, dx = 0. \tag{6.28}$$

K. The general philosophy of evaluation of integrals of the form

$$\int_0^\infty \frac{P(x)}{Q(x)} (\log x)^n\, dx$$

will now be expounded. Let us assume that $P(x)$ and $Q(x)$ are relatively prime polynomials of degrees p and q respectively, with $q > p + 1$; that $Q(z)$ has no real zeros; and that $P(x)/Q(x)$ is an even function. Then if C is the contour of Fig. 6.6 and σ the sum of the residues of $P(z)Q^{-1}(z) (\log z)^n$ in the upper half plane,

$$2\pi i\sigma = \int_C \frac{P(z)}{Q(z)} (\log z)^n\, dz = \int_r^R \frac{P(x)}{Q(x)} (\log x)^n\, dx$$

$$+ \int_{-R}^{-r} \frac{P(x)}{Q(x)} (\log |x| + \pi i)^n\, dx + \int_\gamma \frac{P(z)}{Q(z)} (\log z)^n\, dz \tag{6.29}$$

$$+ \int_\Gamma \frac{P(z)}{Q(z)} (\log z)^n\, dz.$$

Now let $z = R\, e^{i\theta}$. Then for R sufficiently large,

$$\left| \int_\Gamma \frac{P(z)}{Q(z)} (\log z)^n\, dz \right| \leq R \int_0^\pi \frac{|P(R\, e^{i\theta})|}{|Q(R\, e^{i\theta})|} [\log R + \theta]^n\, d\theta$$

$$\leq 4|a_p||b_q^{-1}|R^{p+1-q} \sum_{k=0}^n c_k(\log R)^k,$$

where the c_k are real positive constants. Thus we need only show that

$$\lim_{R \to \infty} R^{p+1-q}(\log R)^k = 0$$

for k finite. But if $q > p + 1$, the above statement is obvious by repeated applications of l'Hospital's rule. Thus

$$\left| \int_\Gamma \frac{P(z)}{Q(z)} (\log z)^n\, dz \right|$$

approaches zero as R increases without limit.

Let $z = r\,e^{i\theta}$. Then for r sufficiently small

$$\left| \int_\gamma \frac{P(z)}{Q(z)} (\log z)^n \, dz \right| \leq r \int_0^\pi \frac{|P(r\,e^{i\theta})|}{|Q(r\,e^{i\theta})|} [\log r + \theta]^n \, d\theta. \qquad (6.30)$$

Now the constant term b_0 of the polynomial $Q(z)$ cannot be zero (for if it were, zero would be a root of $Q(z) = 0$, which violates our hypothesis). Thus by Exercise 3.4 of Chapter 3,

$$|Q(r\,e^{i\theta})| > \frac{1}{2} |b_0|$$

for r sufficiently small. Suppose

$$P(z) = a_p z^p + a_{p-1} z^{p-1} + \cdots + a_s z^s, \qquad 0 \leq s \leq p.$$

Then for r sufficiently small

$$|P(r\,e^{i\theta})| < 2|a_s| r^s.$$

Equation 6.30 then implies that for r sufficiently small

$$\left| \int_\gamma \frac{P(z)}{Q(z)} (\log z)^n \, dz \right| \leq 4|a_s| |b_0^{-1}| r^{s+1} \sum_{k=0}^n c_k (\log r)^k,$$

which approaches zero as r approaches zero.

Equation 6.29 therefore may be written as

$$2\pi i\sigma = \lim_{\substack{R \to \infty \\ r \to 0}} \left[\int_r^R \frac{P(x)}{Q(x)} (\log x)^n \, dx + \int_r^R \frac{P(x)}{Q(x)} (\log x + \pi i)^n \, dx \right],$$

where we have replaced x by $-x$ in the second integral and used the fact that $P(x)/Q(x)$ is an even function, that is, $P(-x)/Q(-x) = P(x)/Q(x)$. Thus we see that

$$\int_0^\infty \frac{P(x)}{Q(x)} (\log x)^n \, dx$$

can be expressed as a linear combination of integrals of the form

$$\int_0^\infty \frac{P(x)}{Q(x)} (\log x)^k \, dx$$

with $k < n$. If $n = 1$,

$$\int_0^\infty \frac{P(x)}{Q(x)} \log x \, dx = \pi i \left[\sigma - \frac{1}{2} \int_0^\infty \frac{P(x)}{Q(x)} \, dx \right].$$

L. As a non-trivial example of the above analysis, let us evaluate the integral

$$I = \int_0^\infty \frac{(\log x)^2}{1 + x^{2n}}\, dx.$$

We see that, if C is the contour of Fig. 6.6,

$$2\pi i\sigma = \int_C \frac{(\log z)^2}{1 + z^{2n}}\, dz = \int_r^R \frac{(\log x)^2}{1 + x^{2n}}\, dx + \int_{-R}^{-r} \frac{(\log |x| + \pi i)^2}{1 + x^{2n}}\, dx. \quad (6.31)$$

Replacing x by $-x$,

$$\int_{-R}^{-r} \frac{(\log |x| + \pi i)^2}{1 + x^{2n}}\, dx = \int_r^R \frac{(\log x + \pi i)^2}{1 + x^{2n}}\, dx = \int_r^R \frac{(\log x)^2}{1 + x^{2n}}\, dx$$

$$+ 2\pi i \int_r^R \frac{\log x}{1 + x^{2n}}\, dx - \pi^2 \int_r^R \frac{dx}{1 + x^{2n}}.$$

Since

$$\int_0^\infty \frac{dx}{1 + x^{2n}} = \frac{\pi}{2n} \frac{1}{\sin \dfrac{\pi}{2n}}$$

from Equation 6.13, we may write Equation 6.31 as

$$2 \int_0^\infty \frac{(\log x)^2}{1 + x^{2n}}\, dx + 2\pi i \int_0^\infty \frac{\log x}{1 + x^{2n}}\, dx = 2\pi i\sigma + \frac{\pi^3}{2n} \csc \frac{\pi}{2n}.$$

Thus

$$\int_0^\infty \frac{(\log x)^2}{1 + x^{2n}}\, dx = \operatorname{Re}[\pi i\sigma] + \frac{\pi^3}{4n} \csc \frac{\pi}{2n} \qquad (6.32)$$

and

$$\int_0^\infty \frac{\log x}{1 + x^{2n}}\, dx = \operatorname{Im}[i\sigma]. \qquad (6.33)$$

We are faced with the task of computing σ. The poles of $(\log z)^2/(1 + z^{2n})$ in the upper half plane occur at the points ω_k,

$$\omega_k = e^{\frac{\pi i}{2n}(2k+1)}, \qquad k = 0, 1, \cdots, n-1,$$

and the residues are given by

$$\sigma = \sum_{k=0}^{n-1} (\log \omega_k)^2 \lim_{z \to \omega_k} \frac{z - \omega_k}{1 + z^{2n}}.$$

Since $|\omega_k| = 1$,

$$\log \omega_k = \log |\omega_k| + \frac{\pi i}{2n}(2k+1) = \frac{\pi i}{2n}(2k+1)$$

and

$$\sigma = \frac{\pi^2}{8n^3} \sum_{k=0}^{n-1} (2k + 1)^2 \rho^{2k+1}, \tag{6.34}$$

where

$$\rho = e^{\pi i/2n} \tag{6.35}$$

Let

$$v = \sum_{k=0}^{n-1} \rho^{2k+1} = \frac{\rho - \rho^{2n+1}}{1 - \rho^2}. \tag{6.36}$$

Then

$$\rho \frac{dv}{d\rho} = \sum_{k=0}^{n-1} (2k + 1)\rho^{2k+1}$$

and

$$\rho \frac{d}{d\rho}\left(\rho \frac{dv}{d\rho}\right) = \sum_{k=0}^{n-1} (2k + 1)^2 \rho^{2k+1}.$$

We may compute the above derivative from the closed form of Equation 6.36. Using the fact that $\rho^{2n} = -1$ enables us to write

$$\sigma = \frac{\pi^2 \rho}{8n^3} \times$$

$$\frac{(1 - \rho^2)[(4n^2 + 4n + 2)(1 - \rho^2) + 8\rho^2] + 4\rho^2[2n(1 - \rho^2) + 2(1 + \rho^2)]}{(1 - \rho^2)^3}. \tag{6.37}$$

If we let

$$S = \sin \frac{\pi}{2n}, \qquad C = \cos \frac{\pi}{2n}, \tag{6.38}$$

then

$$\rho = C + iS, \qquad \rho + \rho^{-1} = 2C,$$
$$\rho^{-1} = C - iS, \qquad \rho - \rho^{-1} = 2iS,$$

and Equation 6.37 can be reduced to the form

$$\sigma = \frac{\pi^2}{8n^3} \frac{\{-2nSC + i[(2n^2 - 1)S^2 - 2C^2]\}}{S^3}.$$

Hence

$$\mathrm{Im}\,[\sigma] = \frac{\pi^2}{8n^3 S^3}[(2n^2 - 1)S^2 - 2C^2] \tag{6.39}$$

and

$$\mathrm{Re}\,[\sigma] = -\frac{C\pi^2}{4n^2 S^2}. \tag{6.40}$$

Now from Equation 6.32,

$$\text{Re}\,[\pi i \sigma] + \frac{\pi^3}{4n}\frac{1}{S} = -\,\text{Im}\,[\pi \sigma] + \frac{\pi^3}{4nS}$$

$$= -\frac{\pi^3}{8n^3 S^3}[(2n^2 - 1)S^2 - 2C^2] + \frac{\pi^3}{4nS} = \frac{\pi^3}{8n^3}\frac{1 + C^2}{S^3}.$$

Recalling the definitions of C and S from Equation 6.38, we may write Equation 6.32 as

$$\int_0^\infty \frac{(\log x)^2}{1 + x^{2n}}\, dx = \frac{\pi^3}{8n^3} \frac{1 + \cos^2 \dfrac{\pi}{2n}}{\sin^3 \dfrac{\pi}{2n}}. \qquad (6.41)$$

Also, from Equations 6.33 and 6.40

$$\text{Im}\,[i\sigma] = \text{Re}\,[\sigma] = -\frac{C\pi^2}{4n^2 S^2},$$

or

$$\int_0^\infty \frac{\log x}{1 + x^{2n}}\, dx = -\frac{\pi^2}{4n^2} \frac{\cos \dfrac{\pi}{2n}}{\sin^2 \dfrac{\pi}{2n}}. \qquad (6.42)$$

6.4 Further Applications

In all the examples of the previous section as well as in the two examples $\int z^{-1} e^{iz}\, dz$ and $\int \cos x\,(1 + x^2)^{-1}\, dx$ of Chapter 4, the contours over which we integrated were essentially semicircular in form (see Figs. 6.5 and 6.6). While this path of integration is perhaps the most useful and common in many problems, it is not always the best nor the most convenient in every problem. In this section we shall consider additional applications of the residue theorem where rectangular or triangular contours are more applicable than semicircular ones. Also, in the next section we shall consider some more bizarre paths of integration when dealing with branch points.

A. As a first example we shall show that

$$\int_{-\infty}^\infty e^{\lambda x}\, \text{sech}\, x\, dx = \pi \sec \frac{\lambda \pi}{2}, \qquad -1 < \lambda < 1. \qquad (6.43)$$

The poles of $e^{\lambda z}\,\text{sech}\, z$ are at the roots of $\cosh z = 0$. Now

$$\cosh z = \cos iz = 0$$

implies

$$iz = (2n + 1)\frac{\pi}{2}, \qquad n = 0, \pm 1, \cdots.$$

Thus the poles of $e^{\lambda z}$ sech z are all simple and purely imaginary, and are given by

$$z = i(2n + 1)\frac{\pi}{2}, \qquad n = 0, \pm 1, \cdots.$$

Let C be the contour illustrated in Fig. 6.7. The only pole of our function inside this contour is at $z = \frac{1}{2}\pi i$. The residue at this point is

$$\sigma = \lim_{z \to \frac{1}{2}\pi i} \frac{\left(z - \frac{1}{2}\pi i\right)e^{\lambda z}}{\cosh z} = -i\, e^{\lambda \pi i/2},$$

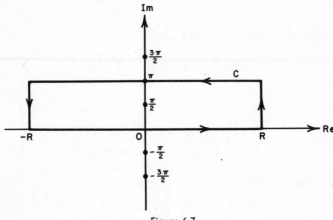

Figure 6.7

and by the residue theorem,

$$\int_C e^{\lambda z}\, \text{sech } z\, dz = 2\pi i\sigma = 2\pi\, e^{\lambda \pi i/2}.$$

Starting at the point $-R$ and integrating around the four straight lines of C, we may also write that

$$\int_C e^{\lambda z}\, \text{sech } z\, dz = \int_{-R}^{R} e^{\lambda x}\, \text{sech } x\, dx + i\int_0^{\pi} e^{\lambda(R+iy)}\, \text{sech}\,(R + iy)\, dy$$

$$+ \int_{R}^{-R} e^{\lambda(x+\pi i)}\, \text{sech}\,(x + \pi i)\, dx \qquad (6.44)$$

$$+ i\int_{\pi}^{0} e^{\lambda(-R+iy)}\, \text{sech}\,(-R + iy)\, dy.$$

Since

$$\cosh (x + \pi i) = -\cosh x,$$

we may write Equation 6.44 as

$$2\pi \, e^{\lambda\pi i/2} = \int_{-R}^{R} e^{\lambda x} \operatorname{sech} x \, dx + e^{\lambda\pi i} \int_{-R}^{R} e^{\lambda x} \operatorname{sech} x \, dx$$

$$+ \; i \int_{0}^{\pi} e^{\lambda(R+iy)} \operatorname{sech} (R + iy) \, dy \qquad (6.45)$$

$$+ \; i \int_{\pi}^{0} e^{\lambda(-R+iy)} \operatorname{sech} (R - iy) \, dy.$$

We shall show that the last two integrals approach zero as R increases without limit. Since

$$\left| \cosh (R \pm iy) \right| = \left| \frac{e^{R\pm iy} + e^{-(R\pm iy)}}{2} \right| \geqq \frac{e^{R} - e^{-R}}{2} > \frac{1}{3} e^{R}$$

for R sufficiently large and

$$\left| e^{\lambda(R+iy)} \right| = e^{\lambda R}, \qquad \left| e^{\lambda(-R+iy)} \right| = e^{-\lambda R},$$

the last two integrals of Equation 6.45 become

$$\left| i \int_{0}^{\pi} e^{\lambda(R+iy)} \operatorname{sech} (R + iy) \, dy \right| < \frac{3\pi e^{\lambda R}}{e^{R}} = 3\pi \, e^{-(1-\lambda)R}$$

and

$$\left| i \int_{\pi}^{0} e^{\lambda(-R+iy)} \operatorname{sech} (R - iy) \, dy \right| < \frac{3\pi e^{-\lambda R}}{e^{R}} = 3\pi \, e^{-(1+\lambda)R}.$$

Since $-1 < \lambda < 1$, both the above expressions tend to zero as R increases without limit.

Returning to Equation 6.45, we may now write

$$2\pi \, e^{\lambda\pi i/2} = \lim_{R\to\infty} \left[(1 + e^{\lambda\pi i}) \int_{-R}^{R} e^{\lambda x} \operatorname{sech} x \, dx \right]$$

or

$$\int_{-\infty}^{\infty} e^{\lambda x} \operatorname{sech} x \, dx = \frac{2\pi e^{\lambda\pi i/2}}{1 + e^{\lambda\pi i}}.$$

A little arithmetic yields Equation 6.43.

B. As another example we shall show that

$$\int_{-\infty}^{\infty} e^{-x^2} \cos 2\lambda x \, dx = \sqrt{\pi} \, e^{-\lambda^2} \qquad (6.46)$$

by integrating e^{-z^2} around the contour of Fig. 6.8 where λ is a positive number, fixed for the discussion. Starting at the point $-R$, we have

$$\int_C e^{-z^2}\,dz = \int_{-R}^R e^{-x^2}\,dx + i \int_0^\lambda e^{-(R+iy)^2}\,dy + \int_R^{-R} e^{-(x+i\lambda)^2}\,dx$$
$$+ i \int_\lambda^0 e^{-(-R+iy)^2}\,dy. \qquad (6.47)$$

Since e^{-z^2} is analytic in and on C, the CIT tells us that

$$\int_C e^{-z^2}\,dz = 0.$$

Thus we may write Equation 6.47 as

$$0 = \int_{-R}^R e^{-x^2}\,dx + i \int_0^\lambda e^{-(R+iy)^2}\,dy - e^{\lambda^2} \int_{-R}^R e^{-x^2} e^{2i\lambda x}\,dx$$
$$+ i \int_\lambda^0 e^{-(-R+iy)^2}\,dy, \qquad (6.48)$$

where we have replaced x by $-x$ in the third integral on the right.

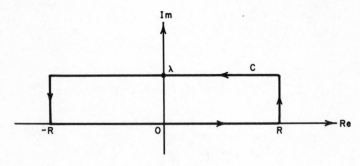

Figure 6.8

We shall now show that the second and fourth integrals of Equation 6.48 approach zero as R increases without limit. Since λ is fixed, $\int_0^\lambda e^{y^2}\,dy$ is a finite number, say M. Thus

$$\left| i \int_0^\lambda e^{-(R+iy)^2}\,dy \right| = \left| \int_0^\lambda e^{-R^2+y^2}\,e^{-2iRy}\,dy \right| \le Me^{-R^2}, \qquad (6.49)$$

which approaches zero as R increases without limit. Similarly the fourth integral on the right of Equation 6.48 tends to zero as R increases without limit.

Equation 6.48 then implies that

$$\int_{-\infty}^{\infty} e^{-x^2}\, dx = e^{\lambda^2} \int_{-\infty}^{\infty} e^{-x^2}(\cos 2\lambda x + i \sin 2\lambda x)\, dx.$$

Equating real and imaginary parts and recalling that

$$\sqrt{\pi} = \int_{-\infty}^{\infty} e^{-x^2}\, dx$$

yields

$$\int_{-\infty}^{\infty} e^{-x^2} \sin 2\lambda x\, dx = 0$$

as well as Equation 6.46.

C. Finally we shall evaluate the *Fresnel integrals*

$$\int_0^{\infty} \cos x^2\, dx$$

and

$$\int_0^{\infty} \sin x^2\, dx$$

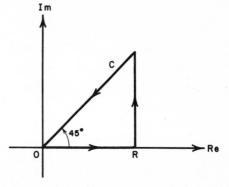

Figure 6.9

by integrating e^{-z^2} around the triangular contour of Fig. 6.9. Starting at the origin, we have

$$\int_C e^{-z^2}\, dz = \int_0^R e^{-x^2}\, dx + i \int_0^R e^{-(R+iy)^2}\, dy,$$

$$\hspace{8cm} (6.50)$$

$$+ \int_{\sqrt{2}R}^0 e^{-(1+i)^2 x^2/2}\, \frac{\sqrt{2}}{2}\, (1 + i)\, dx$$

where we have let $z = \dfrac{\sqrt{2}}{2}(1 + i)x$ on the $45°$ line. Since e^{-z^2} is analytic in and on C, there are no residues and Equation 6.50 becomes

$$0 = \int_0^R e^{-x^2}\, dx + \frac{\sqrt{2}}{2}(1+i) \int_{\sqrt{2}R}^0 e^{-ix^2}\, dx + i \int_0^R e^{-(R+iy)^2}\, dy. \quad (6.51)$$

Since $R^2 - y^2 \geq R(R - y)$ for $R \geq y \geq 0$, it is easy to see that the third integral in the above equation tends to zero as R increases without limit. Equation 6.51 then becomes

$$\int_0^{\infty} e^{-x^2}\, dx = \frac{\sqrt{2}}{2}(1 + i) \int_0^{\infty} e^{-ix^2}\, dx.$$

Since $\displaystyle\int_0^\infty e^{-x^2}\,dx \ = \ \tfrac12\sqrt{\pi}$,

$$\sqrt{\pi} \ = \ \sqrt{2}(1 + i)\int_0^\infty (\cos x^2 - i\sin x^2)\,dx.$$

Equating real and imaginary parts leads to

$$\int_0^\infty \cos x^2\,dx \ = \ \int_0^\infty \sin x^2\,dx \ = \ \frac{\sqrt{2\pi}}{4}. \tag{6.52}$$

6.5 Integration Around Branch Points

In this section we shall consider certain contour integrals whose integrands contain branch points.　Actually the integrals of Section

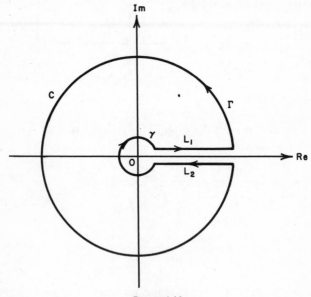

Figure 6.10

6.3 involving $\log x$ had branch points, but because of the type of contour involved only a single sheet of the Riemann surface of $\log z$ had to be considered.

A. Suppose we wish to evaluate the integral

$$\int_0^\infty \frac{x^\lambda}{1 + x}\,dx, \qquad -1 < \lambda < 0.$$

Then, as usual, we consider

$$\int_c \frac{z^\lambda}{1 + z}\,dz$$

over some appropriate contour and apply the residue theorem. Since z^λ has a branch point at $z = 0$, let us exclude this point from C and consider the contour of Fig. 6.10, where Γ is a circle of radius R and γ a circle of radius r. At an appropriate stage in our analysis we shall let R approach infinity and r approach zero. Actually L_1 and L_2 coincide with the real axis, but we have drawn them distinct for clarity in visualizing C. Often we draw C as in Fig. 6.11 to represent exactly the same contour as Fig. 6.10.

Now while L_1 and L_2 coincide in the z-plane, they do not coincide on the Riemann surface of z^λ. That is, they lie on different sheets. We make definite the multi-valued function z^λ by requiring that $z^\lambda = x^\lambda$ for $x > 0$ on L_1. Then $z^\lambda = (ze^{2\pi i})^\lambda = x^\lambda e^{2\pi i\lambda}$ for $x > 0$ on L_2. Another

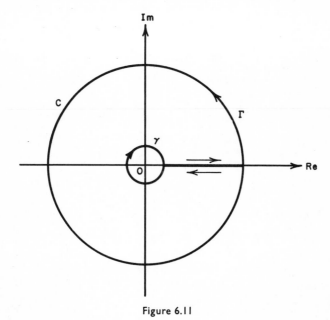

Figure 6.11

way of visualizing C is to imagine the z-plane as slit along the positive real axis. Then L_1 will be on the upper half of the branch cut and L_2 on the lower half.

Since z^λ is now single-valued and analytic in and on C, where C is considered to be drawn on the Riemann surface of z^λ,

$$\int_C \frac{z^\lambda}{1 + z}\, dz = 2\pi i\sigma,$$

where σ is the sum of the residues in C. The only singularity is a pole at the point $z = -1$, which for $r < 1$ and $R > 1$ lies in C. Therefore

$$\sigma = (-1)^\lambda = e^{\lambda \pi i}. \tag{6.53}$$

We may write the contour integral as the sum of the integrals around the curves L_1, Γ, L_2, and γ. It is

$$\int_C \frac{z^\lambda}{1 + z} dz = \int_r^R \frac{x^\lambda}{1 + x} dx + \int_\Gamma \frac{z^\lambda}{1 + z} dz + \int_R^r \frac{x^\lambda e^{2\pi i \lambda}}{1 + x} dx + \int_\gamma \frac{z^\lambda}{1 + z} dz. \tag{6.54}$$

The integral along Γ will be shown to approach zero as R approaches infinity and the integral along γ will be shown to approach zero as r approaches zero. If this be the case, Equations 6.53 and 6.54 imply

$$2\pi i (e^{\lambda \pi i}) = \int_0^\infty \frac{x^\lambda}{1 + x} dx - e^{2\lambda \pi i} \int_0^\infty \frac{x^\lambda}{1 + x} dx$$

or

$$\int_0^\infty \frac{x^\lambda}{1 + x} dx = -\frac{\pi}{\sin \lambda \pi}, \qquad -1 < \lambda < 0. \tag{6.55}$$

Now for $z = R e^{i\theta}$

$$\left| \int_\Gamma \frac{z^\lambda}{1 + z} dz \right| \leqq \left| \int_0^{2\pi} \frac{R^\lambda}{R - 1} R \, d\theta \right| = 2\pi \frac{R^{\lambda+1}}{R - 1},$$

and this approaches zero as R becomes arbitrarily large, since $\lambda < 0$. If $z = r e^{i\theta}$,

$$\left| \int_\gamma \frac{z^\lambda}{1 + z} dz \right| \leq \left| \int_0^{2\pi} \frac{r^\lambda}{1 - r} r \, d\theta \right| = 2\pi \frac{r^{\lambda+1}}{1 - r},$$

and this approaches zero as r tends to zero since $\lambda > -1$.

If we make the change of variable $x = \xi^{2n}$ in Equation 6.55 and let $\lambda = \dfrac{2m - 2n + 1}{2n}$, $n > m \geqq 0$, then

$$\int_0^\infty \frac{\xi^{2m}}{1 + \xi^{2n}} d\xi = \frac{\pi}{2n} \csc \left(\frac{2m + 1}{2n} \right) \pi,$$

which is Equation 6.13.

B. The general philosophy of evaluation of integrals of the form

$$\int_0^\infty \frac{P(x)}{Q(x)} x^\lambda dx, \tag{6.56}$$

where P and Q are relatively prime polynomials, is not difficult to give.

We shall require that $Q(z)$ have no zeros on the non-negative real axis. Thus, in particular, if

$$Q(z) = z^q + b_{q-1}z^{q-1} + \cdots + b_1 z + b_0,$$

we shall have $b_0 \neq 0$. We assume $P(z)$ of the form

$$P(z) = z^p + a_{p-1}z^{p-1} + \cdots + a_s z^s,$$

where $0 \leq s \leq p$ and $a_s \neq 0$. As the analysis proceeds we shall see what restrictions we must impose on p, s, q, and λ in order that the integral of Equation 6.56 exist.

Consider then

$$\int_C \frac{P(z)}{Q(z)} z^\lambda \, dz$$

over the contour of Figs. 6.10 and 6.11. Then, if σ is the sum of the residues of $\dfrac{P(z)}{Q(z)} z^\lambda$ in the whole z-plane,

$$
\begin{aligned}
2\pi i \sigma = \int_C \frac{P(z)}{Q(z)} z^\lambda \, dz &= \int_r^R \frac{P(x)}{Q(x)} x^\lambda \, dx + \int_\Gamma \frac{P(z)\, z^\lambda}{Q(z)} \, dz \\
&+ \int_R^r \frac{P(x)}{Q(x)} x^\lambda e^{2\pi i \lambda} \, dx + \int_\gamma \frac{P(z)}{Q(z)} z^\lambda \, dz
\end{aligned}
\tag{6.57}
$$

for R sufficiently large and r sufficiently small.

Let $z = R\, e^{i\theta}$. Then for R sufficiently large

$$\left| \int_\Gamma \frac{P(z)}{Q(z)} z^\lambda \, dz \right| < 4 \int_0^{2\pi} R^{p-q} \, R^\lambda R \, d\theta = 8\pi \, R^{p+1+\lambda-q},$$

and this will approach zero as R increases without limit if $p + 1 + \lambda - q < 0$. Similarly if $z = r\, e^{i\theta}$, then for r sufficiently small

$$\left| \int_\gamma \frac{P(z)}{Q(z)} z^\lambda \, dz \right| < \int_0^{2\pi} \frac{2|a_s|}{\frac{1}{2}|b_0|} r^\lambda r^s r \, d\theta = 8\pi |a_s| \, |b_0^{-1}| r^{s+\lambda+1},$$

and this will approach zero as r approaches zero if $s + \lambda + 1 > 0$.

Thus under the condition

$$-(s + 1) < \lambda < q - p - 1 \tag{6.58}$$

we may write Equation 6.57 as

$$2\pi i \sigma = \int_0^\infty \frac{P(x)}{Q(x)} x^\lambda \, dx - e^{2\pi i \lambda} \int_0^\infty \frac{P(x)}{Q(x)} x^\lambda \, dx$$

or if λ is not an integer

$$\int_0^\infty \frac{P(x)}{Q(x)} x^\lambda \, dx = -\frac{\pi\sigma e^{-\lambda\pi i}}{\sin \lambda\pi}. \tag{6.59}$$

C. As an application of this formula, let us consider

$$I = \int_0^\infty \frac{x^\lambda}{(1 + x^2)^2} \, dx, \qquad -1 < \lambda < 3. \tag{6.60}$$

We see that Equation 6.58 is satisfied ($q = 4$, $p = s = 0$). Thus

$$\int_0^\infty \frac{x^\lambda}{(1 + x^2)^2} \, dx = -\frac{\pi\sigma e^{-\lambda\pi i}}{\sin \lambda\pi}, \tag{6.61}$$

where σ is the sum of the residues of $z^\lambda/(1 + z^2)^2$ in the whole plane.
    If we let

$$\phi_1(z) = z^\lambda \frac{(z - i)^2}{(z^2 + 1)^2}, \qquad \phi_2(z) = z^\lambda \frac{(z + i)^2}{(z^2 + 1)^2},$$

then, according to Equation 6.2,

$$\sigma = \phi_1'(i) + \phi_2'(-i).$$

Now

$$\phi_1'(z) = z^\lambda[\lambda z^{-1}(z + i)^{-2} - 2(z + i)^{-3}]$$

and

$$\phi_1'(i) = (e^{\pi i/2})^\lambda \left[\frac{i}{4}(\lambda - 1)\right].$$

Similarly,

$$\phi_2'(z) = z^\lambda[\lambda z^{-1}(z - i)^{-2} - 2(z - i)^{-3}]$$

and

$$\phi_2'(-i) = (e^{3\pi i/2})^\lambda \left[-\frac{i}{4}(\lambda - 1)\right].$$

Thus

$$\sigma = \frac{i}{4}(1 - \lambda)\left[e^{3\lambda\pi i/2} - e^{\lambda\pi i/2}\right] \tag{6.62}$$

and

$$I = -\frac{\pi\sigma e^{-\lambda\pi i}}{\sin \lambda\pi} = \frac{\pi}{\sin \lambda\pi} \frac{1 - \lambda}{2} \left[\frac{e^{\lambda\pi i/2} - e^{-\lambda\pi i/2}}{2i}\right]$$

$$\tag{6.63}$$

$$= \frac{\pi}{4}(1 - \lambda)\sec\frac{\lambda\pi}{2}.$$

In terms of the Beta function (see Equation 6.15) we may write

$$\int_0^\infty \frac{x^\lambda}{(1 + x^2)^2} \, dx = \frac{1}{2} \, B\left(\frac{\lambda + 1}{2}, \frac{3 - \lambda}{2}\right). \tag{6.64}$$

D. In certain applications (see, for example, Chapter 9) we must consider complex integrals over certain contours other than circles or straight lines. Two such types of curves are the *loop* and *double loop*. By a loop we mean a contour C which starts at infinity, encloses a branch point, and then recedes to infinity. For example, if α is a branch point of the function $f(z)$, then

$$\int_C f(z) \, dz$$

over the contour of Fig. 6.12 is called a *loop integral*. Occasionally we desire to simplify this integral. That is, we either evaluate it or

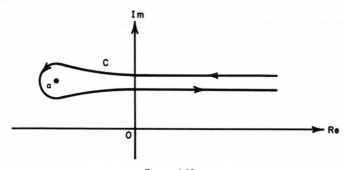

Figure 6.12

express it as an integral over a less complicated contour, say as an integral around a circle or as a real Riemann integral. We illustrate with a simple example.

Let us evaluate

$$\int_C z^\lambda e^{-z} \, dz, \qquad \text{Re}\,[\lambda] > -1, \tag{6.65}$$

over the contour of Fig. 6.12 where $\alpha = 0$. We may draw C more practically as in Fig. 6.13. The line segments L_1 and L_2 coincide with the real axis in the z-plane, but are on different sheets of the Riemann surface for z^λ. (As before, we consider the complex plane as slit along the positive real axis.)

We make the multi-valued function z^λ definite by choosing the branch

$$z^\lambda = e^{\lambda \log z} = e^{\lambda \log x} = x^\lambda$$

for $x > 0$ on L_1. Then

$$z^\lambda = e^{\lambda(\log x + 2\pi i)} = x^\lambda e^{2\pi i \lambda}$$

for $x > 0$ on L_2. Thus Equation 6.65 may be written as

$$\int_C z^\lambda e^{-z}\, dz = \lim_{R \to \infty} \left[\int_R^r x^\lambda e^{-x}\, dx + \int_\gamma z^\lambda e^{-z}\, dz + e^{2\pi i \lambda} \int_r^R x^\lambda e^{-x}\, dx \right],$$

(6.66)

where r is the radius of γ.

Figure 6.13

We assert that if r approaches zero, the integral along γ will vanish. Let $z = r\, e^{i\theta}$. Then

$$\int_\gamma z^\lambda e^{-z}\, dz = i \int_0^{2\pi} (r\, e^{i\theta})^{\lambda+1} e^{-r(\cos\theta + i\sin\theta)}\, d\theta.$$

If we let $\lambda = \lambda_1 + i\lambda_2$, then

$$i\theta\lambda = i\theta(\lambda_1 + i\lambda_2) = i\theta\lambda_1 - \theta\lambda_2$$

and

$$r^\lambda = e^{\lambda \log r} = e^{\lambda_1 \log r} e^{i\lambda_2 \log r} = r^{\lambda_1} e^{i\lambda_2 \log r}.$$

Thus

$$\left| \int_\gamma z^\lambda e^{-z}\, dz \right| \leq r^{1+\lambda_1} \int_0^{2\pi} e^{-\theta\lambda_2} e^{-r\cos\theta}\, d\theta. \qquad (6.67)$$

Since $\lambda_1 = \mathrm{Re}\,[\lambda] > -1$ and the integral on the right of Equation 6.67 is finite, we infer that $\left| \int_\gamma z^\lambda e^{-z}\, dz \right|$ approaches zero as r approaches zero. Equation 6.66 then becomes

$$\int_C z^\lambda e^{-z}\, dz = \lim_{R \to \infty} \left[(e^{2\pi i \lambda} - 1) \int_0^R x^\lambda e^{-x}\, dx \right].$$

Since $\int_0^\infty x^\lambda e^{-x}\,dx$ is a convergent integral (see Exercise 4.11), we see that $\int_C z^\lambda e^{-z}\,dz$ exists and equals

$$\int_C z^\lambda e^{-z}\,dz = (e^{2\pi i\lambda} - 1)\int_0^\infty x^\lambda e^{-x}\,dx.$$

Note that $x^\lambda e^{-x}$ is a complex-valued function of the real variable x. Students of applied mathematics will recognize the integral on the right side of the above expression as the Gamma function $\Gamma(\lambda + 1)$. Thus

$$\int_C z^\lambda e^{-z}\,dz = -(1 - e^{2\pi i\lambda})\Gamma(\lambda + 1), \qquad \mathrm{Re}\,[\lambda] > -1. \qquad (6.68)$$

E. A *double loop* may be described as follows. Let α and β be two branch points of the function $F(z)$. Let C_α be a closed smooth curve

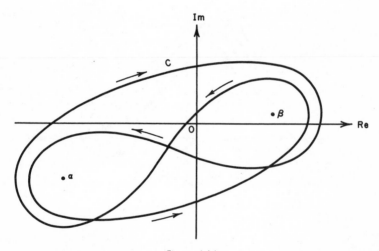

Figure 6.14

encircling α in the positive sense, and C_α^{-1} (read "C_α inverse") be the same curve traversed in the negative sense. Similarly, define C_β and C_β^{-1}. We also require that α be exterior to C_β and β exterior to C_α. Then the contour

$$C = C_\beta^{-1} C_\alpha^{-1} C_\beta C_\alpha,$$

which consists of C_α followed by C_β followed by C_α^{-1} followed by C_β^{-1}, is called a *double loop*. This can be depicted picturesquely as in Fig. 6.14. The advantage of this type of contour is that the multivalued function $F(z)$ returns to its original value after traversing C.

Let us illustrate with the integral

$$I = \int_C f(z)(z - \alpha)^\mu(z - \beta)^\nu \, dz, \qquad (6.69)$$

where α, β, μ, ν are arbitrary complex numbers and $f(z)$ is single-valued and analytic in some connected region containing α and β. Then if we choose any point γ distinct from α and β, we may describe the double loop C as in Fig. 6.15, or more schematically as in Fig. 6.16. This is equivalent to the curve drawn in Fig. 6.14—less glamorous perhaps, but more convenient for practical computation. Of course,

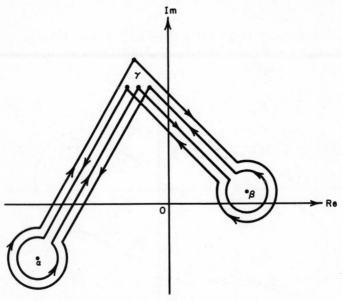

Figure 6.15

we require that the open region in which $f(z)$ is single-valued contain C_α, C_β and their interiors as well as L_α and L_β.

On Fig. 6.16 we have labeled α' and β' as the points where L_α and L_β touch the circles C_α and C_β respectively. The angles that L_α and L_β make with the positive direction of the real axis are indicated by θ and ϕ respectively. If a multi-valued function $F(z)$ traverses a closed contour C', let us denote by $S_{C'}F(z)$ the value of the function after it has completed the circulation. We make the multi-valued functions $(z - \alpha)^\mu$ and $(z - \beta)^\nu$ definite by requiring that at $z = \gamma$

$$(z - \alpha)^\mu = e^{\mu \, \log \, (z-\alpha)} = e^{\mu[\log \, |\gamma-\alpha|+i\theta]}$$

and

$$(z - \beta)^\nu = e^{\nu \log (z-\beta)} = e^{\nu[\log |\gamma-\beta|+i\phi]}.$$

Finally, for simplicity in notation, we let

$$F(z) = f(z)(z - \alpha)^\mu (z - \beta)^\nu.$$

Now we see that

$$\mathbf{S}_{C_\alpha} F(z) = e^{2\pi i \mu} F(z),$$

$$\mathbf{S}_{C_\beta}[\mathbf{S}_{C_\alpha} F(z)] = e^{2\pi i \nu} \mathbf{S}_{C_\alpha} F(z) = e^{2\pi i (\mu+\nu)} F(z),$$

$$\mathbf{S}_{C_\alpha}^{-1}[\mathbf{S}_{C_\beta} \mathbf{S}_{C_\alpha} F(z)] = e^{-2\pi i \mu} \mathbf{S}_{C_\beta} \mathbf{S}_{C_\alpha} F(z) = e^{2\pi i \nu} F(z),$$

$$\mathbf{S}_{C_\beta}^{-1}[\mathbf{S}_{C_\alpha}^{-1} \mathbf{S}_{C_\beta} \mathbf{S}_{C_\alpha} F(z)] = e^{-2\pi i \nu} \mathbf{S}_{C_\alpha}^{-1} \mathbf{S}_{C_\beta} \mathbf{S}_{C_\alpha} F(z) = F(z).$$

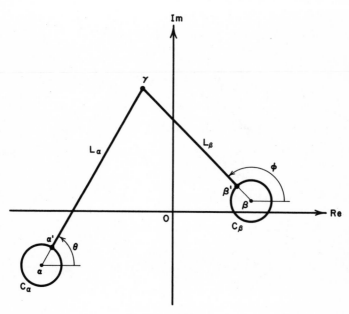

Figure 6.16

Thus, since $C = C_\beta^{-1} C_\alpha^{-1} C_\beta C_\alpha$,

$$\mathbf{S}_C F(z) = F(z)$$

and $F(z)$ returns to its original value after a circulation around C. The curve C is closed on the Riemann surface of $F(z)$, as well as in the z-plane.

We shall now write $\int_C F(z)\,dz$ as a sum of integrals over the constituent contours of Fig. 6.16. Starting at $z = \gamma$, we have

$$\int_C F(z)\,dz = \int_\gamma^{\alpha'} F(z)\,dz + \int_{C_\alpha} F(z)\,dz + e^{2\pi i\mu} \int_{\alpha'}^\gamma F(z)\,dz$$

$$+ e^{2\pi i\mu} \int_\gamma^{\beta'} F(z)\,dz$$

$$+ e^{2\pi i\mu} \int_{C_\beta} F(z)\,dz + e^{2\pi i(\mu+\nu)} \int_{\beta'}^\gamma F(z)\,dz$$

$$+ e^{2\pi i(\mu+\nu)} \int_\gamma^{\alpha'} F(z)\,dz \qquad\qquad (6.70)$$

$$+ e^{2\pi i(\mu+\nu)} \int_{C_\alpha^{-1}} F(z)\,dz + e^{2\pi i\nu} \int_{\alpha'}^\gamma F(z)\,dz + e^{2\pi i\nu} \int_\gamma^{\beta'} F(z)\,dz$$

$$+ e^{2\pi i\nu} \int_{C_\beta^{-1}} F(z)\,dz + \int_{\beta'}^\gamma F(z)\,dz.$$

Since

$$\int_{C_\alpha^{-1}} = \int_{-C_\alpha} = -\int_{C_\alpha}$$

with a similar result when α is replaced by β, and also

$$\int_{\alpha'}^\gamma = -\int_\gamma^{\alpha'}, \qquad \int_{\beta'}^\gamma = -\int_\gamma^{\beta'},$$

we may write Equation 6.70 as

$$\int_C F(z)\,dz = [1 - e^{2\pi i\mu} + e^{2\pi i(\mu+\nu)} - e^{2\pi i\nu}] \int_\gamma^{\alpha'} F(z)\,dz$$

$$+ [e^{2\pi i\mu} - e^{2\pi i(\mu+\nu)} + e^{2\pi i\nu} - 1] \int_\gamma^{\beta'} F(z)\,dz$$

$$+ [1 - e^{2\pi i(\mu+\nu)}] \int_{C_\alpha} F(z)\,dz$$

$$\qquad\qquad (6.71)$$

$$+ [e^{2\pi i\mu} - e^{2\pi i\nu}] \int_{C_\beta} F(z)\,dz$$

$$= -(1 - e^{2\pi i\mu})(1 - e^{2\pi i\nu}) \left[\int_{\alpha'}^\gamma F(z)\,dz + \int_\gamma^{\beta'} F(z)\,dz \right]$$

$$+ (1 - e^{2\pi i(\mu+\nu)}) \int_{C_\alpha} F(z)\,dz + (e^{2\pi i\mu} - e^{2\pi i\nu}) \int_{C_\beta} F(z)\,dz.$$

We consider certain special cases of Equation 6.71. Suppose μ is an integer. Then $(z - \alpha)^\mu$ is single-valued and $e^{2\pi i \mu} = 1$. Equation 6.71 then becomes

$$\int_C F(z)\, dz = (1 - e^{2\pi i \nu}) \int_{C_\alpha + C_\beta} F(z)\, dz.$$

Suppose $f(z)$ has no singularities. Then we may take the radii of C_α and C_β to be equal to $\frac{1}{2}|\beta - \alpha|$ and let α', β', and γ coincide. Thus

$$\int_C F(z)\, dz = (1 - e^{2\pi i (\mu + \nu)}) \int_{C_\alpha} F(z)\, dz + (e^{2\pi i \mu} - e^{2\pi i \nu}) \int_{C_\beta} F(z)\, dz.$$

Suppose $\operatorname{Re}[\mu] > -1$ and $\operatorname{Re}[\nu] > -1$. Then the contours C_α and C_β can be shrunk to points and

$$\int_C F(z)\, dz = -(1 - e^{2\pi i \mu})(1 - e^{2\pi i \nu})\left[\int_\alpha^\gamma F(z)\, dz + \int_\gamma^\beta F(z)\, dz\right].$$

If $f(z)$ has no singularities along the line connecting α to β, we may take γ colinear with α and β. Thus

$$\int_C F(z)\, dz = -(1 - e^{2\pi i \mu})(1 - e^{2\pi i \nu}) \int_\alpha^\beta F(z)\, dz, \qquad (6.72)$$

where the integral is along the straight line segment joining α to β.

The reader can deduce other special cases. One of some practical importance occurs when $f(z) = 1$, $\operatorname{Re}[\mu] > -1$, $\operatorname{Re}[\nu] > -1$, $\alpha = 0$, $\beta = 1$. Then Equation 6.72 becomes

$$\int_C z^\mu (z - 1)^\nu\, dz = -(1 - e^{2\pi i \mu})(1 - e^{2\pi i \nu}) \int_0^1 z^\mu (z - 1)^\nu\, dz.$$

Since $(z - 1)^\nu = (-1)^\nu (1 - z)^\nu = e^{\pi i \nu}(1 - z)^\nu$,

$$\int_C z^\mu (z - 1)^\nu\, dz = -e^{\pi i \nu}(1 - e^{2\pi i \mu})(1 - e^{2\pi i \nu}) \int_0^1 z^\mu (1 - z)^\nu\, dz.$$

Students of applied mathematics will recognize the integral on the right as the Beta function $B(\mu + 1, \nu + 1)$. Thus

$$\int_C z^\mu (z - 1)^\nu\, dz = -e^{\pi i \nu}(1 - e^{2\pi i \mu})(1 - e^{2\pi i \nu}) B(\mu + 1, \nu + 1),$$

or more conventionally,

$$\int_C z^{\mu - 1}(1 - z)^{\nu - 1}\, dz = -(1 - e^{2\pi i \mu})(1 - e^{2\pi i \nu}) B(\mu, \nu),$$

$$\operatorname{Re}[\mu] > 0, \; \operatorname{Re}[\nu] > 0. \tag{6.73}$$

EXERCISES

6.1. Evaluate the following real integrals:

(a) $\displaystyle\int_{-\infty}^{\infty} \frac{dx}{x^2 - x + 2} = \frac{2\pi}{\sqrt{7}}$

(b) $\displaystyle\int_{0}^{\infty} \frac{x^2}{2x^4 + 5x^2 + 2}\, dx = \frac{\pi\sqrt{2}}{12}$

(c) $\displaystyle\int_{0}^{\infty} \frac{dx}{(x^2 + a^2)^2} = \frac{\pi}{4a^3}, \qquad a > 0$

(d) $\displaystyle\int_{0}^{\infty} \frac{dx}{(x^2 + a^2)(x^2 + b^2)} = \frac{\pi}{2ab(a + b)}, \qquad a > 0, b > 0$

(e) $\displaystyle\int_{0}^{\infty} \frac{x^2}{(x^2 + a^2)^3}\, dx = \frac{\pi}{16a^3}, \qquad a > 0$

(f) $\displaystyle\int_{0}^{\infty} \frac{x^6}{(x^4 + 1)^2}\, dx = \frac{3\pi\sqrt{2}}{16}$

6.2. If a, b, ω are real and positive and n is a positive integer, show that

(a) $\displaystyle\int_{0}^{\infty} \frac{\cos \omega x}{(1 + x^2)^2}\, dx = \frac{\pi(\omega + 1)e^{-\omega}}{4}$

(b) $\displaystyle\int_{0}^{\infty} \frac{\cos \omega x}{(x^2 + a^2)(x^2 + b^2)}\, dx = \frac{\pi}{2ab(a^2 - b^2)}\, (ae^{-\omega b} - be^{-\omega a})$

(c) $\displaystyle\int_{-\infty}^{\infty} \frac{\sin \omega x}{x^2 + 4x + 5}\, dx = -\pi e^{-\omega} \sin 2\omega$

(d) $\displaystyle\int_{0}^{\infty} \frac{\sin \omega x}{x(x^2 + a^2)}\, dx = \frac{\pi}{2a^2}\, (1 - e^{-\omega a})$

(e) $\displaystyle\int_{0}^{\infty} \frac{x \sin \omega x}{(x^2 + a^2)^2}\, dx = \frac{\pi\omega}{4a}\, e^{-\omega a}$

(f) $\displaystyle\int_{-\infty}^{\infty} \frac{1 - \cos \omega x}{4n^2\pi^2 - \omega^2 x^2}\, dx = 0$

6.3. Establish the following trigonometric integrals. In all cases a and b are real and n is a positive integer.

(a) $\displaystyle\int_{0}^{2\pi} \frac{dx}{(a + b \cos x)^2} = \frac{2\pi a}{(a^2 - b^2)^{3/2}}, \qquad a > b > 0$

(b) $\displaystyle\int_{0}^{\frac{1}{2}\pi} \frac{dx}{a + \sin^2 x} = \frac{\pi}{2\sqrt{a(a + 1)}}, \qquad a > 0$

(c) $\displaystyle\int_{0}^{\pi} \frac{\cos 2x}{1 + a^2 - 2a \cos x}\, dx = \frac{\pi a^2}{1 - a^2}, \qquad |a| < 1$

(d) $\displaystyle\int_0^\pi \frac{1 + \cos x}{1 + \cos^2 x}\, dx = \frac{\sqrt{\pi}}{2}$

(e) $\displaystyle\int_0^{2\pi} \frac{\sin^2 x}{a + b \cos x}\, dx = \frac{2\pi}{b^2}\,(a - \sqrt{a^2 - b^2}), \qquad a > b > 0$

(f) $\displaystyle\int_0^{2\pi} \frac{\cos nx}{\cosh a + \cos x}\, dx = \frac{2\pi(-1)^n e^{-na}}{\sinh a}, \qquad a > 0$

6.4. Show that

(a) $\displaystyle\int_0^\infty \frac{(\log x)^3}{1 + x^2}\, dx = 0$

(b) $\displaystyle\int_0^\infty \frac{(\log x)^4}{1 + x^2}\, dx = \frac{5}{32}\,\pi^5$

(c) $\displaystyle\int_0^\infty \frac{\log x}{(1 + x^2)^2}\, dx = -\frac{\pi}{4}$

(d) $\displaystyle\int_0^\infty x^\lambda \log (1 + x)\, dx = -\frac{\pi}{(\lambda + 1) \sin \lambda\pi}, \qquad -2 < \lambda < -1$

(e) $\displaystyle\int_{-\infty}^\infty \frac{e^{\lambda x}}{1 + e^x}\, dx = \frac{\pi}{\sin \lambda\pi}, \qquad 0 < \lambda < 1$

(f) $\displaystyle\int_{a-i\infty}^{a+i\infty} \frac{dz}{\lambda^z \sin \pi z} = \frac{2i}{1 + \lambda}, \qquad 0 < \lambda < 1, \qquad 0 < a < 1$

6.5. If λ is real but not necessarily an integer, evaluate

(a) $\displaystyle\int_0^\infty \frac{\sqrt{x}}{x^2 + 2x + 5}\, dx = \frac{\pi}{\sqrt{2}\,\sqrt{5 + \sqrt{5}}}$

(b) $\displaystyle\int_0^\infty \frac{x^\lambda}{x^2 + 3x + 2}\, dx = \frac{\pi}{\sin \lambda\pi}\,[2^\lambda - 1], \qquad |\lambda| < 1$

(c) $\displaystyle\int_0^\infty \frac{x^\lambda}{(x + a)(x + b)}\, dx = \frac{\pi(a^\lambda - b^\lambda)}{(a - b) \sin \lambda\pi}. \qquad |\lambda| < 1, \qquad a > b > 0$

(d) $\displaystyle\int_0^\infty \frac{x^\lambda}{x^4 + 1}\, dx = \frac{\pi}{4}\,\csc \frac{\pi}{4}\,(\lambda + 1), \qquad -1 < \lambda < 3$

(e) $\displaystyle\int_0^\infty \frac{x^\lambda}{x^2 + 1 + 2x \cos \omega}\, dx = \frac{\sin \lambda\omega}{\sin \lambda\pi}\,\frac{\pi}{\sin \omega}, \qquad |\lambda| < 1, \qquad |\omega| < \pi$

CHAPTER 7

Some Properties of Analytic Functions

7.1 Introduction

In the preceding chapters we have inexorably held to our course of developing certain unified portions of complex variable theory. There are, however, many other interesting properties of analytic functions and of functions analytic except for isolated singularities. Rather than interrupt our main thread of discussion, we have ignored these results or else relegated them to the exercises. In the present chapter we should like to prove certain theorems of general interest which are just as much a part of the complex calculus as any of the preceding material. The results of the various sections are of necessity somewhat disjoint. However, we believe that the reader will find each integrated group of theorems a small masterpiece of mathematical beauty illuminating the logic and unity of the theory of analytic functions.

7.2 A Residue Theorem

We start by considering a general residue theorem.

Theorem 1. Let $f(z)$ be single-valued and meromorphic in a connected open set $\mathfrak{A}$. Let $F(z)$ be single-valued and analytic in $\mathfrak{A}$. Let C be a closed smooth curve which, together with its interior, lies in $\mathfrak{A}$. Let $f(z)$ have no poles or zeros on C. If $f(z)$ has poles at the points $\zeta_1, \zeta_2, \cdots, \zeta_r$ in C with multiplicities $p_1, p_2, \cdots, p_r$, respectively, and zeros at the points $z_1, z_2, \cdots, z_s$ in C with multiplicities $q_1, q_2, \cdots, q_s$, respectively, then

$$\int_C F(z) \frac{f'(z)}{f(z)}\, dz = 2\pi i \left[\sum_{i=1}^{s} q_i F(z_i) - \sum_{i=1}^{r} p_i F(\zeta_i) \right]. \qquad (7.1)$$

Proof: If $f(z)$ has a zero at z_i of multiplicity q_i, then in a neighborhood of $z = z_i$, $f(z)$ has the Taylor series expansion

$$f(z) = a_{q_i}(z - z_i)^{q_i} + a_{q_i+1}(z - z_i)^{q_i+1} + \cdots, \qquad a_{q_i} \neq 0,$$

170

and

$$f'(z) = q_i a_{q_i}(z - z_i)^{q_i-1} + (q_i + 1)a_{q_i+1}(z - z_i)^{q_i} + \cdots.$$

Thus

$$\frac{f'(z)}{f(z)} = \frac{q_i}{z - z_i} + R(z - z_i),$$

where $R(z - z_i)$ is an analytic function in the neighborhood of z_i. Thus the residue of $F(z)f'(z)/f(z)$ at $z = z_i$ is

$$q_i F(z_i). \tag{7.2}$$

If $f(z)$ has a pole at ζ_i of multiplicity p_i, then in a neighborhood of $z = \zeta_i$, $f(z)$ has the Laurent series expansion

$$f(z) = b_{-p_i}(z - \zeta_i)^{-p_i} + b_{-p_i+1}(z - \zeta_i)^{-p_i+1} + \cdots, \qquad b_{-p_i} \neq 0,$$

and

$$f'(z) = -p_i b_{-p_i}(z - \zeta_i)^{-p_i-1} + (-p_i + 1)b_{-p_i+1}(z - \zeta_i)^{-p_i} + \cdots.$$

Thus

$$\frac{f'(z)}{f(z)} = -\frac{p_i}{z - \zeta_i} + S(z - \zeta_i),$$

where $S(z - \zeta_i)$ is an analytic function in a neighborhood of ζ_i. Thus the residue of $F(z)f'(z)/f(z)$ at $z = \zeta_i$ is

$$-p_i F(\zeta_i). \tag{7.3}$$

The theorem follows immediately from Equations 7.2 and 7.3.

Under the hypotheses of the above theorem consider the special case $F(z) \equiv 1$. Then

$$\frac{1}{2\pi i} \int_C \frac{f'(z)}{f(z)} \, dz = \sum_{i=1}^{s} q_i - \sum_{i=1}^{r} p_i.$$

Thus if we let Z be the number of zeros of $f(z)$ in C (counting multiplicities) and P the number of poles of $f(z)$ in C (counting multiplicities), then we have the important corollary that

$$\frac{1}{2\pi i} \int_C \frac{f'(z)}{f(z)} \, dz = Z - P. \tag{7.4}$$

If $f(z)$ is analytic in and on C (and $f(z)$ has no zeros on C), then $(2\pi i)^{-1} \int_C [f'(z)/f(z)] \, dz$ is simply the number of zeros of $f(z)$ in C.

We shall deduce still another important consequence of Theorem 1. Suppose C is a smooth curve with initial point α and terminal point β. Let $f(z)$ be single-valued and analytic along C. We may then write

$$f(z) = |f(z)|e^{i \arg f(z)}$$

for any z on C. In particular, the argument of $f(z)$ at α is $\arg f(\alpha)$ and the argument of $f(z)$ at β is $\arg f(\beta)$. We shall call

$$V_C(f) = \arg f(\beta) - \arg f(\alpha)$$

the *variation of the argument* of $f(z)$ along C. This leads to the following theorem.

Theorem 2. Let $f(z)$ be single-valued and meromorphic in a connected open set $\mathfrak{A}$. Let C be a closed smooth curve which, together with its interior, lies in $\mathfrak{A}$. Let $f(z)$ have no poles or zeros on C. Let Z be the number of zeros (counting multiplicities) of $f(z)$ in C and P the number of poles (counting multiplicities) of $f(z)$ in C. Then

$$Z - P = \frac{1}{2\pi} V_C(f). \tag{7.5}$$

Proof: From Equation 7.4

$$Z - P = \frac{1}{2\pi i} \int_C \frac{f'(z)}{f(z)} \, dz = \frac{1}{2\pi i} \log f(z) \Big|_C.$$

Now

$$\log f(z) = \log |f(z)| + i \arg f(z).$$

Since C is closed, $\log |f(z)| \big|_C = 0$. However, $\arg f(z)$ need not return to its original value. Thus

$$\log f(z) \Big|_C = i \, V_C(f),$$

from which the theorem follows.

If $f(z)$ is analytic in C, then $P = 0$ and

$$2\pi Z = V_C(f).$$

We therefore have the following corollary.

Corollary. Let $f(z)$ be single-valued and analytic in and on a closed smooth curve C and not vanish on C. Let Z be the number of zeros of $f(z)$ in C. Then

$$Z = \frac{1}{2\pi} V_C(f). \tag{7.6}$$

As z traverses the curve C, its image $w = f(z)$ will traverse the curve Γ in the w-plane. If Γ does not encircle the origin (or encircles it an equal number of times in the positive and negative sense), then $\arg f(z)$ returns to its original value when z completes C. Thus $V_C(f) = 0$, and hence $Z = 0$. The corollary may be reworded as: the number of zeros of $f(z)$ in C is equal to the number of times the image $f(z)$ encircles the origin in the counterclockwise sense decreased by the number of times it encircles the origin in the negative sense. This result is of importance in applied mathematics. It forms the basis of the Nyquist stability criterion in servomechanism theory and feedback amplifier design.*

7.3 The Fundamental Theorem of Algebra

We recall that an integral or entire function was defined as a single-valued function which was analytic for all z. A classical theorem of Liouville asserts that a bounded entire function must be a constant.

Theorem 3: (*Liouville*). Let $f(z)$ be an integral function which is bounded over the z-plane. Then $f(z)$ is a constant.

Proof: About any point α we can develop $f(z)$ in a power series

$$f(z) = c_0 + c_1(z - \alpha) + c_2(z - \alpha)^2 + \cdots$$

with an infinite radius of convergence. If C is any circle of radius R with center at $z = \alpha$, then by Theorem 16 of Chapter 5

$$c_n = \frac{1}{2\pi i} \int_C \frac{f(z)}{(z - \alpha)^{n+1}} \, dz.$$

By hypothesis there exists an M such that $|f(z)| \leq M$ for all z. Thus

$$|c_n| \leq \frac{1}{2\pi} \frac{M}{R^{n+1}} (2\pi R) = \frac{M}{R^n}. \tag{7.7}$$

Since Equation 7.4 holds for any R, no matter how large, we infer that

$$|c_n| = 0, \qquad n = 1, 2, \cdots.$$

Thus

$$f(z) = c_0.$$

Note that we have no such theorem for real functions. For example, $y = \sin x$ (x real) is single-valued and analytic for all x, is bounded, and yet is not a constant. (Of course if we let x be complex,

---

* See, for example, H. M. James, N. B. Nichols, and R. S. Phillips, *Theory of Servomechanisms*, McGraw-Hill Book Company, 1947.

then we can choose an x such that $|\sin x|$ exceeds any preassigned real number. Hence it is not bounded and Liouville's theorem does not apply.)

An immediate application of Liouville's theorem proves the fundamental theorem of algebra. The reader recalls that in elementary algebra courses it was stated, generally without proof, that every polynomial equation had at least one root. Using the complex calculus we can give a direct proof of this result.

Theorem 4: (*Fundamental theorem of algebra*). Let

$$P(z) = a_0 z^n + a_1 z^{n-1} + \cdots + a_n, \qquad a_0 \neq 0,$$

be a polynomial of degree $n > 0$ where the a_i are complex numbers. Then there exists at least one complex number β such that $P(\beta) \equiv 0$.

Proof: We shall suppose there exists no value of z which makes $P(z)$ vanish and force a contradiction.

Choose a real number $R > 0$ such that

$$|P(z)| > \frac{|a_0||z^n|}{2}$$

for all z with $|z| > R$ (see Exercise 3.4). In particular, we can choose R so large that

$$|P(z)| > 1$$

for $|z| > R$. Since $P(z)$ has no zeros, $P^{-1}(z)$ is analytic throughout the plane and for $|z| > R$,

$$|P^{-1}(z)| < 1.$$

Certainly $P^{-1}(z)$ is bounded in and on a circle of radius R with center at the origin (see Theorem 4 of Chapter 3). Thus $P^{-1}(z)$ is bounded throughout the whole plane. By Liouville's theorem it must be a constant. Thus $P(z)$ must also be a constant—a contradiction to our assumption that $P(z)$ was a polynomial of positive degree.

It is not difficult to show that if $P(z)$ has one root it has n roots. For if β is a root of $P(z) = 0$, we write

$$P(z) = (z - \beta)Q(z),$$

where $Q(z)$ is a polynomial of degree $n - 1$. Applying Liouville's theorem to $Q(z)$ we can prove by a simple induction that $P(z)$ has precisely n roots. However, we shall give a function theoretic proof of this fact.

Theorem 5. Let

$$P(z) = a_0 z^n + a_1 z^{n-1} + \cdots + a_n, \qquad a_0 \neq 0$$

be a polynomial of degree $n > 0$ where the a_i are complex numbers. Then $P(z)$ has precisely n zeros (counting multiplicities).

Proof: Since $|f(z)|$ can be made arbitrarily large for $|z|$ large, there exists a circle C with center at the origin such that $f(z)$ has no zeros in the exterior of C. Since

$$P'(z) = na_0 z^{n-1} + (n-1)a_1 z^{n-2} + \cdots + a_{n-1},$$

the Laurent expansion of $P'(z)/P(z)$ at $z = \infty$ is

$$\frac{P'(z)}{P(z)} = \frac{n}{z} + \frac{1}{z} R(z),$$

where $R(z)$ contains only negative powers of z. Thus, if Γ is a negatively sensed circle with center at $z = 0$ and radius exceeding that of C,

$$\frac{1}{2\pi i} \int_{\Gamma} \frac{P'(z)}{P(z)} \, dz = n,$$

where $-n$ is the residue of $P'(z)/P(z)$ at infinity. Thus by Equation 7.4.

$$n = Z,$$

where Z is the number of zeros of $P(z)$ inside Γ.

7.4 Rational Functions

In Section 3.4 we defined a rational function $R(z)$. Thus

$$R(z) = \frac{P(z)}{Q(z)},$$

where

$$P(z) = a_0 z^p + a_1 z^{p-1} + \cdots + a_p$$

and

$$Q(z) = b_0 z^q + b_1 z^{q-1} + \cdots + b_q, \qquad b_0 \neq 0$$

are polynomials. If $a_0 \neq 0$, then $P(z)$ is a polynomial of degree p. We may assume without loss of generality that P and Q are relatively prime.

By Theorem 5 we may write

$$R(z) = \frac{a_0(z - \alpha_1)(z - \alpha_2) \cdots (z - \alpha_p)}{b_0(z - \beta_1)(z - \beta_2) \cdots (z - \beta_q)}, \tag{7.8}$$

where the α_i are the p roots (multiplicities included) of $P(z) = 0$ and the β_i are the q roots (multiplicities included) of $Q(z) = 0$. It is clear that $R(z)$ has p zeros and q poles. We now wish to consider the poles and zeros of $R(z)$ in the *extended* plane. In this connection we have the following theorem.

Theorem 6. In the extended plane, a rational function has as many zeros as poles.

Proof: We have seen that in the finite part of the plane $R(z)$ has p zeros and q poles. It remains to examine the poles and zeros at $z = \infty$.

If $q > p$, then $z = \infty$ is a zero of multiplicity $q - p$, while if $q < p$, then $z = \infty$ is a pole of multiplicity $p - q$. Finally, if $p = q$, $z = \infty$ is neither a pole nor a zero of $R(z)$.

It is customary to define the *degree*, r, of a rational function $R(z)$ as the larger of the two integers p and q. Thus we see that if $R(z)$ is a rational function of degree r, then it has r zeros and r poles in the extended plane.

If $R(z)$ is a rational function, then

$$\int_C R(z)\, dz = 2\pi i \sigma,$$

where C is any closed smooth curve on which $R(z)$ is analytic and σ is the sum of the residues of $R(z)$ in C. Clearly we can choose C so large that all the poles of $R(z)$ lie interior to C. Thus $R(z)$ is analytic in the exterior of C, that is, in a neighborhood of infinity. But the residue at infinity is

$$\frac{1}{2\pi i} \int_{-C} R(z)\, dz.$$

Thus we have the following theorem.

Theorem 7. The sum of the residues of a rational function in the extended plane is zero.

It is clear from the definition that a rational function is uniquely specified (up to a multiplicative constant) by its poles and zeros. We can also prove the following converse proposition.

Theorem 8. Let $f(z)$ be single-valued and meromorphic in the extended plane. Then $f(z)$ is a rational function.

Proof: Since $f(z)$ is either analytic or has a pole at $z = \infty$, we can draw a circle C of sufficiently large radius such that $f(z)$ is analytic in the exterior of C, except perhaps at $z = \infty$. That is, $f(z)$ is analytic in a neighborhood of infinity. Thus all the poles which occur in the finite part of the plane lie interior to C. We conclude therefore that there can be at most a finite number of such poles. For if there were not, the Bolzano-Weierstrass theorem would imply the existence of a limit point of these poles. Such a point could not be a point of analyticity nor a pole. Let us suppose that the poles occur at the points $\zeta_1, \zeta_2, \cdots, \zeta_r$, with multiplicities $p_1, p_2, \cdots, p_r$, respectively.

In the neighborhood of each ζ_i we can develop $f(z)$ in a Laurent series which has $\phi_i(z)$ for its principal part:

$$\phi_i(z) = \frac{c_{ip_i}}{(z - \zeta_i)^{p_i}} + \frac{c_{i(p_i-1)}}{(z - \zeta_i)^{p_i-1}} + \cdots + \frac{c_{i1}}{z - \zeta_i}.$$

If $f(z)$ has a pole of multiplicity p at $z = \infty$, then the principal part of the Laurent expansion of $f(z)$ at $z = \infty$ is

$$\phi(z) = c_1 z + c_2 z^2 + \cdots + c_p z^p.$$

The function

$$\psi(z) = f(z) - \phi(z) - \sum_{i=1}^{r} \phi_i(z)$$

is therefore devoid of poles in the extended complex plane and by Liouville's theorem must be a constant, say c_0. Thus

$$f(z) = c_0 + \phi(z) + \sum_{i=1}^{r} \phi_i(z),$$

which proves the theorem.

7.5 The Maximum Modulus Theorem

If $f(x)$ is a real continuous function defined on the closed bounded real interval $[a,b]$, we know there exists a point ξ in $[a,b]$ at which $f(x)$ assumes its maximum value. Frequently ξ will be an interior point. Now we also have the result (see Theorem 4 of Chapter 3 and Exercise 3.2) that a complex function $f(z)$ which is analytic and single-valued on a bounded perfect set E has a maximum modulus and actually attains this maximum. The remarkable theorem we wish to prove is that the maximum of $|f(z)|$ *must* occur on the *boundary* of E.

Theorem 9: (*Maximum Modulus*). Let $f(z)$ be single-valued and analytic in and on a closed smooth curve C. Then the maximum value of $|f(z)|$ is attained at a point on C.

Proof: Since C, together with its interior, forms a bounded perfect set, $|f(z)|$ *has* a maximum. Let ζ be any interior point of C. We shall show the existence of a z in a neighborhood of ζ with the property that $|f(z)| > |f(\zeta)|$.

Since $f(z)$ is analytic at $z = \zeta$, we may write

$$f(z) = c_0 + c_1(z - \zeta) + c_2(z - \zeta)^2 + \cdots , \qquad (7.9)$$

and the power series is valid in a neighborhood of ζ. Let Γ be a circle of radius $\delta > 0$ with center at $z = \zeta$ for which the above expression is valid, and such that Γ and its interior lie in the interior of C.

If $c_n = 0$, $n > 0$, then $f(z)$ is a constant and the theorem is trivial. Let us therefore suppose that m is the smallest positive integer with the property that $c_m \neq 0$. Then we may write

$$c_0 = |c_0|e^{i\theta}, \qquad c_m = |c_m|e^{i\phi},$$

where $|c_m| \neq 0$. Furthermore, if we set $z - \zeta = R\, e^{i\psi}$, where $0 < R < \delta$, then Equation 7.9 becomes

$$f(z) = |c_0|e^{i\theta} + |c_m|e^{i\phi}R^m e^{mi\psi} + \sum_{k=1}^{\infty} c_{m+k}R^{m+k}e^{i\psi(m+k)}. \qquad (7.10)$$

Choose a certain radius of Γ with the property that for all z along this radius we have

$$\arg (z - \zeta) = \frac{1}{m}(\theta - \phi).$$

If this is done, Equation 7.10 becomes

$$f(z) = [|c_0| + |c_m|R^m]e^{i\theta} + \sum_{k=1}^{\infty} c_{m+k}R^{m+k}e^{i\psi(m+k)}$$

for all z along this radius. Thus

$$|f(z)| \geq |c_0| + |c_m|R^m - \sum_{k=1}^{\infty} |c_{m+k}|R^{m+k}$$

$$= |c_0| + R^m[|c_m| - \sum_{k=1}^{\infty} |c_{m+k}|R^k].$$

Now choose $R > 0$ so small that

$$\sum_{k=1}^{\infty} |c_{m+k}|R^k < |c_m|.$$

Then
$$|f(z)| > |c_0| = |f(\zeta)|.$$

Another classic theorem in the elementary theory of functions of a complex variable is Rouché's theorem.

Theorem 10: *(Rouché).*   Let $f(z)$ and $g(z)$ be two functions, single-valued and analytic in an open set $\mathfrak{A}$.   Let C be a closed smooth curve which, together with its interior, lies in $\mathfrak{A}$.   Let $f(z)$ have no zeros on C and let $|g(z)| < |f(z)|$ on C.   Then the function $f(z) + g(z)$ has as many zeros in C as $f(z)$ has.

Proof: Let

$$\phi(z;t) = f(z) + tg(z), \qquad 0 \leq t \leq 1.$$

Certainly $\phi(z;t)$ is analytic in and on C.   We assert that $\phi(z;t)$ does not vanish on C.   Suppose it did.   We would then have

$$f(z) = -tg(z),$$

which implies that

$$|g(z)| \geq |tg(z)| = |f(z)|$$

for $0 \leq t \leq 1$.   But this contradicts the hypothesis that $|g(z)| < |f(z)|$.
By Equation 7.4

$$\frac{1}{2\pi i} \int_C \frac{f'(z) + tg'(z)}{f(z) + tg(z)} \, dz = Z(t), \qquad (7.11)$$

where $Z(t)$ is the number of zeros of $\phi(z;t)$ in C.   We shall show that $Z(t)$ is a continuous function of t in $[0,1]$.   If this be so, then, since $Z(t)$ can assume only integral values, $Z(t)$ must be a fixed integer. In particular, $Z(1) = Z(0)$, which implies that $\phi(z;1) = f(z) + g(z)$ has as many zeros in C as $\phi(z;0) = f(z) + 0 \cdot g(z) = f(z)$.

To prove the continuity of $Z(t)$ we write

$$Z(t + h) - Z(t) = \frac{1}{2\pi i} \int_C \left[\frac{\phi'(z;t + h)}{\phi(z;t + h)} - \frac{\phi'(z;t)}{\phi(z;t)} \right] dz$$

or, in expanded form,

$$|Z(t + h) - Z(t)| \leq \frac{|h|}{2\pi} \int_C \frac{|f(z)g'(z) - f'(z)g(z)|}{|f(z) + tg(z)|^2} \, |dz| + \eta,$$

where η is an infinitesimal as h approaches zero.

If two real functions $f(x)$ and $g(x)$ defined on $[a,b]$ coincide for some subinterval I of $[a,b]$, we can say nothing about the relative values* of $f(x)$ and $g(x)$ in the complement of I. For analytic functions the situation is essentially different. In this connection we have the following fundamental theorem.

Theorem 11. Let $f(z)$ be single-valued and analytic on an open set $\mathfrak{A}$. Let $f(z)$ vanish on a set of points in $\mathfrak{A}$ which has a limit point in $\mathfrak{A}$. Then $f(z)$ is identically zero in $\mathfrak{A}$.

Proof: Let α be the limit point of the set of points at which $f(z)$ vanishes. We may write

$$f(z) = c_0 + c_1(z - \alpha) + c_2(z - \alpha)^2 + \cdots,$$

and this series converges in a neighborhood of α. Since $f(z)$ is analytic, it is certainly continuous; and since $f(z)$ vanishes for values of z arbitrarily close to α, we infer $f(\alpha) = 0$ and hence $c_0 = 0$.

Since $f(z)$ is analytic, $f'(z)$ exists at $z = \alpha$. By definition of derivative, $f'(\alpha)$ is the limit of the quotient

$$\frac{f(z) - f(\alpha)}{z - \alpha} = c_1 + c_2(z - \alpha) + c_3(z - \alpha)^2 + \cdots$$

as z approaches α. But

$$\frac{f(z) - f(\alpha)}{z - \alpha} = \frac{f(z)}{z - \alpha}$$

vanishes for points arbitrarily close to α. Thus by the continuity of $f(z)$,

$$f'(\alpha) = \lim_{z \to \alpha} \frac{f(z)}{z - \alpha} = 0$$

and $f'(\alpha) = c_1 = 0$. A similar argument shows that all the c_n are zero and hence $f(z) \equiv 0$.

We have shown that $f(z) \equiv 0$ in a neighborhood of $z = \alpha$. If β is any point in $\mathfrak{A}$, then the Heine-Borel theorem and repeated applications of the above result show that $f(\beta) = 0$.

This theorem can be used, for example, to extend certain results, known to be true in the real domain, to the complex domain. For example, we know that $\sin z$ and $\cos z$ are entire functions, as is

$$f(z) = \sin^2 z + \cos^2 z - 1.$$

Now for z real (say on a segment of the real axis), $f(z) = 0$ By the previous theorem we infer $f(z) = 0$ for *all* z. Thus we have extended

---

* Except in certain special cases.

the well-known identity, $\sin^2 x + \cos^2 x = 1$ for real x, to the complex domain with a single stroke of the pen.

The above example is an illustration of the result known as "the principle of the permanence of functional equations." For suppose $f_i(z)$, $i = 1, 2, \cdots, n$ are n functions single-valued and analytic in some open region $\mathfrak{A}$. Let $P(\zeta_1, \zeta_2, \cdots, \zeta_n)$ be a polynomial in n variables. Then if

$$P(f_1, f_2, \cdots, f_n) \equiv 0 \qquad (7.12)$$

in z in some open or perfect subset of $\mathfrak{A}$ (or merely on a set of points having a limit point in $\mathfrak{A}$), then Theorem 11 implies that Equation 7.12 holds for all z in $\mathfrak{A}$.

The results of the previous theorems can be used to prove a certain topological property of analytic functions. This in turn leads to a short and elegant proof of the maximum modulus theorem (Theorem 9).

Theorem 12. Let $w = f(z)$ be a non-constant function single-valued and analytic in an open region $\mathfrak{A}$. Let α be a point in $\mathfrak{A}$. Then there exists an open neighborhood $\mathfrak{N}_\alpha$ of α in the z-plane lying entirely in $\mathfrak{A}$, such that the image of $\mathfrak{N}_\alpha$ contains an open neighborhood of $f(\alpha)$ in the w-plane.

Proof: The theorem is sometimes stated as "a non-constant analytic function maps open sets into open sets."

The values of z at which $f(z) = f(\alpha)$ cannot have α for a limit point. For if they did we would have $f(z) \equiv f(\alpha)$ by Theorem 11. But this contradicts the hypothesis that $f(z)$ is non-constant. Thus we choose a circle C of radius δ, with center at $z = \alpha$, which is interior to $\mathfrak{A}$ and also has the property that $f(z) \neq f(\alpha)$ for all $z \neq \alpha$ in or on C. The interior of C will be our neighborhood $\mathfrak{N}_\alpha$. Then the function $g(z) = f(z) - f(\alpha)$ is non-zero on C. Since $g(z)$ is continuous and C is perfect, $g(z)$ is bounded away from zero on C. Thus

$$\underset{C}{\text{g.l.b.}} \ |f(z) - f(\alpha)| = \epsilon > 0.$$

Now let $\varXi$ be any complex number such that $|\varXi - f(\alpha)| < \epsilon$. Then since

$$|f(z) - f(\alpha)| > |\varXi - f(\alpha)|, \qquad z \text{ on } C,$$

Rouché's theorem implies that

$$[f(z) - f(\alpha)] + [f(\alpha) - \varXi] = f(z) - \varXi$$

has as many zeros within C as $f(z) - f(\alpha)$ has. Since $f(z) - f(\alpha) = 0$ for $z = \alpha$, we infer that $f(z) - \varXi$ has at least one zero in C. Thus there exists a ζ in $\mathfrak{N}_\alpha$ (that is, $|\alpha - \zeta| < \delta$) such that $f(\zeta) = \varXi$.

Theorem 12 can be used to give a quick proof of the maximum modulus theorem. Under the hypothesis of Theorem 9, let us suppose that $|f(z)|$ attains its maximum at an interior point, say β, of C. Then the image of a neighborhood of β, say $\mathfrak{N}_\beta$, contains a neighborhood of $f(\beta)$ in the w-plane. Thus there exists a ζ in $\mathfrak{N}_\beta$ such that $|f(\zeta)| > |f(\beta)|$—a contradiction.

If we are given a function $w = f(z)$ defined on some region $\mathfrak{B}$, then it is frequently of interest to know under what conditions z is determined as a function of w, say $z = f^{-1}(w)$. This, of course, is a special case of the implicit function theorem.

Theorem 13. Let $w = f(z)$ be single-valued and analytic in an open region $\mathfrak{A}$. Let z_0 be a point in $\mathfrak{A}$ and let $f(z)$ be conformal at $z = z_0$. Then there exists a neighborhood $\mathfrak{N}(w_0)$ of $w_0 = f(z_0)$ in the w-plane, which is covered precisely once by the image of some neighborhood $\mathfrak{N}(z_0)$ of z_0 which is entirely contained in $\mathfrak{A}$.

Proof: We recall from Section 3.11 that $f(z)$ was said to be conformal at a point $z = z_0$ if $f'(z_0) \neq 0$. Since $f(z)$ is analytic at $z = z_0$, we may write

$$f(z) = c_0 + c_1(z - z_0) + c_2(z - z_0)^2 + \cdots,$$

which is valid in a neighborhood of z_0.

Since $f'(z)$ is continuous, there exists a neighborhood of z_0 for which $f'(z) \neq 0$. Now choose a neighborhood $\mathfrak{N}(z_0)$ of z_0 such that the above power series holds, such that $f'(z) \neq 0$ in $\mathfrak{N}(z_0)$, and such that $f(z) \neq f(z_0)$ for all $z \neq z_0$ in $\mathfrak{N}(z_0)$. We also see that z_0 is a *simple* zero of $f(z) - c_0$ in $\mathfrak{N}(z_0)$, since $f'(z_0) = c_1 \neq 0$. By Theorem 12 there exists a neighborhood $\mathfrak{N}(w_0)$ of $f(z_0)$ in the w-plane contained in the image of $\mathfrak{N}(z_0)$. Furthermore, $\mathfrak{N}(w_0)$ has the property that if w_1 is any complex number in $\mathfrak{N}(w_0)$, then there exists a z_1 in $\mathfrak{N}(z_0)$ such that $f(z_1) = w_1$.

Since $f(z) - w_0$ has a simple zero at z_0, it follows from Rouché's theorem (see the end of the proof of Theorem 12) that $f(z) - w_1$ has a *simple* zero in $\mathfrak{N}(z_0)$. Thus there exists precisely *one* z_1 in $\mathfrak{N}(z_0)$ with the property that $f(z_1) = w_1$.

The above analysis shows the existence of a function $z = f^{-1}(w)$ That is defined and single-valued in the neighborhood $\mathfrak{N}(w_0)$ of w_0, and has the further property that

$$f(z) = f(f^{-1}(w)) = w \tag{7.13}$$

for z in the preimage of $\mathfrak{N}(w_0)$.

We also assert that $z = f^{-1}(w)$ is an analytic function of w in a neighborhood of w_0. For, by definition of derivative (if it exists),

$$\frac{d}{dw} f^{-1}(w_1) = \lim_{w \to w_1} \frac{f^{-1}(w_1) - f^{-1}(w)}{w_1 - w} = \lim_{w \to w_1} \frac{z_1 - z}{f(z_1) - f(z)}$$

$$= \lim_{w \to w_1} \left[\frac{f(z_1) - f(z)}{z_1 - z} \right]^{-1}. \tag{7.14}$$

Now

$$\lim_{w \to w_1} z = z_1.$$

Thus

$$f'(z_1) = \lim_{z \to z_1} \frac{f(z_1) - f(z)}{z_1 - z} = \lim_{w \to w_1} \frac{f(z_1) - f(z)}{z_1 - z}.$$

Since $f'(z_1) \neq 0$ for z_1 in $\Re(z_0)$,

$$\lim_{w \to w_1} \left[\frac{f(z_1) - f(z)}{z_1 - z} \right]^{-1} = \left[\lim_{w \to w_1} \frac{f(z_1) - f(z)}{z_1 - z} \right]^{-1} = \frac{1}{f'(z_1)},$$

and Equation 7.14 becomes

$$\frac{d}{dw} f^{-1}(w_1) = \frac{1}{\dfrac{d}{dz} f(z_1)} = \frac{1}{\dfrac{d}{dz} f(f^{-1}(w_1))}. \tag{7.15}$$

7.6 Analytic Continuation

The power series

$$g(z) = 1 + z + z^2 + \cdots + z^n + \cdots$$

converges in the unit circle $\mathfrak{C} : \{|z| < 1\}$ and represents an analytic function. The function $h(z) = \dfrac{1}{1 - z}$ is single-valued and analytic for all $z \neq 1$ and for z in $\mathfrak{C}$ is identical with $g(z)$. Thus there seems to be intrinsic connection between $g(z)$ and $h(z)$. In fact, $h(z)$ is called an *analytic continuation* of $g(z)$. It is the purpose of the present section to investigate such phenomena. We shall begin by giving a precise definition of the term "analytic continuation."

A. Let $f_1(z)$ be single-valued and analytic in and on some closed smooth curve C_1. Let us suppose that the parametric equations of C_1 are

$$C_1 : \begin{cases} x = \phi_1(t) \\ y = \psi_1(t) \end{cases} \quad \alpha_1 \leq t \leq \beta_1.$$

Let $f_2(z)$ be another function, single-valued and analytic in and on a closed smooth curve C_2 with parametric equations

$$C_2: \begin{cases} x = \phi_2(t) \\ y = \psi_2(t) \end{cases} \quad \alpha_2 \leqq t \leqq \beta_2.$$

Let $[a_1, b_1]$ be a subinterval of $[\alpha_1, \beta_1]$ which gives rise to the smooth curve Γ_1 (a part of C_1), and let $[a_2, b_2]$ be a subinterval of $[\alpha_2, \beta_2]$ which gives rise to the smooth curve Γ_2 (a part of C_2). Furthermore, we shall suppose that Γ_1 and Γ_2 coincide (call Γ their common value) but that otherwise the curve C_1 and its interior are disjoint from C_2 and its interior (see Fig. 7.1). Then

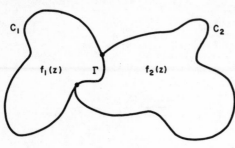

if $f_1(z) = f_2(z)$ for all z on Γ, we shall call $f_2(z)$ an *analytic continuation* of $f_1(z)$, and conversely $f_1(z)$ will be called an analytic continuation of $f_2(z)$. Thus if we let $\mathfrak{E}$ denote the region consisting of C_1 and C_2 and their interiors, we have a function, say $F(z)$ which is single-

Figure 7.1

valued and analytic in $\mathfrak{E}$ (and on the boundary of $\mathfrak{E}$). Explicitly,

$$F(z) = f_1(z) \quad \text{for } z \text{ in or on } C_1,$$

$$F(z) = f_2(z) \quad \text{for } z \text{ in or on } C_2.$$

It is an immediate consequence of Theorem 11 that if an analytic continuation exists, it is unique. For suppose $f_3(z)$ were a function, single-valued and analytic in and on C_2, and suppose furthermore that it equalled $f_1(z)$ for z on Γ. Then, since $f_1(z) = f_2(z)$ on Γ, $G(z) = f_3(z) - f_2(z)$ vanishes on Γ and Theorem 11 implies that $G(z)$ is identically zero throughout C_2 and on its boundary. Thus $f_2(z) \equiv f_3(z)$ in and on C_2 and $f_2(z)$ is unique.

B. We can use the theory of analytic continuation to extend analytic functions beyond their given region of definition. Suppose, for example, it is known that $f(z)$ is analytic at a point $z = \alpha$. Then there exists a power series

$$f(z) = c_0 + c_1(z - \alpha) + c_2(z - \alpha)^2 + \cdots \tag{7.16}$$

that represents this analytic function in a neighborhood of $z = \alpha$. Let $r > 0$ be the radius of convergence of this power series. Thus Equation 7.16 represents an analytic function in the circle $\mathfrak{C}: \{|z - \alpha| < r\}$. Now choose any point β in $\mathfrak{C}$ distinct from α. Since

$f(z)$ is analytic at $z = \beta$, we may develop $f(z)$ in a power series which converges in some circle, say $\mathfrak{D}:\{|z - \beta| < \rho\}$. This circle certainly has points in common with $\mathfrak{C}$. Now it may be that $\mathfrak{D}$ contains points *not* in $\mathfrak{C}$ (see Fig. 7.2). Then we have an analytic continuation of $f(z)$ to the larger region consisting of the union* of $\mathfrak{C}$ and $\mathfrak{D}$. We give a non-trivial example to illustrate this situation.

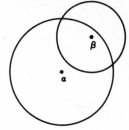

Consider the power series

$$f(z) = \sum_{n=0}^{\infty} \frac{\alpha^{n+1} - \beta^{n+1}}{(\alpha\beta)^{n+1}} z^n, \qquad (7.17)$$

where α and β are non-zero complex numbers. For concreteness we shall assume that

$$|\beta| > |\alpha| > 0. \qquad (7.18)$$

Figure 7.2

If we call c_n the coefficient of z^n in Equation 7.17, we may write it as

$$c_n = \alpha^{-(n+1)}\left[\left(\frac{\alpha}{\beta}\right)^{n+1} - 1\right].$$

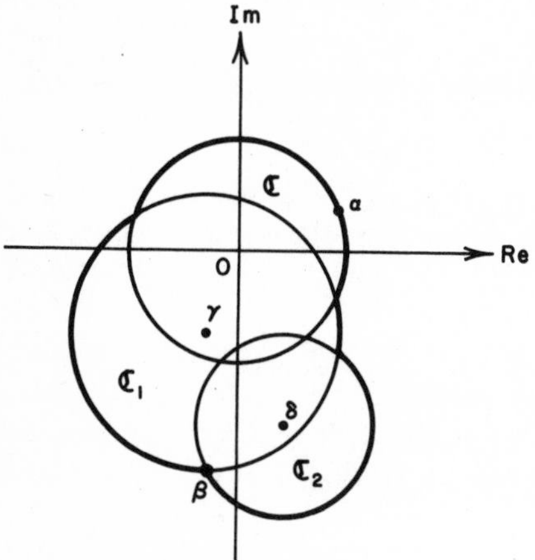

In this form it is not difficult to see that

$$L = \varlimsup_{n \to \infty} \sqrt[n]{|c_n|} = \frac{1}{|\alpha|}$$

and hence that $L^{-1} = |\alpha| > 0$ is the radius of convergence of the power series of Equation 7.17. Thus $f(z)$ represents a function analytic in $\mathfrak{C}:\{|z| < |\alpha|\}$.

Now we shall see if this function admits an analytic continuation. Let us choose a point γ in $\mathfrak{C}$ (see Fig. 7.3) with the property that

$$|\gamma - \alpha| > |\gamma - \beta| > 0. \quad (7.19)$$

Figure 7.3

Then we may write

$$f_1(z) = \sum_{n=0}^{\infty} d_n(z - \gamma)^n, \qquad (7.20)$$

---

* If $\mathfrak{B}_1$ and $\mathfrak{B}_2$ are any two point sets, then by the *union* of $\mathfrak{B}_1$ and $\mathfrak{B}_2$ we mean the set of points $\mathfrak{B}$ contained in $\mathfrak{B}_1$ and $\mathfrak{B}_2$. This is usually written as $\mathfrak{B} = \mathfrak{B}_1 \cup \mathfrak{B}_2$.

which is a convergent power series in some neighborhood of γ. If the region of convergence of $f_1(z)$ reaches outside the circle $|z| = |\alpha|$ we shall have an analytic continuation of $f(z)$ outside $\mathfrak{C}$. Since Equation 7.17 holds at $z = \gamma$,

$$d_k = \frac{f_1^{(k)}(\gamma)}{k!} = \frac{f^{(k)}(\gamma)}{k!}.$$

From Equation 7.17

$$f^{(k)}(\gamma) = k! \sum_{n=k}^{\infty} \binom{n}{k} \left[\frac{\alpha^{n+1} - \beta^{n+1}}{(\alpha\beta)^{n+1}}\right] \gamma^{n-k}.$$

This can be written in closed form. For, by the binomial theorem,

$$\frac{1}{(\beta - \gamma)^{k+1}} = \frac{1}{\beta^{k+1}} \sum_{n=k}^{\infty} \binom{n}{k} \left(\frac{\gamma}{\beta}\right)^{n-k},$$

$$\frac{1}{(\alpha - \gamma)^{k+1}} = \frac{1}{\alpha^{k+1}} \sum_{n=k}^{\infty} \binom{n}{k} \left(\frac{\gamma}{\alpha}\right)^{n-k},$$

and

$$\frac{1}{(\beta - \gamma)^{k+1}} - \frac{1}{(\alpha - \gamma)^{k+1}} = \sum_{n=k}^{\infty} \binom{n}{k} \left[\frac{1}{\beta^{n+1}} - \frac{1}{\alpha^{n+1}}\right] \gamma^{n-k}$$

$$= \frac{f^{(k)}(\gamma)}{k!} = d_k.$$

Hence

$$f_1(z) = \sum_{n=0}^{\infty} \frac{(\alpha - \gamma)^{n+1} - (\beta - \gamma)^{n+1}}{(\alpha - \gamma)^{n+1}(\beta - \gamma)^{n+1}} (z - \gamma)^n. \qquad (7.21)$$

If we write d_n in the form

$$d_n = (\beta - \gamma)^{-(n+1)} \left[1 - \left(\frac{\beta - \gamma}{\alpha - \gamma}\right)^{n+1}\right],$$

it is easy to see in the light of Equation 7.19 that

$$L_1 = \varlimsup_{n \to \infty} \sqrt[n]{|d_n|} = \frac{1}{|\beta - \gamma|}$$

and hence the radius of convergence of $f_1(z)$ is $L_1^{-1} = |\beta - \gamma|$. Thus $f_1(z)$ represents a function analytic in $\mathfrak{C}_1 : \{|z - \gamma| < |\beta - \gamma|\}$. By our choice of values, Equations 7.18 and 7.19, we see that $\mathfrak{C}_1$ covers territory outside of $\mathfrak{C}$.

The process described above yields a function analytic in the region $\mathfrak{C} \cup \mathfrak{C}_1$ which is larger than either $\mathfrak{C}$ or $\mathfrak{C}_1$. We can continue the process. If δ is any point in $\mathfrak{C} \cup \mathfrak{C}_1$, we can expand $f(z)$ in a power series about this point. Either the new circle C_2, with center at δ in which the power series converges, will have its interior $\mathfrak{C}_2$ contained in $\mathfrak{C} \cup \mathfrak{C}_1$ or it may extend beyond. In the latter case we shall obtain a further analytic continuation. This state of affairs is illustrated in Fig. 7.3.

C. Suppose

$$f(z) = c_0 + c_1(z - \alpha) + c_2(z - \alpha)^2 + \cdots$$

is analytic at $z = \alpha$ and R is its radius of convergence. Then $f(z)$ is analytic for all z satisfying the inequality $|z - \alpha| < R$. We assert that $f(z)$ must have at least one singular point *on* the circle $C:\{|z - \alpha| = R\}$. For if $f(z)$ were analytic at every point of C, then the radius of convergence of $f(z)$ would exceed R (see Exercise 3.10), which contradicts the definition of circle of convergence.

D. Let Γ be a smooth curve with initial point α and terminal point β. Let $f(z)$ be a function analytic at $z = \alpha$. We wish to consider the problem of analytically continuing $f(z)$ along Γ to β. Since $f(z)$ is analytic at α, there exists a circle C_1 with center at $z = \alpha$ such that $f(z)$ is analytic in C_1. Now it may be that β is interior to C_1. Then if Γ is also interior to C_1, we will have achieved our continuation. Suppose this is not the case. Let z_1 be the first point* of Γ which belongs to C_1. Choose a point t' with the property that $t_1 > t' > \alpha$ and let z' be the corresponding point of Γ (of necessity in C_1). Then we can expand $f(z)$ about the point z' in a convergent power series. Let C_2 be the circle of convergence of this power series. Then it may be that β lies in C_2 and Γ in the interiors of C_1 and C_2. In this case we have the desired result. If not, we continue the process. Two cases arise:

(i) After a finite number (say n) of such analytic continuations we may reach β. That is, β is interior to C_n and Γ is in the union of the interiors of the circles $C_1, C_2, \cdots, C_n$. In this case we say $f(z)$ can be *continued analytically* along Γ to β and we shall call β a *regular point* of $f(z)$ relative to Γ or relative to the analytic continuation along Γ.

(ii) There may exist a point γ on Γ distinct from α (but which may coincide with β) with the property that $f(z)$ can be continued analytically into every neighborhood of γ but not to γ itself. In this case we call γ a *singular point* of $f(z)$ relative to Γ or relative to the analytic continuation along Γ.

E. Let $f(z)$ be analytic at $z = \alpha$. Then $f(z)$ can be expanded in a power series about $z = \alpha$. Let us denote this power series by the

---

* By this we mean: Let t be the parameter used in describing Γ, say $a \leqq t \leqq b$. Let $t_1 > a$ be the smallest value of t with the property that $z_1 = z(t_1) = x(t_1) + iy(t_1)$ is a point of C_1. Then we shall call z_1 the first point of Γ which belongs to C_1.

symbol $E(z;\alpha)$, and its circle of convergence by $\mathfrak{C}$. We shall call $E(z;\alpha)$ an *analytic element*. About every point β in $\mathfrak{C}$ we can develop $f(z)$ in powers of $z - \beta$ to obtain a new analytic element $E(z;\beta)$. Each analytic element converges in the interior $\mathfrak{C}_\beta$ of some circle of positive radius. Now it may be that the union $\mathfrak{D}$ of the $\mathfrak{C}_\beta$ contains points of the z-plane not in $\mathfrak{C}$. If this be the case, we have effected an analytic continuation of $f(z)$. If $\mathfrak{D}$ coincides with $\mathfrak{C}$, then we shall call the boundary of $\mathfrak{C}$ the *natural boundary* of $f(z)$. For example, the unit circle $|z| = 1$ is the natural boundary for

$$f(z) = \sum_{n=1}^{\infty} z^{n!}.$$

If there exist points of $\mathfrak{D}$ not in $\mathfrak{C}$ we can use these points to construct

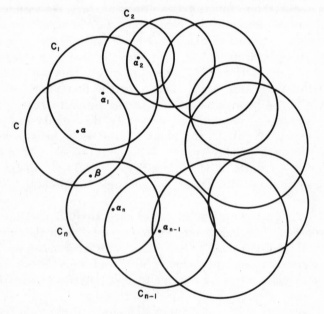

Figure 7.4

additional analytic elements. The totality of analytic elements obtained in this fashion is called a *monogenic analytic function*.

A monogenic analytic function may be multi-valued. For example, consider Fig. 7.4. Let $f(z)$ be analytic at $z = \alpha$ and let C be its circle of convergence. Suppose it is possible to analytically continue $f(z)$ as shown in the diagram. The point β is now in both C and C_n. However, the elements $E(z;\alpha)$ and $E(z;\alpha_n)$ may not yield the same value at $z = \beta$. Thus a Riemann surface is defined on which the monogenic analytic function is single-valued. As a concrete illustration let us consider the familiar function $f(z) = \sqrt{z}$. We shall make the multi-valued function definite by requiring that $f(z) = +\sqrt{x}$ for

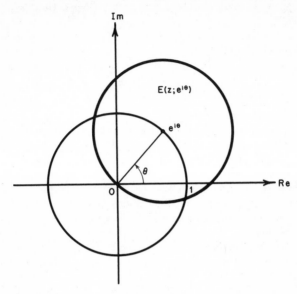

Figure 7.5

$z = x + i0 > 0$. Then, for instance, at every point $z = e^{i\theta}$ on the unit circle (see Fig. 7.5) we may construct an analytic element $E(z;e^{i\theta})$,

$$E(z;e^{i\theta}) = e^{i\theta/2} \sum_{n=0}^{\infty} \frac{(-1)^{n-1}(2n)!}{2^{2n}(n!)^2(2n-1)} e^{-ni\theta}(z - e^{i\theta})^n.$$

It is easy to see, for example, that

$$E(z;e^{i0}) = -E(z;e^{i2\pi}).$$

EXERCISES

7.1. In the general residue theorem (Theorem 1) let $F(z) = \log z$ and assume that the origin is neither a pole nor a zero of $f(z)$. Show that

$$\int_0^{2\pi} \log |f(R\,e^{i\theta})|\,d\theta = 2\pi \log \left| f(0)R^{s-r}\frac{\zeta_1\zeta_2\cdots\zeta_r}{z_1z_2\cdots z_s} \right|.$$

This is *Jensen's formula*.

7.2. Let

$$f(z) = \sum_{n=0}^{\infty} c_n z^n$$

be an integral function such that for every $R > 0$ the inequality $|f(z)| \leqq e^R$ is valid whenever $|z| \leqq R$. Prove that $|c_n| \leqq e^n n^{-n}$ for all $n > 0$.

7.3. Let $R(z)$ be a rational function of degree $r > 0$. Prove that $R(z)$ assumes every complex value exactly r times in the extended plane.

7.4. Verify by direct calculation that the sum of the residues of

$$f(z) = \frac{z + 3i}{z(z^2 + 1)}$$

in the extended plane is zero.

7.5. Let $f(z)$ be an entire function that is not a polynomial. Then if m is any positive integer and M_1 and M_2 are any positive constants, prove that there exists a point ζ such that $|\zeta| > M_1$ and $|f(\zeta)| > M_2 |\zeta|^m$.

7.6. (i) Prove the *minimum modulus theorem*: Let $f(z)$ be single-valued and analytic in and on a closed smooth curve C. Let $f(z) \neq 0$ in the interior of C. Then the minimum value of $|f(z)|$ is assumed at a point on C.

(ii) Prove the maximum modulus and minimum modulus theorems, assuming the analyticity of $f(z)$ *in* C but only the continuity of $f(z)$ *on* C.

7.7. Let $f(z)$ be an integral function and let $f'(z) \neq 0$ on the unit circle. Let n be an integer. Prove that for $|n|$ sufficiently large the function $n[f(z + 1/n) - f(z)]$ has the same number of zeros as $f'(z)$ within the unit circle.

7.8. Using Rouché's theorem prove that a polynomial of degree n has precisely n roots.

7.9. Let $f(z)$ be analytic and single-valued in and on the square $\Re: \{-a \leqq x \leqq a, \; -a \leqq y \leqq a\}$. If $|f(z)| \leqq |xy|$ on the boundary of $\Re$, prove that $|f'(0)| < \frac{1}{2}a$.

7.10. Let $f(z)$ be single-valued and analytic in the unit circle $|z| < 1$. If $|f(z)| \leqq 1$ and $f(0) = 0$, prove that $|f(z)| \leqq |z|$ and $|f'(0)| \leqq 1$. Show that equality holds only if $f(z) = z\,e^{i\theta}$.

7.11. Let $f(z)$ be analytic and single-valued in a strip containing the positive real axis. If $f(z)$ is real for all z in the real interval $0 < z < 1$, show that $f(z)$ is real valued at every point of the positive real axis.

7.12. Let Γ be a smooth curve with initial point α and terminal point β. Let $f(z)$ be analytic at $z = \alpha$ and suppose that β is a regular point of $f(z)$ relative to the analytic continuation along Γ. Show that the value of $f(z)$ at β is independent of the sequence of analytic elements used to go from α to β along Γ.

7.13. Let C be a simple closed curve (not necessarily rectifiable). Construct a function analytic in the interior of C which has C for its natural boundary.

CHAPTER 8

Conformal Mapping

8.1 Introduction

In Section 3.2 we mentioned that a function f of a complex variable z could be considered as a *mapping* of the domain of f on a region of the image plane called the range. Sections 3.11 and 3.12 were devoted to a more detailed discussion of the properties of such transformations. In particular, we called a mapping $w = f(z)$ *conformal* at a point $z = z_0$ in the domain of f if $f'(z_0) \neq 0$. The utility of conformal mapping stems from the invariance of solutions of Laplace's equation under such transformations. It is our intention in this chapter to study analytic functions from the viewpoint of mappings (or transformations) of part of the z-plane into the w-plane.

The examples of Section 3.11 seemed to indicate that if two curves in the z-plane intersected at a given angle, then their images, under a conformal transformation, would also intersect at the same angle. Our first result will be to prove this premise. While this property is important—leading, for example, to the fact that orthogonal coordinate systems are transformed into orthogonal coordinate systems—it does not play a forward role in the theory. That is, we shall be interested in how certain conformal maps transform certain point sets in the z-plane and how, given two point sets, we can find a conformal map which transforms one into the other. The fact that angles are preserved is of secondary importance in such problems.

After proving the preservation of angles under conformal maps we shall give various examples. For purposes of illustration we shall generally consider the images of circles and straight lines, and regions bounded by combinations of such curves. Of course, the reader may readily apply our methods to more complicated configurations. When mapping regions it may happen that the mapping function $f(z)$ has a zero derivative for some point of the domain, that is, $f(z)$ ceases to be conformal. Nevertheless, it is still customary even in such cases to speak of the "conformal map of the domain." No confusion arises from such a convention.

We have used the term *transformation* as a synonym for *mapping* or *function*. In line with this point of view it is sometimes convenient to represent a function $w = f(z)$ by the notation (common in various other branches of mathematics),

$$w = \mathbf{T}z. \tag{8.1}$$

This is to be thought of as a transformation $\mathbf{T}$ operating on z and yielding w. If $\zeta = g(w)$ is an analytic function of w, then if we write

$$\zeta = \mathbf{S}w,$$

the function of a function rule $\zeta = g(f(z))$ may be expressed in symbolic form by the *composition* $\mathbf{ST}$ of the transformations $\mathbf{S}$ and $\mathbf{T}$, viz.,

$$\zeta = \mathbf{ST}z. \tag{8.2}$$

This is to be thought of as $\mathbf{T}$ operating on z and the result transformed according to the rule of $\mathbf{S}$. The notations of Equations 8.1 and 8.2 are sometimes convenient, and we shall use them in certain portions of our theory.

8.2 The Fundamental Property

We mentioned in Section 3.11 that a conformal transformation preserved angles. Let us verify this contention in a more general

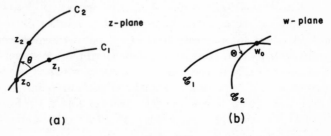

Figure 8.1

setting. Let C_1 and C_2 be two smooth curves which intersect at the point $z = z_0$ in the z-plane at the angle θ (see Fig. 8.1a). Let $z_1 \neq z_0$ be a point on C_1 and $z_2 \neq z_0$ a point on C_2. Then we may write

$$z_1 - z_0 = \delta_1 e^{i\theta_1}$$

$$z_2 - z_0 = \delta_2 e^{i\theta_2}.$$

Without loss of generality, we assume $\delta_1 = \delta_2$ (say, $= \delta$). Then

$$\frac{z_2 - z_0}{z_1 - z_0} = e^{i(\theta_2 - \theta_1)}$$

and

$$\lim_{\delta \to 0} \arg \frac{z_2 - z_0}{z_1 - z_0} = \lim_{\delta \to 0} (\theta_2 - \theta_1) = \theta.$$

Now let $w = f(z)$ be a function single-valued and analytic at $z = z_0$. We may write

$$f(z) = a_0 + a_n(z - z_0)^n + a_{n+1}(z - z_0)^{n+1} + \cdots, \qquad a_n \neq 0,$$

where $n \geq 1$ and this power series converges in a neighborhood of $z = z_0$. Under this transformation let $w_0 = f(z_0)$ and let C_1 be mapped into $\mathscr{C}_1$, C_2 into $\mathscr{C}_2$. Then the angle between $\mathscr{C}_1$ and $\mathscr{C}_2$ is

$$\Theta = \lim_{\delta \to 0} \arg \frac{w_2 - w_0}{w_1 - w_0}, \tag{8.3}$$

where $w_1 = f(z_1)$ and $w_2 = f(z_2)$.

Now

$$\frac{w_1 - w_0}{(z_1 - z_0)^n} = a_n + a_{n+1}(z_1 - z_0) + \cdots$$

$$\frac{w_2 - w_0}{(z_2 - z_0)^n} = a_n + a_{n+1}(z_2 - z_0) + \cdots,$$

and Equation 8.3 may be written

$$\Theta = \lim_{\delta \to 0} \arg \left[\frac{\dfrac{w_2 - w_0}{(z_2 - z_0)^n}}{\dfrac{w_1 - w_0}{(z_1 - z_0)^n}} \frac{(z_2 - z_0)^n}{(z_1 - z_0)^n} \right]$$

$$\tag{8.4}$$

$$= \lim_{\delta \to 0} \arg \left(\frac{z_2 - z_0}{z_1 - z_0} \right)^n = n \lim_{\delta \to 0} \arg \left(\frac{z_2 - z_0}{z_1 - z_0} \right) = n\theta.$$

Thus the angle θ is magnified n times. If, in particular $f'(z_0) \neq 0$, then $n = 1$,

$$f(z) = a_0 + a_1(z - z_0) + a_2(z - z_0)^2 + \cdots, \qquad a_1 \neq 0$$

and

$$\Theta = \theta. \tag{8.5}$$

In this case we say the mapping is *conformal*. Note that not only the *magnitude*, but the *sense* of the angle as well is preserved. If $f'(z_0) = 0$, we shall call z_0 a *critical point* of the transformation $w = f(z)$.

As a corollary we remark that if $f(z)$ is conformal at $z = z_0$, then the inverse function $z = f^{-1}(w)$ exists and is single-valued and analytic at w_0 (see Theorem 13 of Chapter 7).

8.3 Some Simple Examples

A. Perhaps the simplest transformation after the *identity transformation* $w = z$ is the general *translation*

$$w = z + \alpha, \tag{8.6}$$

where α is an arbitrary complex number. Clearly this mapping is conformal and one to one for all z, since

$$\frac{dw}{dz} = 1 \neq 0.$$

The identity transformation corresponds to $\alpha = 0$.

In this trivial example it is clear that every point z in the z-plane is translated an amount $|\alpha|$ in the direction $\arg \alpha$. Straight lines are mapped into parallel straight lines. This is clear geometrically. However, if we wish to be analytical, we need only write

$$\alpha = \alpha_1 + i\alpha_2.$$

Then if

$$y = ax + b \qquad a, b \text{ real}$$

is a straight line in the z-plane, its image under the conformal mapping of Equation 8.6 is

$$(v - \alpha_2) = a(u - \alpha_1) + b$$

or

$$v = au + (b + \alpha_2 - a\alpha_1). \tag{8.7}$$

If C is a circle with center at $z = z_0$ and radius r, then its image in the w-plane is a circle with center at $w = \alpha + z_0$ and with the same radius r. Analytically, we may write C as

$$|z - z_0| = r.$$

Then under the transformation of Equation 8.6

$$|w - \alpha - z_0| = r \tag{8.8}$$

is the image of C.

B. Another trivial example of a conformal map is the *rotation* $w = \lambda z$, where λ is a complex number of unit modulus. Let us consider the slightly more general transformation

$$w = \beta z, \tag{8.9}$$

where β is any complex number unequal to zero.   Since

$$\frac{dw}{dz} = \beta \neq 0,$$

the mapping is conformal for all z.

If we write $\beta = |\beta|e^{i\theta}$, then it is clear that every point z in the z-plane is transformed in a one to one fashion into a new point w whose magnitude is $|\beta|$ times $|z|$ and whose argument has been increased by the angle θ.   We sometimes refer to Equation 8.9 as a *rotation* (by the angle θ) and a *stretching* or *contraction* (depending on whether $|\beta| > 1$ or $|\beta| < 1$ respectively).   If $|\beta| = 1$ we have pure rotation as previously mentioned.

Since $\beta \neq 0$, we may write Equation 8.9 as

$$x + iy = z = \frac{\bar{\beta}}{|\beta|^2}\, w = \frac{(\beta_1 - i\beta_2)}{|\beta|^2}\,(u + iv), \qquad (8.10)$$

where $\beta = \beta_1 + i\beta_2$ and $|\beta| \neq 0$.   If we use the real and imaginary parts of Equation 8.10, it is easy to see that a straight line

$$Ax + By + C = 0$$

in the z-plane goes over into the rotated straight line

$$(A\beta_1 - B\beta_2)u + (A\beta_2 + B\beta_1)v + C|\beta|^2 = 0. \qquad (8.11)$$

The circle $C:\{|z - z_0| = r\}$, with center at $z = z_0$ and radius r, becomes

$$\left| \frac{w}{\beta} - z_0 \right| = r$$

or

$$|w - \beta z_0| = |\beta|r$$

under the transformation of Equation 8.9.   That is, the image of C is a circle with center at βz_0 and radius $|\beta|r$.

C. If we write Equation 8.6 as

$$w = \mathbf{T}z$$

and Equation 8.9 as

$$w = \mathbf{S}z,$$

then the transformation **L**,

$$\mathbf{L} = \mathbf{TS}, \qquad (8.12)$$

is the most general *linear* transformation, since

$$\mathbf{L}z = \mathbf{TS}z = \mathbf{T}(\mathbf{S}z) = \mathbf{T}(\beta z) = \beta z + \alpha, \qquad (8.13)$$

where α and β are arbitrary complex numbers ($\beta \neq 0$).   Of course, **ST** is also a linear transformation since $\mathbf{ST}z = \mathbf{S}(z + \alpha) = \beta z + \beta\alpha$.

D. A less transparent example is

$$w = \log z.$$

We shall make this multi-valued function definite by taking the principal

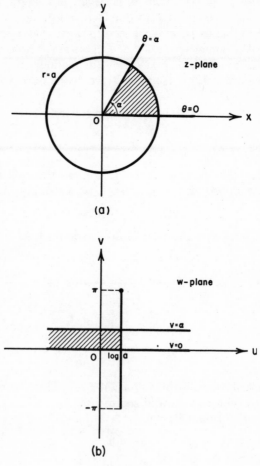

(a)

(b)

Figure 8.2

branch $-\pi < \arg z \leqq \pi$.   Since $dw/dz = 1/z$, the mapping is conformal except at $z = 0$.   If we write z in polar form as

$$z = r\, e^{i\theta},$$

then

$$w = u + iv = \log r + i\theta.$$

We see that if $\theta = 0$ the positive real axis is mapped into the u-axis. A straight line

$$\theta = \alpha, \qquad -\pi < \theta \leq \pi$$

in the z-plane is mapped into the straight line

$$v = \alpha$$

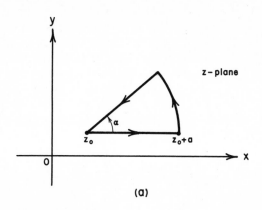

(a)

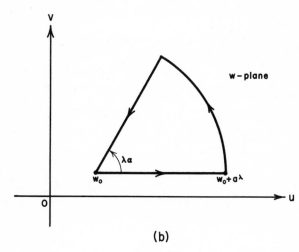

(b)

Figure 8.3

in the w-plane.   A circle with center at the origin and radius a,

$$r = a > 0,$$

is mapped onto the line segment

$$\log a + i\theta, \qquad -\pi < \theta \leq \pi$$

in the w-plane.

These results are illustrated in Fig. 8.2. It is easy to see that the shaded sector in the z-plane is mapped onto the shaded region of the w-plane.

E. Consider

$$w = w_0 + (z - z_0)^\lambda, \qquad (8.14)$$

where λ is a positive real number (but not necessarily an integer). This function has a branch point at $z = z_0$ (if λ is not an integer) and hence will be multi-valued. We make its value definite by requiring that if $z - z_0$ is real and positive, then $(z - z_0)^\lambda$ is real and positive. If we write

$$z - z_0 = r\,e^{i\theta}, \qquad w - w_0 = R\,e^{i\Theta},$$

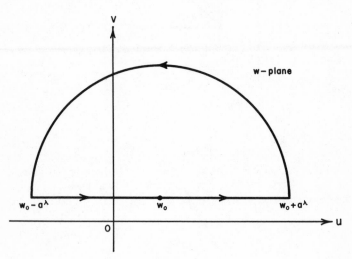

Figure 8.4

then

$$R = r^\lambda$$

and

$$\Theta = \lambda\theta + 2n\pi,$$

where n is an integer. If $\theta = 0$, then $\Theta = 2n\pi$ and horizontal lines are mapped onto horizontal lines. The ray $\theta = \alpha$ is mapped onto the ray $\Theta = \lambda\alpha + 2n\pi$, and the circle $r = a$ onto the circle $R = a^\lambda$. These results appear in Fig. 8.3, where the sector in the z-plane is mapped onto the sector of the w-plane. As a corollary, if we choose $\alpha = \pi/\lambda$, then the sector of Fig. 8.3a is mapped onto the semicircle of Fig. 8.4.

Sometimes it will be convenient to write

$$w = w_0 + (z_0 - z)^\lambda$$

in place of Equation 8.14 (notice that we have reversed z and z_0). Then

$$w - w_0 = (z - z_0)e^{\lambda\pi i(1+2n)}$$

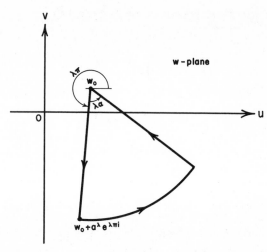

Figure 8.5

and the sector of Fig. 8.3a is mapped onto the sector of Fig. 8.5, where we have chosen the sheet of $(z - z_0)e^{\lambda\pi i(1+2n)}$ corresponding to $n = 0$.

8.4 The Inverse Transformation

If we write

$$w = \frac{1}{z},$$

then the transformation is conformal for all $z \neq 0$, since $dw/dz = -z^{-2}$. Every point in the plane except $z = 0$ is transformed in a one to one fashion into the w-plane (with the exception of $w = 0$). In the extended plane there are no exceptions. If $z \neq 0$, then its image w has magnitude equal to $1/|z|$ and argument, $\arg w = -\arg z$.

Let us examine what happens to straight lines and circles under this conformal mapping. In particular, consider first the line

$$y = ax + b. \tag{8.15}$$

One way to determine the map is to use the straightforward arithmetic of Section 3.11. Another useful device, especially when we are considering straight lines and circles, is to transform to polar form. This we did in the previous section. For our present problem we shall use the following approach.

Since

$$x = \text{Re}\,[z] = \frac{z + \bar{z}}{2}, \qquad y = \text{Im}\,[z] = \frac{z - \bar{z}}{2i}, \qquad (8.16)$$

we may write Equation 8.15 in terms of z and $\bar{z}$ as

$$z - \bar{z} = ai(z + \bar{z}) + 2bi$$

or

$$z(1 - ia) - \overline{z(1 - ia)} = 2bi.$$

By making the transformation $w = 1/z$ in the above equation, we obtain

$$\bar{w}(1 - ia) - w(1 + ia) = 2ibw\bar{w}. \qquad (8.17)$$

If we write w as

$$w = u + iv,$$

Equation 8.17 becomes

$$b(u^2 + v^2) + v + au = 0. \qquad (8.18)$$

If $b \neq 0$, that is, if $y = ax + b$ does not pass through the critical point $z = 0$, then Equation 8.18 represents a circle of radius $(1/2b)\sqrt{1 + a^2}$ with center at $(-a/2b,\ -1/2b)$. If $b = 0$, then Equation 8.18 is a straight line

$$v + au = 0, \qquad (8.19)$$

where the critical point $z = 0$ corresponds to the point at infinity in the w-plane. Note that the straight line of Equation 8.19 also passes through the origin of the w-plane.

Consider now a circle

$$x^2 + y^2 + ax + by + c = 0 \qquad (8.20)$$

in the z-plane. By using the substitutions of Equation 8.16 in Equation 8.20 and simplifying, we obtain

$$z\bar{z} + \left(\frac{a}{2} + \frac{b}{2i}\right)z + \left(\frac{a}{2} - \frac{b}{2i}\right)\bar{z} + c = 0.$$

Under the transformation $w = 1/z$ this becomes

$$c(u^2 + v^2) + au - bv + 1 = 0, \qquad (8.21)$$

where we have again used the fact that $w = u + iv$. Thus if $c \neq 0$, Equation 8.21 represents a circle. If $c = 0$, that is, if the circle of Equation 8.20 passes through the critical point $z = 0$, then Equation 8.21 represents the straight line

$$au - bv + 1 = 0$$

in the w-plane.

In summary then we can draw up the following table.

z-plane	Image in w-plane
Straight line through the origin	→ Straight line through the origin
Straight line *not* through origin	→ Circle through the origin
Circle through the origin	→ Straight line *not* through origin
Circle *not* through origin	→ Circle *not* through origin

If we consider straight lines as limiting cases of circles, we may say: *the transformation* $w = 1/z$ *always takes circles into circles.*

The transformation $w = 1/z$ is closely related to the geometric construction known as the *inversion of the circle*. Consider a circle

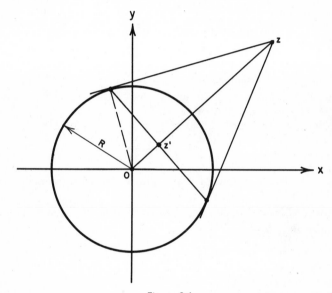

Figure 8.6

of radius R with center at the origin. Let z be any point outside the circle. Then we define a point z' by the following geometric construction. From z draw tangents to the circle. The intersection of the chord connecting the two points of tangency with the secant joining 0 to z is defined as z'. The points z and z' are called *conjugates*. Clearly points *on* the circle (called the *circle of inversion*) are self-conjugate. From the similar triangles of Fig. 8.6 we see that

$$|z||z'| = R^2.$$

Hence, in particular, if $R = 1$,

$$|z'| = \frac{1}{|z|},$$

and from the figure,

$$\arg z' = \arg z.$$

Thus inversion is a conformal transformation with reversal of angles. (Recall that if $w = 1/z$, then $|w| = 1/|z|$ and $\arg w = -\arg z$.) One can deduce numerous properties of inversion by elementary techniques. Some of these results will be found in the exercises.

8.5 The Bilinear Transformation

The transformation

$$w = \frac{\alpha z + \beta}{\gamma z + \delta}, \tag{8.22}$$

where α, β, γ, δ are complex numbers with the property that

$$\Delta = \alpha\delta - \beta\gamma \neq 0, \tag{8.23}$$

is called a *bilinear transformation* (see Exercise 3.12). We impose the condition of Equation 8.23 in order that Equation 8.22 represent a conformal transformation.* For

$$\frac{dw}{dz} = \frac{\Delta}{(\gamma z + \delta)^2}$$

and if $\Delta = 0$, every point of the z-plane would be a critical point. The image of $z = -\delta/\gamma$ (for $\gamma \neq 0$) is $w = \infty$.

The term *bilinear* stems from the fact that if we solve Equation 8.22 for z we obtain

$$z = -\frac{\delta w - \beta}{\gamma w - \alpha}, \tag{8.24}$$

which is of the same form as Equation 8.22.

The transformation is one to one. For suppose two distinct values of z, say z_0 and z_1, gave rise to the same w. Then Equation 8.22 would imply

$$\frac{\alpha z_0 + \beta}{\gamma z_0 + \delta} = \frac{\alpha z_1 + \beta}{\gamma z_1 + \delta}$$

or

$$\Delta z_0 = \Delta z_1.$$

Thus if $z_0 \neq z_1$, we would have to have $\Delta = 0$. But this contradicts our hypothesis (Equation 8.23).

---

* Also, if $\Delta = 0$, then $\alpha z + \beta$ and $\gamma z + \delta$ would be linearly dependent and hence w would reduce to a constant, which of course implies and is implied by the fact that $dw/dz = 0$ for all z.

We shall now show how the bilinear transformation of Equation 8.22 can be obtained by the composition of translations, rotations (with stretching or contraction), and inversions. Towards this end, define the following transformations:

$$\mathbf{T}_a z = z + a$$

$$\mathbf{S}_b z = bz \tag{8.25}$$

$$\mathbf{V} z = \frac{1}{z}.$$

Then, assuming for the moment that $\gamma \neq 0$, we have

$$\mathbf{T}_{\delta/\gamma} z = z + \frac{\delta}{\gamma}$$

$$\mathbf{S}_\gamma \mathbf{T}_{\delta/\gamma} z = \mathbf{S}_\gamma \left(z + \frac{\delta}{\gamma} \right) = \gamma z + \delta \tag{8.26}$$

and $\mathbf{S}_\gamma \mathbf{T}_{\delta/\gamma}$ is the linear transformation of Section 8.3 C. Continuing, we operate with $\mathbf{V}$ on Equation 8.26,

$$\mathbf{V}\mathbf{S}_\gamma \mathbf{T}_{\delta/\gamma} \, z = \mathbf{V}(\gamma z + \delta) = \frac{1}{\gamma z + \delta},$$

and then with the operator $\mathbf{S}$,

$$\mathbf{S}_{-\Delta/\gamma}\mathbf{V}\mathbf{S}_\gamma \mathbf{T}_{\delta/\gamma} z = \frac{-\Delta}{\gamma(\gamma z + \delta)}.$$

Finally

$$\mathbf{T}_{\alpha/\gamma}\mathbf{S}_{-\Delta/\gamma}\mathbf{V}\mathbf{S}_\gamma \mathbf{T}_{\delta/\gamma} z = \frac{\alpha z + \beta}{\gamma z + \delta}.$$

Thus the most general bilinear transformation can be obtained by successive applications of the three simple mappings of Equations 8.25. In particular, we can conclude from our previous discussions that *a bilinear transformation maps circles into circles*, where again we are using the tacit convention that a straight line is to be considered as a limiting case of a circle.

In the above paragraph we assumed $\gamma \neq 0$. If $\gamma = 0$, then since $\Delta \neq 0$, we must have both α and δ unequal to zero. Then it is easy to see that

$$\mathbf{S}_{\alpha/\delta}\mathbf{T}_{\beta/\alpha} z = \mathbf{S}_{\alpha/\delta}\left(z + \frac{\beta}{\alpha} \right) = \frac{\alpha z + \beta}{\delta},$$

which is the desired bilinear transformation in the case $\gamma = 0$, that is, it is now a *linear* transformation.

Suppose now that z_1, z_2, z_3, z_4 are four distinct points in the z-plane. Then the ratio

$$\frac{(z_1 - z_2)(z_3 - z_4)}{(z_2 - z_3)(z_4 - z_1)}$$

obtained by an obvious permutation of the subscripts is called the *cross ratio* of the four numbers. We shall show that the cross ratio is invariant under a bilinear transformation. To prove this, let w_i be the image of z_i, $i = 1, 2, 3, 4$. Then we see that

$$w_i - w_j = \frac{\varDelta(z_i - z_j)}{\zeta_i \zeta_j},$$

where $\zeta_i = \gamma z_i + \delta$. By some more simple algebra

$$\frac{(w_1 - w_2)(w_3 - w_4)}{(w_2 - w_3)(w_4 - w_1)} = \frac{\dfrac{\varDelta(z_1 - z_2)}{\zeta_1 \zeta_2} \dfrac{\varDelta(z_3 - z_4)}{\zeta_3 \zeta_4}}{\dfrac{\varDelta(z_2 - z_3)}{\zeta_2 \zeta_3} \dfrac{\varDelta(z_4 - z_1)}{\zeta_4 \zeta_1}} \tag{8.27}$$

$$= \frac{(z_1 - z_2)(z_3 - z_4)}{(z_2 - z_3)(z_4 - z_1)},$$

as we wished to prove.

Equation 8.22 depends on only three parameters. Suppose we specify that three distinct points z_1, z_2, z_3 are to be mapped into three other points w_1, w_2, w_3 that are distinct from each other. Then the required bilinear transformation can be found from Equation 8.27 by letting z play the role of z_4 and w the role of w_4.

8.6 Elliptic Integral

All of our previous examples of conformal mappings used elementary functions. Let us now consider the non-elementary function

$$w = \int_0^z \frac{dz}{\sqrt{(1 - z^2)(1 - k^2 z^2)}} \tag{8.28}$$

as a transformation where $0 < k < 1$. This is an *elliptic integral* of the first kind. We shall determine what region in the w-plane is the image of the upper half of the z-plane. Since the integrand of Equation 8.28 is multi-valued, some care must be exercised.

Let us indulge ourselves with the luxury of examining in detail

$$f(z;k) = \frac{1}{\sqrt{(1 - z^2)(1 - k^2 z^2)}}. \tag{8.29}$$

Clearly $f(z;k)$ has branch points at $z = \pm 1$ and $z = \pm 1/k$. The Riemann surface of $f(z;k)$ can be drawn as illustrated in Fig. 8.7. More conveniently we can draw it as in Fig. 8.8 where the heavy lines between $-1/k$ and -1 and between 1 and $1/k$ are the branch cuts.

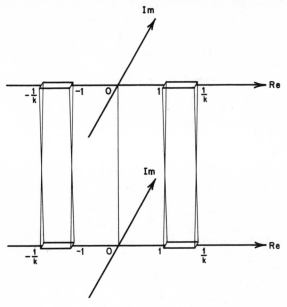

Figure 8.7

Our first task will be to assign appropriate values to the two sheets. We shall define $f(0;k)$ as $+1$ on the upper sheet. With this information the value of $f(z;k)$ at any point of the Riemann surface is uniquely determined. In particular, we are interested in the values of $f(z;k)$ on the real axis.

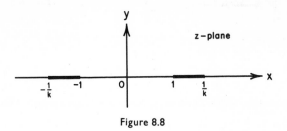

Figure 8.8

Since $f(0;k) = +1$, the value of $f(z;k)$ for z real and small must be close to $+1$. Let

$$z = r\, e^{i\theta}.$$

Then we may write

$$f(z;k) = |f(z;k)|e^{-i\phi/2}e^{-i\psi/2}, \qquad (8.30)$$

where

$$\phi = \arg(1 - z^2) = \arg(1 - r^2\cos 2\theta - i\,r^2\sin 2\theta)$$
$$\psi = \arg(1 - k^2z^2) = \arg(1 - k^2r^2\cos 2\theta - i\,k^2r^2\sin 2\theta). \qquad (8.31)$$

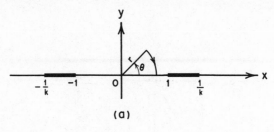

(a)

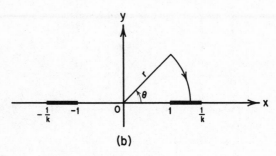

(b)

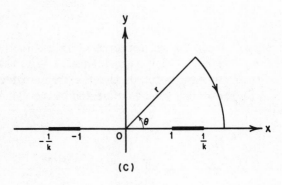

(c)

Figure 8.9

By the continuity of $f(z;k)$ near $z = 0$ we shall require that

$$\phi = 0, \quad \psi = 0 \quad \text{when } \theta = 0, \quad 0 < r < 1. \qquad (8.32)$$

Let us determine the values of $f(z;k)$ on the upper half of the upper plane of Fig. 8.7. Using the continuity of the arguments (see Fig. 8.9 and Equations 8.31), we see that if θ is small and positive, then ϕ is small and negative when $0 < r < 1$, while $\phi + \pi$ is small and positive when $1 < r < \infty$. Similarly, if θ is small and positive, ψ is small and negative when $0 < r < 1/k$, while $\psi + \pi$ is small and positive when $1/k < r < \infty$. Thus we may construct the following self-explanatory table which gives the values of $f(z;k)$ on the upper half of the top plane along the positive real axis.

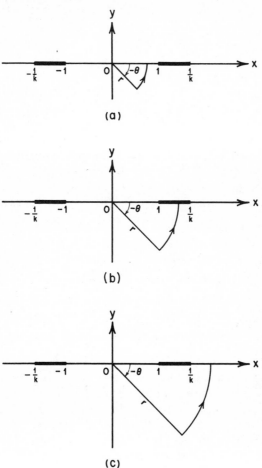

(a)

(b)

(c)

Figure 8.10

TABLE 8.1

	ϕ	ψ	$f(z;k)$
$0 < r < 1$	0	0	$|f(z;k)|$
$1 < r < 1/k$	$-\pi$	0	$i\,|f(z;k)|$
$1/k < r < \infty$	$-\pi$	$-\pi$	$-\,|f(z;k)|$

By an identical argument (see Fig. 8.10), again using the continuity of the arguments, we see that if θ is small and negative, then ϕ is small and positive when $0 < r < 1$, while $\phi - \pi$ is small and negative when $1 < r < \infty$. Also, if θ is small and negative, ψ is small and positive when $0 < r < 1/k$, while $\psi - \pi$ is small and negative when $1/k < r < \infty$. Thus the values of $f(z;k)$ on the lower half of the top plane along the positive real axis are given in Table 8.2. As we anticipated, the values

TABLE 8.2

	ϕ	ψ	$f(z;k)$
$0 < r < 1$	0	0	$\lvert f(z;k)\rvert$
$1 < r < 1/k$	π	0	$-i\lvert f(z;k)\rvert$
$1/k < r < \infty$	π	π	$-\lvert f(z;k)\rvert$

for $0 < z < 1$ and $1/k < z < \infty$ are identical, being on the same sheet, but the values of $f(z;k)$ for $1 < r < 1/k$ permute since this segment represents a branch cut.

We return now to Equation 8.28 and assume z is real and positive.

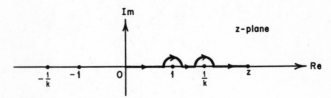

Figure 8.11

Let us integrate from 0 to z along the real axis where we shall assume that the path of integration is on the upper sheet of the Riemann surface whose values are defined by Table 8.1. Actually, we should consider Equation 8.28 relative to the contour illustrated in Fig. 8.11 (assuming $z > 1/k$), since the integral is improper at $z = 1$ and $z = 1/k$. However, it is easy to see that the integrals over these small semi-circles vanish. Thus if we define

$$K(k) = \int_0^1 f(z;k)\,dz$$

$$i\,K'(k) = \int_1^{1/k} f(z;k)\,dz \qquad (8.33)$$

$$-L(k) = \int_{1/k}^{\infty} f(z;k)\,dz,$$

the numbers K, K', and L are real and positive by virtue of Table 8.1. Actually, the last of Equations 8.33 defining L is an infinite integral; more precisely we should write

$$\lim_{R\to\infty} \int_{1/k}^{R} f(z;k)\,dz,$$

but it is easy to see that this integral converges. In fact, if we make the change of variable $z = 1/\zeta k$, we have

$$-L(k) = \int_{1/k}^{\infty} \frac{dz}{\sqrt{(1-z^2)(1-k^2 z^2)}} = -\int_0^1 \frac{d\zeta}{\sqrt{(1-\zeta^2)(1-k^2\zeta^2)}}$$

$$= -K(k)$$

or

$$L(k) = K(k). \tag{8.34}$$

Also, if we set

$$k' = \sqrt{1-k^2}$$

(and hence $0 < k' < 1$) and make the change of variable

$$z = (1 - k'^2\zeta^2)^{-1/2}$$

in the second of Equations 8.33, we infer that

$$i\,K'(k) = \int_1^{1/k} \frac{dz}{\sqrt{(1-z^2)(1-k^2 z^2)}} = \int_0^1 \frac{d\zeta}{\sqrt{(1-\zeta^2)(1-k'^2\zeta^2)}}$$

$$= i\,K(k')$$

or

$$K'(k) = K(k'). \tag{8.35}$$

Notice the symmetry of K and k with and without the prime.

Returning now to the problem of conformal mapping, we see that

$$w(1) = \int_0^1 f(z;k)\,dz = K$$

$$w\!\left(\frac{1}{k}\right) = \int_0^{1/k} f(z;k)\,dz = \int_0^1 f(z;k)\,dz + \int_1^{1/k} f(z;k)\,dz$$

$$= K + i\,K'$$

$$w(\infty) = \int_0^{\infty} f(z;k)\,dz = \int_0^{1/k} f(z;k)\,dz + \int_{1/k}^{\infty} f(z;k)\,dz$$

$$= K + i\,K' - L = i\,K',$$

since $K = L$ by Equation 8.34. The conformal map is illustrated in

Fig. 8.12.   That part of the rectangle in the left half of the w-plane is
determined by an argument similar to the ones used in the above
analysis.

   While we have the elliptic integral under consideration let us
mention another interesting fact.   If a Jordan curve C is drawn in

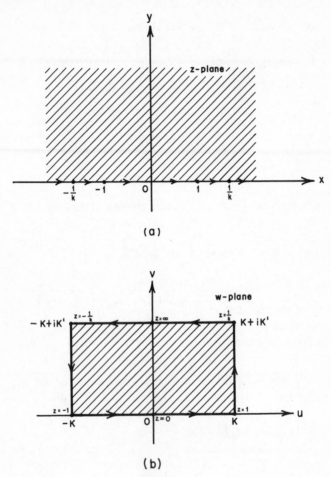

(a)

(b)

Figure 8.12

the z-plane, then any continuous curve connecting an interior point
of C to an exterior point must contain a point of C (see Theorem 8 of
Chapter 2).   One can easily verify that if any Jordan curve is drawn
on the Riemann surface of $f_1(z) = \sqrt{z - \alpha}$ or $f_2(z) = \sqrt{(z - \alpha)(z - \beta)}$,
$(\alpha \neq \beta)$, the same situation prevails.   Note that both $f_1(z)$ and $f_2(z)$
have two sheets and two branch points.   The branch points of $f_1(z)$

are $z = \alpha$, ∞, and those of $f_2(z)$ are $z = \alpha$, β. However, the situation is essentially different for the function $f(z;k)$ of Equation 8.29. Consider Fig. 8.13. Then it is clear that C' is a continuous curve

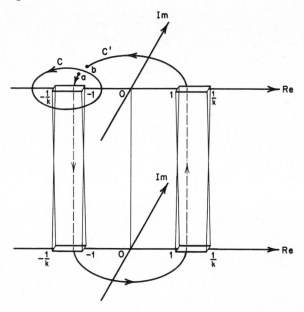

Figure 8.13

connecting a (an interior point of C) to b (an exterior point of C) without crossing C. Another way of looking at this result is the following: Every Jordan curve divides the z-plane (and also the Riemann

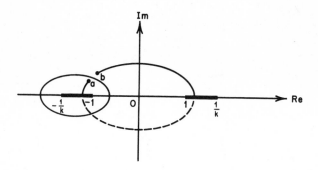

Figure 8.14

surfaces of f_1 and f_2) into two pieces, while the closed curve C does *not* divide the Riemann surface of $f(z;k)$ into two pieces. This topological property is expressed by saying that the plane (and the Riemann surfaces of f_1 and f_2) have *genus* zero while the Riemann surface of $f(z;k)$ has *genus* one. Since the extended plane can be mapped in a one to one fashion on the Riemann sphere (see Section 5.9), it is customary to say that the sphere has genus zero. A torus has genus one and, for example, a button with three holes has genus three. Similarly, as an example, the Riemann surface of

$$\sqrt{(z - \alpha_1)(z - \alpha_2)(z - \alpha_3)(z - \alpha_4)(z - \alpha_5)},$$

($\alpha_i \neq \alpha_j$ for $i \neq j$) has genus two.

The complicated picture of Fig. 8.13 can be drawn more simply as in Fig. 8.14, where it is understood that the dashed portions of the curve are on a sheet of the Riemann surface different from the solid portions.

8.7 The Schwarz-Christoffel Transformation

In the previous sections of this chapter we considered problems of *analysis* as distinct from *synthesis*. That is, we took a given region or

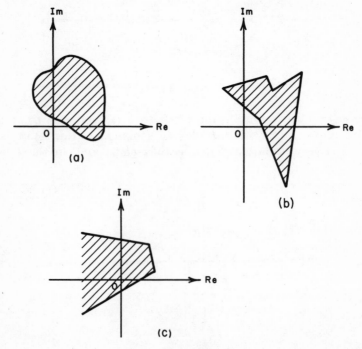

Figure 8.15

curve and a given conformal transformation and inquired what the image of the point set was under the given mapping. A problem of *synthesis* starts with two given regions and determines what transformation maps one region onto the other. Thus, for example, we could inquire what functions would map the various regions of Fig. 8.15 onto some canonical domain such as a half plane. At the outset it is not clear that such functions exist.

We shall develop a method for finding transformations which map regions of the type illustrated in Fig. 8.15b and 8.15c onto the half plane. Such mappings are generally called *Schwarz-Christoffel transformations*. Thus a Schwarz-Christoffel transformation maps a polygon (which may have a vertex at $z = \infty$ as illustrated in Fig. 8.15c) onto a half plane.

Using the example of the elliptic integral of Section 8.6 of this

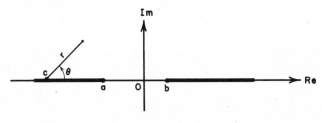

Figure 8.16

chapter as our motivation, we are invited to examine the transformation.

$$w = \int_c^z \frac{dz}{(a - z)^\lambda (b - z)^\mu}, \qquad c < a < b, \qquad (8.36)$$

where λ and μ are real numbers less than one. It is therefore appropriate first to discuss the function

$$g(z) = \frac{1}{(a - z)^\lambda (b - z)^\mu}. \qquad (8.37)$$

This function has branch points at $z = a$ and $z = b$ and possibly at $z = \infty$ (depending on the values of λ and μ). Thus we may represent one sheet of its Riemann surface as in Fig. 8.16, where we have assumed for definiteness that $b > a$. If we specify the value of $g(z)$ at one point of one sheet of the Riemann surface, all other values at every point of every sheet are uniquely determined by continuity. Suppose then that c is any number less than a. Then $a - c$ and $b - c$ are both positive real numbers. Let us define

$$g(c) = \frac{1}{(a - c)^\lambda (b - c)^\mu} > 0, \qquad (8.38)$$

where we have taken c on the *upper* half of the cut (see Fig. 8.16).

As in the last section we write

$$g(z) = |g(z)|e^{-\lambda i \phi}e^{-\mu i \psi},\qquad(8.39)$$

where

$$\phi = \arg{(a - z)}, \qquad \psi = \arg{(b - z)}.$$

If we let $z - c = r\,e^{i\theta}$, then

$$\phi = \arg{[(a - c) - (z - c)]} = \arg{[(a - c) - r\cos\theta - i\,r\sin\theta]}$$

$$\psi = \arg{[(b - c) - (z - c)]} = \arg{[(b - c) - r\cos\theta - i\,r\sin\theta]},\qquad(8.40)$$

where $a - c$, $b - c$, and r are all positive real numbers.

Since $g(z)$ is to be real and positive for $z = c$ on the upper cut, we must have $\phi = \psi = 0$ for $\theta = 0$ since λ and μ are unrestricted. Then the same argument as was used in the case of the elliptic integral enables us to construct Table 8.3. This table gives us the values of $g(z)$ on the real axis corresponding to the upper half plane of the sheet of the Riemann surface illustrated in Fig. 8.16. By continuity we see

TABLE 8.3

	ϕ	ψ	$g(z)$
$0 < r < a - c$	0	0	$\|g(z)\|$
$a - c < r < b - c$	$-\pi$	0	$\|g(z)\|e^{\lambda\pi i}$
$b - c < r < \infty$	$-\pi$	$-\pi$	$\|g(z)\|e^{(\lambda+\mu)\pi i}$

that $g(z) = |g(z)|$ for z real and less than c on the upper cut of the sheet. This can also be demonstrated analytically by noting that

$$\lim_{\substack{\theta\to\pi\\\theta<\pi}} \phi = 0 = \lim_{\substack{\theta\to\pi\\\theta<\pi}} \psi,$$

since for θ in the second quadrant, $a - c - r\cos\theta$ and $b - c - r\cos\theta$ are both positive for any $r > 0$.

Since $\lambda < 1$ and $\mu < 1$, no difficulties arise because of the improperness of the integral of Equation 8.36 at $z = a, b$. Thus we have

$$w(a) = \int_c^a g(z)\,dz = A$$

$$w(b) = \int_c^b g(z)\,dz = \int_c^a g(z)\,dz + \int_a^b g(z)\,dz = A + Be^{\lambda\pi i}$$

$$w(\infty) = \int_c^\infty g(z)\,dz = \int_c^b g(z)\,dz + \int_c^\infty g(z)\,dz = A + Be^{\lambda\pi i} + Ce^{(\lambda+\mu)\pi i},$$

where A, B, C are positive constants. If $\lambda + \mu > 1$, the infinite real integral

$$\int_b^\infty \frac{dx}{(x-a)^\lambda(x-b)^\mu} \qquad (8.41)$$

converges absolutely and hence C is finite. If $\lambda + \mu \leq 1$, the integral diverges and C is infinite. These situations are illustrated in Fig. 8.17.

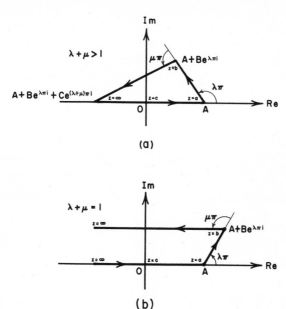

(a)

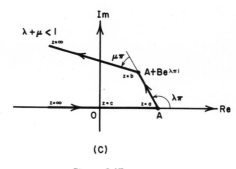

(b)

(c)

Figure 8.17

If the reader has any qualms about the triangle of Fig. 8.17a being closed, he may draw a large semicircle with center at $z = c$ in the upper half of the sheet illustrated in Fig. 8.16 and apply the Cauchy integral theorem.

Suppose now we are given a triangle (see Fig. 8.18), allowing even the case where one vertex may be at infinity (see Figs. 8.17b and 8.17c). Then can we conformally map this into a half plane? The answer is certainly yes. For if we write

$$w = \int_c^z \frac{dz}{(a-z)^{\alpha-1}(b-z)^{\beta-1}}, \qquad c < a < b, \qquad (8.42)$$

then, as we have just seen, this transformation maps the upper half plane of the z-plane into the triangle of Fig. 8.19b. The triangles of

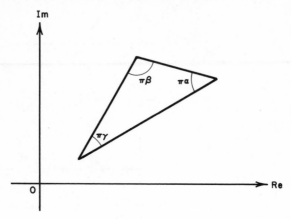

Figure 8.18

Figs. 8.18 and 8.19b are similar. Hence by a linear transformation (see Section 8.3)

$$\zeta = kw + k' \qquad (8.43)$$

we can make the two triangles coincide. Thus we have effected a mapping of a half plane onto an arbitrary triangle. Equation 8.42 is a Schwarz-Christoffel transformation.

Note that a and b ($a \neq b$) are arbitrary in Equation 8.42, although their numerical values will affect those of k and k' in Equation 8.43. If we consider the general case, we see that the transformation

$$w = \int_0^z \frac{dz}{(z-a_1)^{\lambda_1}(z-a_2)^{\lambda_2}\cdots(z-a_n)^{\lambda_n}}, \qquad (8.44)$$

where $0 < a_1 < a_2 < \cdots < a_n$, $\lambda_i < 1$, $i = 1, 2, \cdots, n$, and $\sum_{i=1}^{n} \lambda_i > 1$, will map the half plane into the polygon of Fig. 8.20. If $\sum \lambda_i \leq 1$,

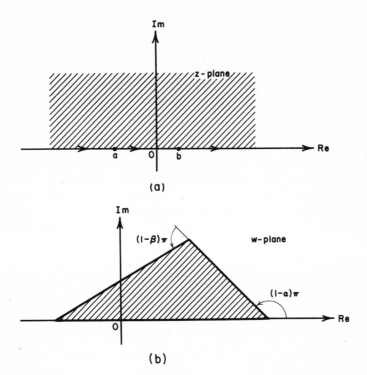

(a)

(b)

Figure 8.19

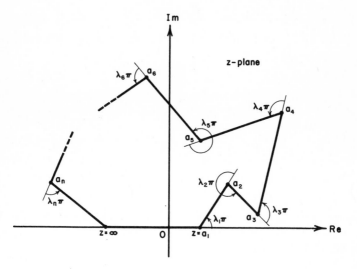

Figure 8.20

the polygon will have a vertex at $z = \infty$. Thus if we are given an arbitrary polygon, we can immediately infer the values of the λ's of Equation 8.44 that will map the half plane into a polygon with the same angles. In order to get the image polygon and the original polygon similar, all the values of the a_i's can no longer be chosen arbitrarily. Once we have similar polygons, a linear transformation will bring them into coincidence.

There is a famous theorem of Riemann which states, essentially, that any simply connected domain can be conformally mapped onto a half plane (for example, the region of Fig. 8.15a). However, the proof does not indicate how to construct such a function, that is, it is a pure existence proof. Thus from the practical viewpoint we have available only such simple mappings as given, for example, by the bilinear transformation and the polygonal Schwarz-Christoffel transformation.

EXERCISES

8.1. Let z and z' be two points which are conjugates with respect to the circle of inversion. Let C be a circle through z and z'. Prove that C cuts the circle of inversion orthogonally.

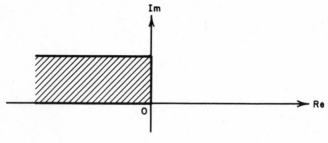

Figure 8.21

8.2. Let C_1 and C_2 be two circles which orthogonally cut the circle of inversion. If C_1 and C_2 intersect at z and z', show that z and z' are conjugates.

8.3. Show that the totality of bilinear transformations with composition as the binary operation form a group.*

8.4. Show that

$$w = \alpha\left(\frac{z - \bar{\beta}}{z - \beta}\right),$$

where $|\alpha| = 1$ and $\mathrm{Im}\,[\beta] < 0$ is the most general bilinear transformation which maps the upper half of the z-plane onto the unit circle in the w-plane.

---

* See, for example, K. S. Miller, *Elements of Modern Abstract Algebra*, Harper & Brothers, 1958, p. 1.

8.5. Find a necessary and sufficient condition on four distinct points in order that their cross ratio be a real number.

8.6. Show that the most general bilinear transformation which maps the upper half of the z-plane onto the upper half of the w-plane is one in which α, β, γ, δ are real and $\Delta > 0$.

8.7. Show that

$$w = \int_0^z \frac{dz}{(1 - z^2)^{2/3}}$$

maps the upper half of the z-plane onto an equilateral triangle in the w-plane.

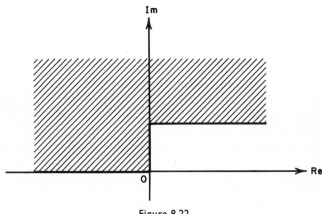

Figure 8.22

8.8. Find the Schwarz-Christoffel transformation which maps a half plane onto the shaded region of Fig. 8.21.

8.9. Find the Schwarz-Christoffel transformation which maps a half plane onto an isosceles triangle.

8.10. Determine the mapping which takes a half plane onto the shaded area of Fig. 8.22.

CHAPTER 9

The Method of Laplace Integrals

9.1 Introduction

One of the most interesting applications of the complex calculus is to the subject of differential equations. We shall present a certain facet of the theory of linear differential equations in the complex domain in this chapter. The topic of linear differential equations in the complex domain could easily be made the subject matter for a treatise the size of this book.* However, we shall only study a particular branch known as the *method of Laplace integrals*. We recall from elementary differential equation theory that the solution of linear differential equations with non-constant coefficients can rarely be written in terms of elementary functions. However, the method of Frobenius† indicates that, under rather broad conditions, solutions can be determined in the form of infinite series. Sometimes these infinite series can be converted to integrals. We shall give an example below. The method of Laplace integrals considers the problem of determining an integral representation directly from the differential equation itself. The techniques we use form an excellent non-trivial application of the theory of contour integration expounded in Chapter 6.

Our plan of attack will be as follows. In Section 9.2 we shall introduce the notion of the *adjoint operator*, fundamental in our future discussions. We shall then define a Laplace integral and give several examples. The remainder of the chapter will be devoted to a treatment of a certain subclass of differential equations (those with linear coefficients) for which very explicit results may be obtained.

Before we embark on this program let us consider an example of

---

* See, for example, E. L. Ince, *Ordinary Differential Equations*, Longmans, Green and Company, Ltd., 1927, Part II; F. J. Murray and K. S. Miller, *Existence Theorems*, New York University Press, 1954, chap. 6.

† See, for example, K. S. Miller, *Engineering Mathematics*, Rinehart and Company, 1956, p. 85.

an integral solution of a differential equation. Students of applied mathematics will recognize

$$z^2 \frac{d^2w}{dz^2} + z \frac{dw}{dz} + z^2w = 0$$

as Bessel's equation of order zero. By the method of Frobenius one solution* is readily determined to be

$$J_0(z) = \sum_{k=0}^{\infty} \frac{(-1)^k}{(k!)^2} \left(\frac{z}{2}\right)^{2k}. \tag{9.1}$$

This power series has an infinite radius of convergence. Using the integral formula

$$\int_0^{\pi/2} \cos^{2k} \theta \, d\theta = \frac{\pi(2k)!}{2^{2k+1}(k!)^2},$$

which may be obtained from the Beta function, enables us to write Equation 9.1 as

$$J_0(z) = \frac{1}{\pi} \sum_{k=0}^{\infty} \frac{(-1)^k}{(2k)!} 2^{2k+1} \left(\frac{z}{2}\right)^{2k} \int_0^{\pi/2} \cos^{2k} \theta \, d\theta.$$

Since the infinite series

$$\sum_{k=0}^{\infty} \frac{(-1)^k}{(2k)!} (z \cos \theta)^{2k}$$

converges uniformly and absolutely for all θ, we may interchange the order of integration and summation to write

$$J_0(z) = \frac{2}{\pi} \int_0^{\pi/2} \left[\sum_{k=0}^{\infty} \frac{(-1)^k (z \cos \theta)^{2k}}{(2k)!} \right] d\theta$$

$$= \frac{2}{\pi} \int_0^{\pi/2} \cos (z \cos \theta) \, d\theta. \tag{9.2}$$

This is the desired integral representation for $J_0(z)$. It is known as a *Lommel integral*.

9.2 The Adjoint Operator

The notion of an integrating factor plays an important role in the theory of first order linear differential equations. In an attempt to

* *Op. cit.*, p. 118.

generalize this idea to nth order equations we are led to the concept of the *adjoint operator*.

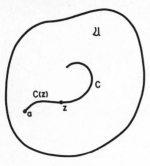

Consider two functions $u(z)$ and $v(z)$ which are analytic and single-valued in some simply connected open region $\mathfrak{A}$. Let C be a smooth curve in $\mathfrak{A}$. Let a be a fixed point on C and z a variable point. We shall denote that portion of the curve from a to z by $C(z)$ (see Fig. 9.1). If we integrate the expression

$$\int_{C(z)} v(z)u^{(k)}(z)\, dz$$

Figure 9.1

by parts, we obtain (see Exercise 4.4)

$$\int_{C(z)} v(z)u^{(k)}(z)\, dz = v(z)\, u^{(k-1)}(z)\Big|_{C(z)} - \int_{C(z)} v'(z)u^{(k-1)}(z)\, dz.$$

Repeated integration by parts leads by a simple induction to

$$\int_{C(z)} v(z)u^{(k)}(z)\, dz = \sum_{j=0}^{k-1} (-1)^j v^{(j)}(z)u^{(k-1-j)}(z)\Big|_{C(z)}$$

$$+ (-1)^k \int_{C(z)} v^{(k)}(z)u(z)\, dz. \tag{9.3}$$

Now let

$$\mathbf{L} = p_0(z)\frac{d^n}{dz^n} + p_1(z)\frac{d^{n-1}}{dz^{n-1}} + \cdots + p_n(z). \tag{9.4}$$

be a linear differential operator of the nth order where the $p_i(z)$ have, at most, isolated singularities in $\mathfrak{A}$ and are analytic on C. Also, let $p_0(z)$ be bounded away from zero on C. Then

$$\int_{C(z)} v(z)\mathbf{L}u(z)\, dz = \sum_{k=0}^{n} \int_{C(z)} [v(z)p_{n-k}(z)]u^{(k)}(z)\, dz$$

$$= \sum_{k=0}^{n} \left\{ \sum_{j=0}^{k-1} (-1)^j [v(z)p_{n-k}(z)]^{(j)}u^{(k-1-j)}(z)\Big|_{C(z)} \right. \tag{9.5}$$

$$\left. + (-1)^k \int_{C(z)} [v(z)p_{n-k}(z)]^{(k)}u(z)\, dz \right\}.$$

We define

$$\mathbf{L}^{+}v = (-1)^n \frac{d^n}{dz^n}(p_0 v) + (-1)^{n-1}\frac{d^{n-1}}{dz^{n-1}}(p_1 v) + \cdots - \frac{d}{dz}(p_{n-1}v) + p_n v$$

$$\tag{9.6}$$

as the *adjoint differential equation* and call $\mathbf{L}^+$ the *adjoint operator* (or *formal adjoint* or *Lagrange adjoint* of $\mathbf{L}$). Equation 9.5 may then be written as

$$\int_{C(z)} [v(z)\mathbf{L}u(z) - u(z)\mathbf{L}^+v(z)]\, dz = P[u(z), v(z)]\Big|_{C(z)}, \qquad (9.7)$$

where

$$P[u(z), v(z)] = \sum_{k=0}^{n} \sum_{j=0}^{k-1} (-1)^j [v(z)p_{n-k}(z)]^{(j)} u^{(k-1-j)}(z)$$

$$= [v(z)p_{n-1}(z)]u(z)$$
$$+ [v(z)p_{n-2}(z)]u'(z) - [v(z)p_{n-2}(z)]'u(z)$$
$$+ [v(z)p_{n-3}(z)]u''(z) - [v(z)p_{n-3}(z)]'u'(z) \qquad (9.8)$$
$$+ [v(z)p_{n-3}(z)]''u(z)$$
$$+ \cdots$$
$$+ [v(z)p_0(z)]u^{(n-1)}(z) - [v(z)p_0(z)]'u^{(n-2)}(z) + \cdots$$
$$+ (-1)^n [v(z)p_0(z)]^{(n-1)}u(z).$$

is called the *Lagrange bilinear concomitant*.

It is often more convenient to write Equation 9.7 as

$$v(z)\mathbf{L}u(z) - u(z)\mathbf{L}^+v(z) = \frac{d}{dz} P[u(z), v(z)]. \qquad (9.9)$$

9.3 Laplace Integrals

Our objective is to express a solution of

$$\mathbf{L}w(z) = 0 \qquad (9.10)$$

in the form

$$w(z) = \int_C K(z,\zeta)v(\zeta)\, d\zeta, \qquad (9.11)$$

where the kernel $K(z,\zeta)$, the function $v(\zeta)$, and the contour C are all to be determined.

Suppose that a kernel $K(z,\zeta)$ can be found such that

$$\mathbf{L}_z K(z,\zeta) = \mathbf{M}_\zeta K(z,\zeta), \qquad (9.12)$$

where $\mathbf{M}$ is some linear differential operator.* Then from Equation 9.11

$$\mathbf{L}_z w(z) = \int_C \mathbf{L}_z K(z,\zeta)v(\zeta)\, d\zeta$$
$$= \int_C v(\zeta)\mathbf{M}_\zeta K(z,\zeta)\, d\zeta. \qquad (9.13)$$

---

* We use subscripts to indicate on which variable the linear differential operator operates. For example, Equation 9.10 may be written as $\mathbf{L}_z w(z) = 0$.

Let $\mathbf{M}^+$ be the formal adjoint of $\mathbf{M}$. Then

$$v(\zeta)\mathbf{M}_\zeta K(z,\zeta) - K(z,\zeta)\mathbf{M}_\zeta^+ v(\zeta) = \frac{\partial}{\partial\zeta} P_\zeta[K(z,\zeta), v(\zeta)], \qquad (9.14)$$

where $P_\zeta[K(z,\zeta), v(\zeta)]$ is the Lagrange bilinear concomitant. Equation 9.13 then becomes

$$\mathbf{L}_z w(z) = \int_C K(z,\zeta)\mathbf{M}_\zeta^+ v(\zeta)\, d\zeta + P_\zeta[K(z,\zeta), v(\zeta)]\bigg|_C. \qquad (9.15)$$

In order that Equation 9.11 be a solution of Equation 9.10, the right-hand member of Equation 9.15 must vanish. Thus $v(\zeta)$ must be a solution of

$$\mathbf{M}_\zeta^+ v = 0$$

and the contour C must be so chosen that

$$P_\zeta[K(z,\zeta), v(\zeta)]\bigg|_C = 0.$$

Let us specialize our problem. Suppose that the coefficients $p_i(z)$ appearing in $\mathbf{L}$ are polynomials of degree at most m. Then we may write

$$\mathbf{L}_z = \sum_{r=0}^{n} \sum_{s=0}^{m} a_{rs} z^s \frac{d^r}{dz^r}.$$

Now consider the operator

$$\mathbf{M}_\zeta = \sum_{r=0}^{n} \sum_{s=0}^{m} a_{rs}\zeta^r \frac{d^s}{d\zeta^s}.$$

Clearly

$$\mathbf{L}_z e^{z\zeta} = \sum_{r=0}^{n} \sum_{s=0}^{m} a_{rs} z^s \zeta^r e^{z\zeta} = \mathbf{M}_\zeta e^{z\zeta}.$$

Consequently the equation $\mathbf{L}_z w = 0$ is satisfied by

$$w(z) = \int_C e^{z\zeta} v(\zeta)\, d\zeta, \qquad (9.16)$$

where $v(\zeta)$ is a solution of the differential equation $\mathbf{M}_\zeta^+ v = 0$ and the contour C is so chosen that

$$P_\zeta[e^{z\zeta}, v(\zeta)]\bigg|_C = 0.$$

Equation 9.16 is known as a *Laplace integral*.

There exists a reciprocal relation between $v(\zeta)$ and $w(z)$. We shall show that

$$\mathbf{L}_z^+ e^{-z\zeta} = \mathbf{M}_\zeta^+ e^{-z\zeta}. \tag{9.17}$$

If we assume this for the moment, then the equation $\mathbf{M}_\zeta^+ v = 0$ is satisfied by

$$v(\zeta) = \int_\Gamma e^{-z\zeta} w(z)\, dz$$

for an appropriately chosen contour Γ. For,

$$\mathbf{M}_\zeta^+ v(\zeta) = \int_\Gamma \mathbf{M}_\zeta^+ e^{-z\zeta} w(z)\, dz = \int_\Gamma w(z) \mathbf{L}_z^+ e^{-z\zeta}\, dz$$

$$= \int_\Gamma e^{-z\zeta} \mathbf{L}_z w(z)\, dz + P_z[e^{-z\zeta}, w(z)]\Big|_\Gamma$$

and $\mathbf{L}_z w(z) = 0$, while Γ is so chosen that the concomitant vanishes.

To prove Equation 9.17 we note that

$$\mathbf{L}_z^+ u = \sum_{r,s} a_{rs}(-1)^r \frac{d^r}{dz^r} (z^s u)$$

$$\mathbf{M}_\zeta^+ u = \sum_{r,s} a_{rs}(-1)^s \frac{d^s}{d\zeta^s} (\zeta^r u).$$

Therefore it suffices to show that

$$(-1)^r \frac{\partial^r}{\partial z^r} z^s e^{-z\zeta} = (-1)^s \frac{\partial^s}{\partial \zeta^s} \zeta^r e^{-z\zeta}. \tag{9.18}$$

But

$$\frac{\partial^{r+s}}{\partial z^r \partial \zeta^s} e^{-z\zeta} = (-1)^s \frac{\partial^r}{\partial z^r} z^s e^{-z\zeta}$$

and

$$\frac{\partial^{s+r}}{\partial \zeta^s \partial z^r} e^{-z\zeta} = (-1)^r \frac{\partial^s}{\partial \zeta^s} \zeta^r e^{-z\zeta}.$$

Now since $e^{-z\zeta}$ considered as a function of z and ζ is analytic, we may interchange the order of differentiation. That is,

$$\frac{\partial^{r+s}}{\partial z^r \partial \zeta^s} e^{-z\zeta} = \frac{\partial^{s+r}}{\partial \zeta^s \partial z^r} e^{-z\zeta}.$$

Thus

$$(-1)^{r+s} \frac{\partial^{r+s}}{\partial z^r \partial \zeta^s} e^{-z\zeta} = (-1)^r \frac{\partial^r}{\partial z^r} z^s e^{-z\zeta}$$

$$= (-1)^s \frac{\partial^s}{\partial \zeta^s} \zeta^r e^{-z\zeta}$$

$$= (-1)^{s+r} \frac{\partial^{s+r}}{\partial \zeta^s \partial z^r} e^{-z\zeta},$$

which proves Equation 9.18.

9.4 Linear Coefficients

Let us first consider the case where the coefficients of $\mathbf{L}$ are linear, viz.,

$$\mathbf{L}_z w = (a_0 z + b_0) \frac{d^n w}{dz^n} + (a_1 z + b_1) \frac{d^{n-1} w}{dz^{n-1}} + \cdots \tag{9.19}$$
$$+ (a_n z + b_n) w = 0, \qquad a_0 \neq 0.$$

Then

$$\mathbf{M}_\zeta u = P(\zeta) \frac{du}{d\zeta} + R(\zeta) u, \tag{9.20}$$

where

$$P(\zeta) = a_0 \zeta^n + a_1 \zeta^{n-1} + \cdots + a_n$$
$$R(\zeta) = b_0 \zeta^n + b_1 \zeta^{n-1} + \cdots + b_n.$$

Hence

$$\mathbf{M}_\zeta^+ v = -P(\zeta) \frac{dv}{d\zeta} + [R(\zeta) - P'(\zeta)] v$$

and $v(\zeta)$ is a solution of

$$P(\zeta) \frac{dv}{d\zeta} - Q(\zeta) v = 0, \tag{9.21}$$

where

$$Q(\zeta) = R(\zeta) - P'(\zeta).$$

The bilinear concomitant is

$$\frac{d}{d\zeta} P[u,v] = v\mathbf{M}u - u\mathbf{M}^+ v$$

$$= v(\zeta) \left[P(\zeta) \frac{du}{d\zeta} + R(\zeta) u \right] + u(\zeta) \left[P(\zeta) \frac{dv}{d\zeta} - Q(\zeta) v \right]$$

$$= P(\zeta)[uv' + u'v] + [R(\zeta) - Q(\zeta)] uv$$

$$= P(\zeta) \frac{d(uv)}{d\zeta} + P'(\zeta) uv.$$

Thus

$$P_\zeta[e^{z\zeta}, v(\zeta)] = P(\zeta)v(\zeta)e^{z\zeta}.$$

Let us assume for the moment that the roots of $P(\zeta) = 0$ are distinct,* say $\alpha_1, \alpha_2, \cdots, \alpha_n$. Then from Equation 9.21

$$v^{-1}\frac{dv}{d\zeta} = \frac{Q(\zeta)}{P(\zeta)} = \mu + \frac{\lambda_1}{\zeta - \alpha_1} + \cdots + \frac{\lambda_n}{\zeta - \alpha_n}$$

and

$$v(\zeta) = e^{\mu\zeta}(\zeta - \alpha_1)^{\lambda_1}\cdots(\zeta - \alpha_n)^{\lambda_n}.$$

Therefore the integral

$$w(z) = \int_C e^{z\zeta}v(\zeta)\,d\zeta$$

satisfies $\mathbf{L}_z w = 0$, provided the contour C is chosen so that $P_\zeta[e^{z\zeta}, v(\zeta)]$ vanishes (identically in z) with respect to the contour C (which, of course, is independent of z).   Explicitly

$$a_0 F(\zeta)\Big|_C = 0,$$

where

$$F(\zeta) = e^{(\mu+z)\zeta}(\zeta - \alpha_1)^{1+\lambda_1}\cdots(\zeta - \alpha_n)^{1+\lambda_n}. \tag{9.22}$$

If the real parts of two of the λ's are greater than -1, say $\mathrm{Re}\,[\lambda_j] > -1$, $\mathrm{Re}\,[\lambda_k] > -1$, $j \neq k$, then

$$w(z) = \int_C e^{z\zeta}v(\zeta)\,d\zeta$$

will be a solution where C is any smooth curve joining α_j and α_k and not passing through any other α_r with $\mathrm{Re}\,[\lambda_r] \leq -1$. If some λ is a negative integer, then C may be chosen as a circle, about the corresponding α, which encloses no other root of $P(\zeta) = 0$. Then the function $F(\zeta)$ returns to its initial value after a circuit around C. Finally consider the case where the λ's are unrestricted. Consider any two, say λ_j and λ_k, $(j \neq k)$. Let β be a point distinct from the α's. Then C may be taken as the double loop† with respect to α_j and α_k which encloses no other α_i.

Except in the case where λ is a negative integer, only $n - 1$ distinct integrals which satisfy $\mathbf{L}_z w = 0$ may be formed. A set of n distinct contour integrals which satisfy the equation cannot be obtained without some restriction on z. Suppose, for instance, that $\mathrm{Re}\,[z + \mu] > 0$.

---

* See Section 9.6 for the case of equal roots.
† See Section 6.5E.

Then the single loop contour* illustrated in Fig. 9.2 is suitable.   It is, of course, assumed that no other α lies on or in the contour.   In general, n integrals of this type will exist.

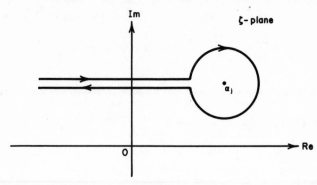

Figure 9.2

9.5 Examples of Contour Integrals as Solutions

A. Kummer's differential equation is

$$\mathbf{L}_z w = z \frac{d^2 w}{dz^2} + (c - z) \frac{dw}{dz} - aw = 0.$$

We shall suitably restrict c and a at a later time.   Now

$$\mathbf{M}_\zeta u = (\zeta^2 - \zeta) \frac{du}{d\zeta} + (c\zeta - a)u$$

and

$$\mathbf{M}_\zeta^+ v = (\zeta - \zeta^2) \frac{dv}{d\zeta} + [(c - 2)\zeta + (1 - a)]v = 0.$$

Thus

$$v^{-1} \frac{dv}{d\zeta} = - \frac{(c - 2)\zeta + (1 - a)}{\zeta(1 - \zeta)} = \frac{a - 1}{\zeta} + \frac{c - a - 1}{\zeta - 1}$$

and

$$v = \zeta^{a-1}(\zeta - 1)^{c-a-1}.$$

Hence

$$w(z) = \int_C e^{z\zeta} \zeta^{a-1}(\zeta - 1)^{c-a-1} \, d\zeta,$$

where C is chosen so that

$$P_\zeta[e^{z\zeta}, v(\zeta)] = \zeta^a(\zeta - 1)^{c-a} e^{z\zeta} \bigg|_C = 0.$$

* See Section 6.5D.

Now assume Re $[c]$ > Re $[a]$ > 0. Then the straight line from 0 to 1 is acceptable,

$$w(z) = \int_0^1 e^{z\zeta}\zeta^{a-1}(\zeta - 1)^{c-a-1}\, d\zeta.$$

Since $0 \leq \zeta \leq 1$, write

$$\hat{w}(z) = \int_0^1 e^{z\zeta}\zeta^{a-1}(1 - \zeta)^{c-a-1}\, d\zeta.$$

Let $z\zeta = t$. Then aside from a constant factor

$$\hat{w}(z) = z^{1-c}\int_0^z e^t t^{a-1}(z - t)^{c-a-1}\, dt$$

is the confluent hypergeometric function $_1F_1(a,c\,;z)$,

$$_1F_1(a,c\,;z) = \frac{\Gamma(c)}{\Gamma(a)\Gamma(c - a)}\, \hat{w}(z).$$

B. Consider the differential equation

$$\mathbf{L}_z w = z\,\frac{d^2w}{dz^2} - (3z + 7)\,\frac{dw}{dz} + (2z + 10)w = 0.$$

Then

$$\mathbf{M}_\zeta u = (2 - 3\zeta + \zeta^2)\,\frac{du}{d\zeta} + (10 - 7\zeta)u$$

and

$$\mathbf{M}_\zeta^+ v = -(2 - 3\zeta + \zeta^2)\,\frac{dv}{d\zeta} + (13 - 9\zeta)v = 0.$$

Integrating $\mathbf{M}_\zeta^+ v = 0$,

$$v^{-1}\,\frac{dv}{d\zeta} = -\frac{4}{\zeta - 1} - \frac{5}{\zeta - 2}$$

and

$$v(\zeta) = (\zeta - 1)^{-4}(\zeta - 2)^{-5}.$$

Thus

$$w(z) = \int_C e^{z\zeta}(\zeta - 1)^{-4}(\zeta - 2)^{-5}\, d\zeta,$$

provided C is chosen so that

$$P_\zeta[e^{z\zeta}, v(\zeta)] = (\zeta - 1)^{-3}(\zeta - 2)^{-4}e^{z\zeta}\Big|_C = 0.$$

Since P_ζ is single-valued, let C be a circle around $\zeta = 1$ of radius $\frac{1}{2}$.

Then if we expand $e^{z\zeta}$ and $(\zeta - 2)^{-5}$ in powers of $\zeta - 1$ and multiply them together, the coefficient of $(\zeta - 1)^3$ is

$$e^z\left(\frac{5}{2} z^2 + 15z + 35 + \frac{1}{6} z^3\right).$$

Hence

$$w(z) = e^z(z^3 + 15z^2 + 90z + 210).$$

Also

$$e^{z\zeta} = e^{2z} + ze^{2z}(\zeta - 2) + \frac{z^2}{2} e^{2z}(\zeta - 2)^2 + \frac{z^3}{6} e^{2z}(\zeta - 2)^3$$

$$+ \frac{z^4}{24} e^{2z}(\zeta - 2)^4 + \cdots$$

and

$$\frac{1}{(\zeta - 1)^4} = 1 - 4(\zeta - 2) + 10(\zeta - 2)^2 - 20(\zeta - 2)^3$$

$$+ 35(\zeta - 2)^4 + \cdots,$$

while

$$\frac{e^{z\zeta}}{(\zeta - 1)^4} = \cdots + e^{2z}\left[\frac{1}{24} z^4 - \frac{2}{3} z^3 + 5z^2 - 20z + 35\right](\zeta - 2)^4 + \cdots.$$

Thus

$$w(z) = e^{2z}(z^4 - 16z^3 + 120z^2 - 480z + 840)$$

is another solution.

C. Let

$$\mathbf{L}_z w = 4z \frac{d^2 w}{dz^2} - 3 \frac{dw}{dz} - (4z - 1)w = 0.$$

Then the following sequence of formulas is immediate:

$$\mathbf{M}_\zeta u = (4\zeta^2 - 4) \frac{du}{d\zeta} - (3\zeta - 1) u$$

$$\mathbf{M}_\zeta^+ v = -(4\zeta^2 - 4) \frac{dv}{d\zeta} = (11\zeta - 1)v = 0$$

$$v^{-1} \frac{dv}{d\zeta} = -\frac{11\zeta - 1}{4\zeta^2 - 4} = -\frac{3}{2} \frac{1}{\zeta + 1} - \frac{5}{4} \frac{1}{\zeta - 1}$$

$$P_\zeta[e^{z\zeta}, v(\zeta)] = e^{z\zeta}(\zeta + 1)^{-1/2}(\zeta - 1)^{-1/4}.$$

Thus

$$w(z) = \int_C e^{z\zeta}(\zeta + 1)^{-3/2}(\zeta - 1)^{-5/4} \, d\zeta,$$

where C is chosen so that P_ζ vanishes.   That is, C is the double loop,

$$C = C_1^{-1}C_0^{-1}C_1C_0,$$

where C_0 is a circuit around $\zeta = -1$ in the positive sense, C_1 is a circuit around $\zeta = +1$ in the positive sense, and C_0^{-1} and C_1^{-1} are the same curves, respectively, in the negative sense.

9.6 Repeated Linear Factors

Suppose $\alpha_1 = \alpha_2$ is a double root of $P(\zeta) = 0$.   Then in this case

$$v^{-1}\frac{dv}{d\zeta} = \mu + \frac{\lambda_1}{\zeta - \alpha_1} + \frac{\nu_1}{(\zeta - \alpha_1)^2} + \frac{\lambda_3}{\zeta - \alpha_3} + \cdots + \frac{\lambda_n}{\zeta - \alpha_n}.$$

Integrating,

$$v(\zeta) = e^{\mu\zeta}e^{-\nu_1/(\zeta-\alpha_1)}(\zeta - \alpha_1)^{\lambda_1}(\zeta - \alpha_3)^{\lambda_3}\cdots(\zeta - \alpha_n)^{\lambda_n}$$

and the bilinear concomitant $P[e^{z\zeta}, v(\zeta)]$ becomes

$$a_0e^{(\mu+z)\zeta}e^{-\nu_1/(\zeta-\alpha_1)}(\zeta - \alpha_1)^{1+\lambda_1}(\zeta - \alpha_3)^{1+\lambda_3}\cdots(\zeta - \alpha_n)^{1+\lambda_n}.$$

For convenience in notation and with no real loss of generality, let us assume $n = 2$, $\alpha_1 = \alpha$, $\nu_1 = \nu$, $\lambda_1 = \lambda$.   Then

$$v(\zeta) = e^{\mu\zeta}e^{-\nu/(\zeta-\alpha)}(\zeta - \alpha)^\lambda. \tag{9.23}$$

Thus we must obtain two distinct contours relative to α.   One such contour is described in Fig. 9.2.   To obtain a second we consider the limiting case as $\alpha_1 \to \alpha_2$ of the double loop encircling these points. It must be such that the concomitant

$$e^{(\mu+z)\zeta}e^{-\nu/(\zeta-\alpha)}(\zeta - \alpha)^{1+\lambda}$$

vanishes.   If we write

$$\zeta - \alpha = |\zeta - \alpha|e^{i\phi}, \qquad \nu = |\nu|e^{i\psi},$$

then

$$\left|e^{-\nu/(\zeta-\alpha)}\right| = \left|e^{-Ae^{i(\psi-\phi)}}\right| = e^{-A\cos(\psi-\phi)}, \tag{9.24}$$

where $A = |\nu|/|\zeta - \alpha|$.   Since A approaches infinity as ζ approaches α, we must have $A\cos(\psi - \phi) > 0$ in order that the exponential factor approach zero.   This implies $\cos(\psi - \phi) > 0$ or

$$\psi - \frac{1}{2}\pi < \phi < \psi + \frac{1}{2}\pi. \tag{9.25}$$

Thus a closed loop starting and ending at α but such that its gradient is discontinuous at $\zeta = \alpha$ and satisfies the above inequalities, is appropriate. For example, the contour C of Fig. 9.3 is adequate.

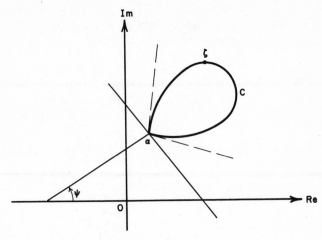

Figure 9.3

9.7 Constant Coefficients

Let us consider the case where the coefficients are constant, viz.,

$$\mathbf{L}_z w = b_0 \frac{d^n w}{dz^n} + b_1 \frac{d^{n-1}w}{dz^{n-1}} + \cdots + b_n w = 0, \qquad b_0 \neq 0. \qquad (9.26)$$

Then, referring to Section 9.4, the adjoint operator $\mathbf{M}_\zeta^+$ is a scalar and $v(\zeta)$ need only satisfy the algebraic equation

$$R(\zeta)v(\zeta) = 0,$$

where

$$R(\zeta) = b_0 \zeta^n + b_1 \zeta^{n-1} + \cdots + b_n.$$

Thus the method appears to break down.

However, returning to the basic formulation, we are searching for a solution in the form

$$w(z) = \int_C e^{z\zeta} v(\zeta)\, d\zeta \qquad (9.27)$$

for appropriate C and $v(\zeta)$. Therefore, if we place Equation 9.27 in Equation 9.26, there results

$$\mathbf{L}_z w = \int_C b_0 \zeta^n e^{z\zeta} v(\zeta)\, d\zeta + \int_C b_1 \zeta^{n-1} e^{z\zeta} v(\zeta)\, d\zeta + \cdots + \int_C b_n e^{z\zeta} v(\zeta)\, d\zeta$$

$$= \int_C e^{z\zeta} R(\zeta) v(\zeta)\, d\zeta = 0.$$

Thus it suffices to choose for $v(\zeta)$ any function such that $R(\zeta)v(\zeta)$ is analytic in some region and the C can be chosen as any closed smooth curve in this region.

Let $f(\zeta)$, where

$$f(\zeta) = R(\zeta)v(\zeta),$$

be such an analytic function. Then

$$v(\zeta) = \frac{f(\zeta)}{R(\zeta)}.$$

Suppose β is a root of multiplicity r of $R(\zeta) = 0$. Then we may write

$$v(\zeta) = \frac{B_1}{\zeta - \beta} + \frac{B_2}{(\zeta - \beta)^2} + \cdots + \frac{B_r}{(\zeta - \beta)^r} + u(\zeta).$$

If C is a contour which encloses β but no other root of $R(\zeta) = 0$, then $u(\zeta)$ is analytic in and on C. Hence

$$w(z) = \int_C [B_1(\zeta - \beta)^{-1} + B_2(\zeta - \beta)^{-2} + \cdots + B_r(\zeta - \beta)^{-r} + u(\zeta)]e^{z\zeta}\,d\zeta.$$

Now let

$$I_k = \int_C B_k(\zeta - \beta)^{-k}e^{z\zeta}\,d\zeta.$$

Writing

$$e^{z\zeta} = e^{z\beta} + ze^{z\beta}(\zeta - \beta) + \cdots + \frac{z^{k-1}e^{z\beta}(\zeta - \beta)^{k-1}}{(k-1)!} + \cdots,$$

we see by the Cauchy integral formula that

$$I_k = \frac{2\pi i}{(k-1)!}\, z^{k-1}e^{z\beta}B_k = C_k z^{k-1}e^{z\beta}.$$

Thus

$$w(z) = e^{\beta z}(C_1 + C_2 z + \cdots + C_r z^{r-1})$$

is the desired solution corresponding to the root β of multiplicity r.

EXERCISES

9.1. Let C be a circle of radius r with center at the origin. If z is large and real and p is not an integer, show that

$$z^{p+1}\int_C \zeta^p e^{z\zeta}\,d\zeta = 2i \sin p\pi \int_0^{rz} t^p e^{-t}\,dt,$$

where we have made the change of variable $z\zeta = -t$.

9.2. Consider the integral

$$w_j(z) = e^{z\alpha_j} \int_{C_j} e^{z\zeta}(\zeta - \alpha_1)^{\lambda_1}(\zeta - \alpha_2)^{\lambda_2}\cdots(\zeta - \alpha_n)^{\lambda_n}\, d\zeta$$

over the single loop contour of Fig. 9.2 Show that $w_j(z)$ is asymptotic to

$$2i\, e^{z\alpha_j} z^{-(\lambda_j+1)} \sin \lambda_j \pi \Gamma(\lambda_j + 1)$$

for z large and real, provided λ_j is not an integer.

9.3. Using the results of the previous exercise, show that if $\mathrm{Re}\,[\alpha_1] > \mathrm{Re}\,[\alpha_2] > \cdots > \mathrm{Re}\,[\alpha_n]$ and $\mathrm{Im}\,[\alpha_j] \neq \mathrm{Im}\,[\alpha_k]$, $j \neq k$; $j, k = 1, 2, \cdots, n$, then the n solutions $w_j(z)$, $j = 1, 2, \cdots, n$ of $\mathbf{L}w(z) = 0$ are linearly independent.

9.4. Show that if $\mathrm{Re}\,[z] < 0$, $\mathrm{Re}\,[\lambda] > 0$, then

$$w(z) = \int_0^\infty e^{z\zeta}\zeta^{\lambda-1}(\zeta + 1)^{\mu-1}\, d\zeta$$

is a solution of

$$z\frac{d^2w}{dz^2} + (\lambda + \mu + z)\frac{dw}{dz} + \lambda w = 0.$$

9.5. Derive the integral representation of $J_0(z)$ directly from Bessel's equation of order zero.

9.6. Bessel's equation with purely imaginary argument and order zero is

$$z\frac{d^2w}{dz^2} + \frac{dw}{dz} - zw = 0.$$

Show that

$$I_0(z) = \frac{2}{\pi}\int_0^{\pi/2} \cosh\,(z \sin \theta)\, d\theta$$

and determine $\quad K_0(z) \quad \left(= \int_0^\infty e^{-z\cosh\theta}\, d\theta, \qquad \mathrm{Re}\,[z] > 0 \right)$ up to a non-zero multiplicative constant.

9.7. Show by the method of Laplace integrals that

$$w(z) = \int_0^\infty \zeta e^{-\zeta^2/2} \sin\frac{z}{\zeta}\, d\zeta$$

is a solution of the differential equation

$$z\frac{d^3w}{dz^3} - w = 0.$$

9.8. Investigate the integral solutions of

$$(az + b)\frac{d^2w}{dz^2} + 2a\frac{dw}{dz} + (cz + d)w = 0,$$

where a, b, c, d are non-zero constants.

References

Ahlfors, L. V., *Complex analysis*, McGraw-Hill Book Company, Inc., 1953.

Churchill, R. V., *Introduction to complex variables and applications*, McGraw-Hill Book Company, Inc., 1948.

Dienes, P., *The Taylor series*, Oxford, Clarendon Press, 1931.

Franklin, P., *Functions of complex variables*, Prentice-Hall, Inc., 1958.

Ince, E. L., *Ordinary differential equations*, Longmans, Green and Company, Ltd., 1927.

Knopp, K., *Theory of functions*, Dover Publications, Part I, 1945, Part II, 1947.

Miller, K. S., *Advanced real calculus*, Harper & Brothers, 1957.

Murray, F. J., and Miller, K. S., *Existence theorems for ordinary differential equations*, New York University Press, 1954.

Nehari, Z., *Conformal mapping*, McGraw-Hill Book Company, Inc., 1952.

Newman, M. H. A., *Elements of the topology of plane sets of points*, Cambridge University Press, 1939.

Osgood, W. F., *Functions of a complex variable*, G. E. Stechert and Company, 1938.

Pierpont, J., *Functions of a complex variable*, Ginn and Company, 1914.

Ritt, J. F., *Theory of functions*, King's Crown Press, rev. ed., 1949.

Titchmarsh, E. C., *The theory of functions*, Oxford University Press, 1939, second edition.

Index